Mortimer Ostow, M.D.

DRUGS IN
PSYCHOANALYSIS
AND
PSYCHOTHERAPY

BASIC BOOKS, INC.

Publishers / New York

© 1962 BY BASIC BOOKS PUBLISHING CO., INC.
LIBRARY OF CONGRESS CATALOG CARD NUMBER: 62-15830
MANUFACTURED IN THE UNITED STATES OF AMERICA
DESIGNED BY LAUREL WAGNER

DRUGS IN PSYCHOANALYSIS AND PSYCHOTHERAPY

This book is dedicated to the psychiatrists of the newer generations, who will understand that a sound psychiatry must be securely based upon a sound psychology, which is the physiology of the mind; but who will not on that account neglect the study of the physiology of the brain, nor disdain to exploit it for the benefit of their patients and their science. A sound psychology must be firmly rooted in clinical data, must conform to the biologic nature of man, and must contribute significantly to the comprehension of normal and pathologic behavior. The only psychology that complies with these requirements is the psychoanalytic metapsychology of Freud.

Acknowledgments

In the course of writing a book such as this, one incurs many obligations. Among those to whom I am obligated, I must list first my patients. Their confidence in me and tolerance of my occasional blunders has made the collection of this material and formulation of this method possible. Most, though not all, have profited, and none has, to my knowledge, been hurt.

To my distinguished teacher, Herman Nunberg, I am obligated for the vision of what psychoanalytic psychology really is, and for the realization that when I fail, the failure is almost always the consequence of my imperfect understanding, and seldom the consequence of defect in Freud's theory.

My close colleague, Sidney S. Furst, has always been helpful, reviewing my work, challenging my conclusions, checking my observations, and testing my hypotheses in his own clinical material. Nathan S. Kline and John C. Saunders have made their large and intelligent experience with the drug therapy of mental illness freely available to me at all times, and have assisted me with more than one difficult problem. Harold Rifkin has provided information and advice most graciously and wisely in the area of internal medicine. Finally, I must thank Martha Crossen for the benefit of her impressive editorial experience and judgment.

MORTIMER OSTOW

New York
May 1962

CONTENTS

DRUGS IN PSYCHOANALYSIS AND PSYCHOTHERAPY

CHAPTER I

Should Drugs Be Used
in Psychoanalysis
and Psychotherapy?

ONE DOES NOT LIGHTLY PROPOSE a variation in the technique of psychoanalysis. It is not that our method is so efficient or so easy or so obviously reduced to its ultimate form that deters a responsible analyst from venturing to alter it. Its limitations are only too obvious and have been described and deplored throughout Freud's writings (*e.g.* Freud, 1937c) and in the writings of many other able analysts (*see* Nunberg, 1943). But the classical technique was crystallized out of years of experience in which useless devices were rejected and useful ones concentrated and refined. It is not likely that in the absence of radically new methods of obtaining, understanding, and communicating information, a significant and valuable innovation will be devised. Those that are proposed, if they purchase any advantage at all, purchase it at the cost of some counterbalancing loss; generally the loss greatly outweighs the gain. For this reason, conscientious and able analysts, aware as they are of the difficulties of the method, have come to look askance at suggested variations. They are skeptical of novel modes of psychologic intervention, but even more skeptical of nonpsychologic maneuvers. Perhaps it is oversimplifying to say that the analyst's diffidence is based upon his experience that the variant techniques fail. That would be bad enough. What is worse is the fact that when these innovations are put into practice by their proponents, it often becomes clear that the essence and foundation of the analytic method are undermined.

It has not been difficult for analysts to remain aloof from organic therapies. Until the advent of the newer pharmaceutic agents, organic modalities have had little to offer to the analyst. Electric shock therapy has been able to dissipate the occasional melancholia that has supervened in an analysis, or the acute schizophrenic breakdown in the preschizophrenic patient. While this contribution is indeed valuable, the procedure has no therapeutic potency for undoing the constant personality malfunction, the neurotic disorder into which the acute melancholia or schizophrenia may obtrude from time to time. Further, the mental confusion it brings about interrupts the analysis and prevents analytic examination of the events of the psychosis and of the process of recovery. Surgical procedures have, in general, given so little for the irreversible loss they exact that the morality of using them may be questioned. Sedatives and hypnotics can be and have been employed by some analysts to deal with the occasional emergencies, the acute anxiety attacks, the panics, the suicidal impulses that every psychiatrist encounters. What has the analyst lost by doubting the usefulness of these organic methods for his essential task of freeing the patient from the neurotic forces that tyrannize him?

A rigid, imperceptive defense of the psychoanalytic technique, as if it were canonized, was not Freud's attitude. The current technique is the historical precipitate of many kinds of approach. The question of technical variation to make analysis more efficient is discussed extensively in one of Freud's last papers, "Analysis Terminable and Interminable" (1937c); there the problems that require solution are examined together with the inherent limitations of the method. In his final, uncompleted, and posthumously published *Outline*, Freud (1940a) concluded his chapter on technique as follows: "The future may teach us how to exercise a direct influence, by means of particular chemical substances, upon the amounts of energy and their distribution in the apparatus of the mind. It may be that there are other undreamed of possibilities of therapy. But for the moment we have nothing better at our disposal than the technique of psychoanalysis, and for that reason, in spite of its limitations it is not to be despised." Dr. Nunberg has informed me that Freud spoke of anticipating a time when it would be possible to use chemical substances during a therapeutic analysis in order to direct the analysis into the most fruitful channels. We have, of course, not yet achieved the capacity to make such fine adjustments as this kind of regulation would require, but I believe that with the drugs now available we can, on occasion, make coarse adjustments of sufficient consequence to determine whether an analysis can be conducted and whether a patient can be saved.

In contrast to other physical modalities of psychiatric therapy, the use of psychopharmaceutic agents lends itself to combination with psychoanalysis and psychotherapy for three reasons. First, the therapy is gentle and does not disrupt ego function. Therefore it does not impede psychologic investigation and interpretation, nor does it damage the transference. Second, when properly employed, it actually facilitates the psychotherapeutic work. Third, the chemical substances can be used to achieve quickly though temporarily, the same ultimate therapeutic influence that we achieve more lastingly though slowly and painstakingly by psychologic means. I refer to a redistribution of psychic energies within the psychic apparatus. This, I believe, is the *tertium comparationis* whereby psychoanalytic therapy and pharmacotherapy can be compared, related, and coordinated with each other.

The psychoanalyst will wonder whether the administration of a drug can fail to distort the transference relation. I believe that this is not an important consideration for the following reasons. First, in most instances in which I advocate the introduction of pharmacotherapy, the alternative to it—hospitalization or electric shock therapy—would create an even more serious distortion of the transference. In many cases, the alternative is to withhold analysis altogether for fear of reactivating a psychosis. Second, I do not question the desirability of maintaining a ritualized, constant affective distance from the patient. Against this uniform background, the transference fantasies projected by the patient stand out all the more clearly. But while such uniformity is desirable, it is essential only that all transactions with the patient be deliberate and controlled so that fantasy may be contrasted with reality. For example, no analyst will hesitate to offer a seriously depressed patient more assurance, more time, or more affection than he ordinarily does. Third, the administration of medication to a patient has unconscious meanings which can be analyzed as readily as the unconscious meanings of all the other contrived and fortuitous features of the therapeutic contact, such as disposition of the office furniture, the analyst's name, arrangements for payment of fees, an illness, and so on. Fourth, the patient's motivation to work in the analysis and to struggle against his resistances derives not only from his wish to overcome his discomfort but also in a large measure from the positive features of the transference relation. These often receive powerful reinforcement when the physician effects almost magical relief from the horrors of psychosis. Many aspects of the implications for the transference of drug administration in the course of an ongoing psychoanalysis will be taken up in some detail further.

ADVANTAGES AND LIMITATIONS
OF DRUG THERAPY

I think that I can best express my own point of view by citing in an abbreviated anticipatory way some of the things the drugs can do and what they cannot do. Let me state clearly at the outset that no pharmaceutic agent that is currently available can do what analysis does. A drug can, by means which we shall discuss below, undo the ego distortion and disruption which are responsible for the florid symptoms of an acute neurotic or psychotic crisis. Moreover, so long as it is used, it may contain the pathogenic forces and keep the patient relatively free of the symptoms which characterized his crises. If the particular episode of illness was precipitated by a temporary temptation or frustration which no longer exists, the patient may even remain well for a while after the medication is withdrawn. Except in the case of purely traumatic illness, however, the pathogenic process will sooner or later reassert itself, and unless it is countered by one of these pharmaceutic agents, it will once more bring about the clinical picture of neurosis or psychosis. The pathogenic tendency, arising as it does from constitutional roots and early childhood experience, cannot be affected by any chemical agent. It can be influenced only by psychoanalysis. Without analysis it will continue to enlarge and to encroach more and more upon the ongoing psychodynamic processes of daily life. The therapeutic effect of the drugs is comparable to the effect of the corticosteroids in an inflammatory disease, of insulin in diabetes, of digitalis upon a weakened heart muscle; while the effect of psychoanalysis is in some ways comparable to relieving an obstruction of some fluid-conducting hollow viscus.

What can the drugs do? They can reconstitute a fragmented ego so as to make psychoanalysis possible for patients otherwise too ill to participate in it. They can protect the patient and the analysis during the occasional acute exacerbations of illness which may occur during analysis. They can diminish to a significant degree the danger in the case of some suicidal patients. They can protect the patient who becomes disturbed during his analyst's absence. I believe they can often overcome addiction, which is ordinarily a serious obstacle to analysis. I also believe that ultimately we shall be able to use them to facilitate the indolent analysis. These are striking clinical advantages. But the pharmaceutic agents can also contribute to psychoanalytic theory. They permit the analyst to treat and hence to observe conditions with which he cannot ordinarily deal. From these observations new insights are bound to emerge. Further, each administration of a chemical substance constitutes an experiment in psychology and so offers a method of experimental investigation of psychoanalytic problems. I shall discuss each of these issues below.

In my opinion there is no reason or justification for the administration of any pharmaceutic agent in the ordinary analysis of patients whose self-control, reality-testing and capacity for detached self-observation are sufficient to permit the psychoanalytic process and to meet the minimal requirements of daily living. Psychoanalytic technique is assuredly difficult. To develop a good technique the analyst must know psychoanalytic theory well, must have had a thorough and successful personal analysis, must be honest and dedicated, and must have experience with the method as it applies to the many different varieties of patients. The tyro, as a result of his inexperience or inexpertness, will probably tend to turn to these drugs when he runs into difficulties which are best handled analytically. Not only would it be bad analytic technique for him to do so, but it is not even likely to work. Conflicts and dynamic defenses will yield only to proper genetic and dynamic interpretation; they cannot be dissipated by drugs. The drugs, however, have specific, unique effects, and when invoked judiciously, they can give the analyst a considerably greater measure of control over certain problem situations which would otherwise resist the analytic process.

WHAT IS THE ROLE OF DRUGS IN PSYCHOTHERAPY?

The term *psychotherapy* denotes treatment by psychologic methods. In the larger sense, psychoanalysis is merely one mode of psychotherapy. When the two terms are used in the same discussion, the latter generally refers to a less intensive and less rigorous procedure. This less intensive treatment is offered when the clinical situation does not warrant analysis—for example, when the patient is too old or the illness too trivial; when the psychiatrist is not trained to analyze, or when circumstances compel him to accept responsibility for a patient for whom he has insufficient time; and, unfortunately, when a patient requires analysis but cannot afford it. I shall not digress here to consider the several techniques of psychotherapy. Practicing psychotherapy, the psychiatrist is less constrained by the rigorous strictures of analytic technique and generally feels free to improvise and to adopt any device that may seem promising to him. Psychotherapy is generally considered to be a lesser task than analysis, and to require a lesser skill. In my opinion, the opposite is true. The analyst acts upon information that he obtains, and he sees his patient so often that he can wait until the information is forthcoming. The therapist must work with considerably less information and is often compelled to act on the basis of poorly supported guesses. At any rate, since psychotherapy is less clearly delineated than psychoanalysis, one might expect less reluctance on the part of psychotherapists to accept innovations such as drug therapy.

I can imagine that, in time, the introduction of drug therapy into psychiatry may do much to increase interest in psychotherapy and to improve its practice. The reader will learn that, in my opinion, the only way to select, combine, and regulate medication rationally is to assess the state of the patient's ego function. This can be done only in relatively undirected interviews. Moreover, as the patient improves, the interviews will naturally be occupied with a review of the patient's relations to love objects, to work, to rivals, and so on. Hence the attempt to offer a sound pharmacotherapy will automatically involve the psychiatrist in simultaneous psychotherapy. Skill in pharmacotherapy will require at least minimal skills in psychotherapeutic techniques.

THE PROBLEM OF THE
REMISSION PERSONALITY

There are those who will ask: If medication can control or prevent psychotic episodes, why should one consider analysis in such cases at all? In answering, one might refer to the potential toxicity of these drugs given over long periods of time, to the difficulties in the fine regulation of dosage, to the fact that episodes may be triggered abruptly by unexpected events. In a good number of cases, however, skillful administration of drugs will indeed keep a patient free of overt psychotic symptoms for several years, and perhaps indefinitely. We must still answer the question in principle then: Assuming that with drug therapy alone one can prevent overt psychotic episodes, is there any reason to advise psychoanalysis? My unequivocal answer is yes. Observation shows that the same pathogenic tendencies which at times issue in psychosis, also exist in the remission personality, and seriously impair its function. The "normal" individual who unexpectedly breaks down with an acute schizophrenia is frequently a person who has always remained aloof and apart, separate, and in an ultimate sense not participating and responding, even though he may have seemed to conform to the mores of society. His isolation leaves him disappointed and unhappy. His parents, his spouse, and his children suffer from it as much as he. If the acute breakdown creates the opportunity to bring him into analysis, that opportunity should certainly be seized.

Many patients to whom energizing drugs are given, emerge from their melancholia and immediately or shortly pass into a paranoia, a schizophrenia, or a hysteric or phobic neurosis. These developments have been reported in the literature as "complications" of the treatment, or as "toxic effects" of the drugs. It is as if the diabetes or renal disease which one might find when a patient emerges from a coma were considered a "complication" of the treatment of the coma. It is my impression that the psychosis or neurosis which comes to light when a melancholia is dissipated is a primary pathologic disorder into which the melancholia had intruded as an intercurrent ictus. I shall discuss this sequence of events in considerably greater detail further on. I mention it here merely to demonstrate the point that a melancholia does not appear in a vacuum, so that offering chemotherapy for it provides an opportunity to induct the patient into analysis not merely for the prevention of melancholia but also for the treatment of the pathologic soil in which the melancholia grows. Similarly, no thoughtful psychiatrist who is concerned with patients rather than with diagnoses will consider his obligation to an alcoholic or drug addict discharged when he has managed by chemical means to reduce the pathologic craving. While the preoccupation with getting and using the intoxicant may seem to be the proximate cause of the patient's downfall, there can be no doubt that he is driven to this preoccupation by misery arising in serious disorder of his relations to those he loves, or should love. Obliterating the craving will not undo the fundamental disorder, and here too, only good analysis can offer anything like a definitive solution.

My experience, acquired in the six years since the introduction of psychopharmaceuticals, is essentially different from the material described in the literature. The data are drawn from daily observation of thirteen patients for whom I prescribed one or more of these chemical substances during the course of psychoanalysis; five other patients, for whom analysis was impossible, were seen in frequent psychotherapeutic sessions at least three times a week. In a few instances, the drugs were administered over a period of several weeks, in most instances for several months, and in the remaining few instances for several years. In order to check the observations and hypotheses which arose from this intensive study, I also undertook to treat another group of thirty-three patients, relying primarily upon the drugs for clinical improvement. These patients I saw either for a limited time, lasting no more than a few weeks, or over a longer period at relatively infrequent intervals of one or two weeks. This kind of experience, of course, has its limitations. With such small samples from a nonhomogeneous population, statistical methods are inapplicable. It is impossible to detect fine differences among the several drugs in each category. Toxicity certainly cannot be ascertained. Individual idiosyncrasy can create serious distortion of the net clinical impressions. Yet the advantages of this kind of intensive study cannot be duplicated by any other method of investigation. There is no other way to observe the day to day changes in the dynamics and energetics of the psyche, in the patient's feelings, his interests, and capacities. The actual workings of the drugs become visible and the differences among them show up with a clarity that cannot be achieved by even the largest series of patients classified by the usual gross nosologic criteria. Of course, it is not only the actions of the drugs that are elucidated by this method of psychoanalyzing patients under the influence of selected medication. For the first time the psychiatrist has an opportunity to watch the evolution and dissolution of psychotic states in "slow motion." The individual peculiarities of one or two patients may temporarily obscure some of the regularities that are to be detected, but except in the case of a most improbable concatenation of atypical events, the observer is not likely to be misled into seeing things that are not there. While I rely primarily upon my experience with analytic patients for source data, I like to check my inferences and the techniques that follow from them by observing the course of a larger number of patients whose treatment is primarily pharmacologic. In this way, not only are my conclusions confirmed or on occasion contradicted, but patterns which escape notice in daily observation become evident as one stands back from the picture. It is analogous to examining slide sections now under a low power lens, now under a high power lens.

Before employing any pharmaceutic agent, the psychiatrist must, of course, familiarize himself with the literature published by the manufacturer. While the technical chemical properties of the drug will hold little interest for him, and the results of animal tests only slightly more, the safe dose, the toxic potentialities, the side effects, complications and contraindications must be kept in mind. I have often found manufacturers' statements regarding the psychic effects of the drugs and their diagnostic indications to be of little value, and sometimes even misleading. Most of the reports in the psychiatric literature, in which the properties of a drug are judged by its effect on large groups of patients, are equally uninformative. It is difficult to obtain from these published data definite, consistent, and reliable criteria for administering any given substance. By now it has become clear that drugs cannot be selected on the basis of diagnosis, or on the basis of the existence of any given symptom or symptom complex. The criteria I shall propose, which are independent of nosologic and symptomatic entities, have served me and others who have tried this method, as dependable indicators for the choice and administration of the various medications in clinical use.

There is no longer any question of the revolutionary change in the practice of psychiatry brought about by the introduction of pharmacotherapy. This has occurred largely as the result of the aggressive and intensive research activities conducted by the pharmaceutical manufacturing industry, a unique development in the study of mental disease. At the same time there has developed a set of special problems, relating to claims and recommendations for the use of new drugs released for general distribution, and to marketing practices. The inevitable conflict between a bold experimental approach to new modes of therapy and cautious concern for the welfare of the individual has been complicated by the ambiguous role of the manufacturer as scientific investigator. I question the wisdom and benefit to the public of a premature freezing of recommendations for the use of new agents by regulatory agencies, for I find that the initial clinical studies of such recently introduced drugs often miss a true assessment of their actions. Free and extensive trials by many physicians over several years are necessary to reach a sound assessment of new therapies, since ultimately only experience can teach us the full therapeutic and toxic potential of any drug.

I find questionable, too, the preliminary testing procedures currently employed by drug manufacturers. In an effort to predict what effect a new substance may have on mental illness, the manufacturers' pharmacologists turn to animal experiments. From such unnatural tests as aversive and operant conditioning, squirrel cage running, maze learning, and response to prodding, generalizations are made which are then applied in a psychologically naive way to normal and pathologic human behavior. I would guess that much more could be inferred about the action of a new agent if its effect on total, natural animal behavior were examined, using the techniques of ethology. Starting with such data relating to the influence of a chemical on the instinctual life of an animal and applying the metapsychology of mental illness, I believe it should be possible to predict the therapeutic effects of new substances with considerably greater accuracy. I emphasize once more, however, that a final assessment requires clinical experience.

In these remarks I am assuming that where it is indicated and available, authentic psychoanalysis is the most efficacious, technically elegant, and clinically definitive procedure. Where analysis is not the procedure of choice, whether because the patient is too old, or the disease too chronic and severe, or because financial resources are insufficient, similar considerations also apply to less intensive psychotherapy.

CHAPTER II

Psychic Energy,
Psychic Function,
and the Drugs

In almost all psychological systems that have been devised, some account is taken of a quantitative strength factor. It may be called a "conative" element, a "drive" component, vigor, and so on. Piotrowski, on a more sophisticated level, is able to discern in Rorschach studies indications of conflict between opposing forces, above and beyond the well-known inferences regarding content of the central psychic complexes and defenses (Piotrowski and Bricklin, 1958; Piotrowski and Levin, 1959). For example, he considers that responses to light shading in the Rorschach pattern reflect energy control by the ego.

In describing responses to the newer psychopharmaceutic agents, and in attempting to work out therapeutic indications and prognostic criteria, strength or vigor concepts have been devised and used *ad hoc*. Freyhan, recently discussing pharmacologic effects, speaks of psychokinetic activity which, he claims, is reduced by tranquilizers (Freyhan, 1960). In one of the early reserpine studies, Luttrell and Morrison constructed a measure of "biological activity" with numerical notation (Luttrell and Morrison, 1955). I believe that what is discerned in each case is one manifestation or another of what Freud called "psychic energy," which is the intrapsychic component of instinctual energy.

The concept of a psychic energy, arising within instinctual

sources and driving the dynamic processes, is one of the earliest, most vital, and most characteristic of Freud's constructs. Acceptance of this idea can often be used as a shibboleth to distinguish between the authentic psychoanalyst on the one hand, and the "neopsychoanalyst" on the other. It is my impression, though, that many of those who most articulately support the libido theory do not really exploit it fully in their day to day clinical work. Using the term "cathexis" as a synonym for "interest," and "libido" for "desire," is not really applying libido theory in clinical practice. Any kind of psychiatric work with the newer drugs requires, in my opinion, the constant application of libido theory, and the interest and insights which experience with the pharmaceutic agents can generate may restore psychic energetics to its rightful place in the metapsychology of therapy.

THE LIBIDO THEORY

Even in the unpublished letters and notes which antedate his first psychoanalytic publications, Freud spoke of libido, sexual tension, and sexual desire (Freud, 1954). Variations in the distribution of this entity, as between physical and psychic, between discharge by gratification and accumulation by frustration, determined the evolution of such clinical consequences as anxiety neurosis, hysteria, neurasthenia, and melancholia. In addition to the concept of overall quantitites of libido which create symptoms, Freud also attempted to describe individual psychic processes such as perception, cognition, thought, memory, and affect as determined by the passage of "quantity" over neural pathways. In his early *Studies on Hysteria* he describes the process whereby the cathexis, that is, the charge of psychic excitation, passes from a single idea to raise the energy level of the psyche as a whole (Freud and Breuer, 1895d). Specifically, the perception of the love object becomes a source of excitation which progressively involves more and more of the ego, excluding other ideas, until ultimately, in orgasm, the sexual excitement alone prevails. In *The Interpretation of Dreams* Freud makes extensive use of the concepts of psychic excitation, cathexis, and the "principle of constancy" to explain the nature, the purpose, and the content of dreams (Freud, 1900a). The principle of constancy expresses the tendency of the ego to maintain a constant energy level within the psychic apparatus by discharging surplus excitation. He refers in the same work to libido as the psychic excitation contributed by the sexual instincts. Here, the distinction between the impulse driving a specific mental process and an energy level in the psychic apparatus as a whole is obscured, for in analyzing the content of a dream, as well as an individual symptom, the dynamic evolution of an instinctual impulse and its vicissitudes are the principal determining factors. The only reference to the influence of the ego's energy content upon its mode of function in dreams is the supposition that the capacity for hallucinatory representation and regression to primary process are at least partly to be ascribed to the cessation of afferent sensory flow during sleep.

In *Three Essays on the Theory of Sexuality*, Freud clearly defines libido as a "quantitatively variable force which could serve as a measure of processes and transformations occurring in the field of sexual excitation" (Freud 1905d). He distinguishes it from "the energy which must be supposed to underlie mental processes in general" by virtue of its "special origin." He supposes that sexual excitation is introduced into the psychic apparatus by stimulation of erogenous zones, resulting from a charge of functional centers in the nervous system with "substances (that) arise from the sexual metabolism," and occasionally by intoxication with exogenous chemicals. "It should be the task of a libido theory of neurotic and psychotic disorders," he says, "to express all of the observed phenomena and inferred processes in terms of the economics of the libido . . . but [psychoanalysis] is unable to make any immediate distinction between the ego libido and the other forms of energy operating in the ego." These remarks were added to the original 1905 manuscript in 1915, and in 1920 he cautioned against following the example of Jung in watering down the meaning of libido to psychic instinctual force in general. Libido denotes only the energy of the sexual instincts. The ego instincts, that is, those instincts that ensure self-preservation, are a second source of energy. Freud's subsequent revision of his instinct theory resulted in his postulation of the erotic instinct and the death instinct as the only two sources of instinctual energy (Freud, 1920g). *Wit and Its Relation to the Unconscious*, written also in 1905, contains a masterful analysis of the psychology of wit, comedy, and humor, based on considerations of psychic energetics alone (Freud, 1905c).

In the 1915 supplement to the *Three Essays*, Freud employed the term *ego libido* to denote the "mental representation" of the quantity of libido "whose production, increase or diminution, distribution and displacement, should afford us possibilities for explaining the psychosexual phenomena observed." As he develops the term, it seems to represent both the quantity of libido contained within the ego and the libidinal investment of the ego as opposed to the object. Presumably, Freud meant to imply that the libido contained by the ego, which is not devoted to the cathexis of the object, establishes the narcissistic cathexis of one's own ego. If cathexis denotes the psychic investment of an image or idea, and if the psychic interest is sexual, then the term "libidinal cathexis" refers to the investment of intrapsychic images and ideas with sexual excitation. Each sexual impulse or fantasy consists of a libidinal cathexis attached to ideational content (Freud, 1909a).

In his earlier writings, Freud's chief interest was descriptive and clinical. He investigated the classical dynamic patterns, genetic sequences, and the symptomatic manifestations to which they give rise. Energetics played a considerably smaller role than genetics, dynamics, and topographical considerations. He was interested in the circumstances that evoked an increase in libido, and he used a concept which he subsequently had to discard, namely, that accumulated libido was transformed into anxiety.

With his discussion of the Schreber case, and other papers written at about the same time, Freud began to give more attention to the total libido level and the ego's capacity to contain it (Freud, 1911c, 1912c). A relative plethora of the first, and deficiency of the second, no matter how created, could cause neurosis. This concept of an ego innervated by a quantity of libido, which might on occasion be too great for the ego to contain, is the theoretical basis of the approach to be presented in this book. Freud described repression as a withdrawal of libido from the object, and the clinical outcome is seen as a consequence of that withdrawal. When the withdrawal is partial or brief, the outcome may be neurosis, or merely normal relinquishment of an object. When libido is withdrawn from the images of all real objects, psychosis results. The detached libido is reflected back into the ego and creates megalomania. Once the libido seems to strive to reach objects again via delusional relations, we see an attempt at restitution of the lost world of objects. This condition is characteristic of paranoid schizophrenia. If the attempt at repair is restricted to hallucinations, the restitutional process does not reach real objects, and recovery is less likely. In his theoretical discussion of the Schreber case, Freud poses the following problem: If libido, the energy of the sexual instincts, comprises only a portion of the total energy available to the ego, why does withdrawal of libido from objects seem to terminate all contact with the world of reality? This question foreshadows the revision of instinct theory in 1920, to the effect that the so-called ego instincts, too, are in essence libidinal, constituting the narcissistic portion of the total energy flux. When libido is withdrawn from objects, no contact with the world remains (Freud, 1920g).

It is important to note that in his discussion of psychosis, Freud developed the notion that some symptoms are to be ascribed to purely energetic events. Hitherto, he had suggested the idea that anxiety was merely a transmutation of excessive libido, and that there were some neuroses which were essentially expressions of pathologic accumulation of libido due to purely physical influences such as sexual continence. These were the *aktual Neurosen,* anxiety neurosis, neurasthenia, and hypochondria (Freud, 1895b). Now, after more than a decade of intensive study of the genetic and dynamic determinants of symptom formation, Freud, in dealing with psychosis, turned again to energetics for an explanation of certain phenomena. The "end of the world" fantasy which is almost universally encountered at the beginning of schizophrenia, is ascribed to a complete withdrawal of libido from the objects of the real world. Megalomania is ascribed to a reinvestment of object libido into the ego. Psychotic hypochrondria is due to an excessive libidinal cathexis of a single organ of the subject's body, following the withdrawal of libido from external objects. When this cathexis of the ego or of an organ first occurs it is pleasurable, for there is a renewal of satisfaction, deriving now from oneself, to replace the arrested gratification from objects. As the libidinal cathexis of the ego or the body becomes excessive, however, this pleasure gives way to pain.

Delusions and hallucinations are the outcome of attempts to restore libidinal object relations. Even in nonpathologic areas of psychic function, in object choice, in fluctuations of self-regard, in the genesis of guilt, the economy of the libido plays a determining role.

In the series of papers on metapsychology, including and following "On Narcissism," Freud gives close attention to the energetics of the psychologic processes which also had hitherto been described chiefly in dynamic terms. In fact, he defines the term "metapsychology" as follows: "I propose that when we have succeeded in describing a psychical process in its dynamic, topographic, and economic aspects, we should speak of it as a *metapsychological* presentation" (Freud, 1915d, p. 181). In a footnote, he deplores the neglect of "the economic standpoint" (Freud, 1917e, p. 255). (Freud uses the term "economic" to denote the subject of the generation, distribution, and dissipation of psychic energies, just as we might speak of the "economy" of metabolism.) As previously, he speaks sometimes of the vicissitudes of individual instinctual derivatives, such as wishes or fantasies, and sometimes of energetic changes which beset the entire ego. The former case applies, of course, to the neuroses, and the latter to the psychoses. For our purposes, it is important to note that he elaborates the concept that psychic energy in general, and libido in particular, arise from instinctual sources in the Ucs. (the unconscious, which in later terminology includes the id as well as unconscious portions of the ego). The Pcs. (the preconscious, in later terminology, the preconscious portion of the ego) also has a store of energy which it can use, (1) to reinforce the charge of a preconscious idea which is simultaneously being charged by the Ucs.; (2) to oppose the entry of an Ucs. cathexis (charge) into the Pcs. by creating an anticathexis; or (3) to activate a Pcs. idea as a result simply of conscious volition (Freud, 1915e). In the case of neurosis or normal behavior, each individual impulse and idea undergoes its own development and vicissitudes. In the case of psychosis, the entire energy content of the ego is affected at once. The concept of the ego as a "reservoir" of instinctual energy from which libido can be extended to objects, and to which libido can be withdrawn, begins to take shape (Freud, 1914c, p. 76; 1920g., p. 51).

"The complex of melancholia," Freud says, "behaves like an open wound, drawing to itself cathectic energies. . . . from all directions, and emptying the ego until it is totally impoverished." Further, he wonders "whether an impoverishment of ego libido directly due to toxins may not be able to produce certain forms of the disease [melancholia]" (Freud, 1917e, p. 253). We shall deal with the concept of impoverishment of the ego in melancholia a little later in our discussion. Let us note at this point, though, that Freud explains the impoverishment as the result of the ego's defensive activities against the trauma of object loss. He says that the injury "binds" the ego's energy so that it is no longer available for other purposes (Freud, 1917d; see also Freud, 1920g, p. 30). He also points out that energy available to the ego can be employed to "bind," that is to neutralize the effect of any disturbing stimulus, whether of internal origin such as somatic pain or an instinctual impulse, or external, for example, a painful percept. An ego, therefore, which has an inadequate supply of energy, is unprepared to deal with the stimuli which impinge upon it. In 1926, Freud observed that when the ego is depleted of available energy it exhibits a generalized inhibition in its function (Freud, 1926d, p. 90). We shall find these ideas helpful in comprehending the manifestations of melancholia.

As has been mentioned before, in 1920 (*Beyond the Pleasure Principle*) Freud found it necessary to revise his classification of instincts (Freud, 1920g). The ego or self-preservative instincts which he had hitherto distinguished from and opposed to the sexual instincts, had to be considered "narcissistic forms" of the latter. It was Freud's interest in the "narcissistic neuroses," that is, paranoia and schizophrenia, which led him to realize that the intensification of narcissistic ego libido in these states occurred as a result of the withdrawal of libido from objects. He considered that the entire group of "erotic" instincts, whether aimed at the ego or at objects, was to be differentiated from other ego instincts, all of which could probably be understood as manifestations of death instincts. The death instincts are assumed to be a set of drives appearing in all living organisms, which tend to lead the organism back to its prenatal state of nonexistence. The continuing life of the organism is to be attributed to a temporary inactivation of the death instincts by the power of the erotic instincts. They are able to defer death by driving the organism through a "long circuit" (as opposed to a short circuit) or a detour, but the individual organism must ultimately succumb to its death instincts. The concept itself, and the argumentation leading up to it, seem abstruse, philosophic, and somewhat distant from clinical experience and therapy. Yet Freud was driven to this conclusion by certain clinical observations, namely, the need to repeat in dream and fantasy certain traumatic experiences, and the perversions of sadism and masochism. Little as we know of the nature and fluctuations of libido, or of the energy of the erotic instincts, we know less of the energy of the death instincts, to which Freud did not even assign a specific name. The death instincts, he said, "work silently." Few analysts have been able to accept this hypothesis of the existence of aggressive instincts. I have tried to relate the theory to the distinction between interspecific and intraspecific instincts, that is, the instincts which determine the organism's behavior with respect to organisms of different species, as opposed to those which determine its behavior with respect to organisms of the same species (Ostow, 1958d). It has struck me that in using energy theory to regulate the administration of drugs, only libido need be considered—not the energy of the death instincts. The latter are seen to come into operation in response to painful experience; their activation cannot be self-initiated. The erotic instincts, however, require no triggering stimulus, and their activation may be accounted for entirely by fluctuations of libido.

The ways in which the energies of Eros and the death instincts influence each other are taken up by Freud in papers of the early twenties, notably *The Ego and the Id* and *Inhibitions, Symptoms, and Anxiety* (Freud, 1923b; 1926d). Freud proposes that normally the destructive energies of the death instincts are tamed by being "fused" with libido. Under certain circumstances, "defusion" occurs and the destructive tendencies are liberated to express themselves in action and symptom. Defusion follows: (1) regression (of the id), that is, reversion of the dominant sexual modality to an infantile form; (2) identification, that is, assuming the characteristics of a loved object as if to become that person; and (3) sublimation, that is, altering the aim and object of an instinct so that it tends now toward some nonsensual activity rather than toward physical satisfaction. The libidinal energies which the ego obtains by its narcissistic cathexis are used to support and drive ego activities after they have been "desexualized." In other words, the impetus belonging to erotic instinctual impulses which have been repressed can be diverted from their somatic objectives and can lend their drive to activities which are not directly physical but which, in their synthetic, creative, constructive operations nevertheless express the primary tendency of Eros.

Regression of the id induces defusion with a liberation of aggressive energies by permitting unfused and unsublimated pregenital, sadistic, and masochistic energies to emerge into consciousness

The creation of a consistent theory of psychologic processes also profits from the energy theory. Dreams, errors, humor, and fantasy can all be elucidated when seen as consequences of the attempt of an instinctual impulse to traverse the channels, barriers, and resistances of the preconscious ego. Finally, and most important from the point of view of this study, Freud was able to account for some of the manifestations of psychosis—paranoia, schizophrenia, and melancholia—as the outcome of profound energetic changes in the ego. We shall be occupied with the further development of this last approach.

INSTINCTUAL ENERGY IN ETHOLOGY

The psychoanalytic concept of a fluid motivational impulse generated by instinctual sources has, in the past quarter century, found support in the hypothetical constructs of the ethologists. Lorenz, one of the most original and perceptive of these, terms this fluid motivating entity "action specific energy." He implies that each individual instinctual behavior pattern, as time passes, accumulates what seems to be a discharge pressure. A number of phenomena create this impression. First, the threshold for the triggering of an instinctual act sinks lower and lower as time passes following performance of the act. For example, an animal raised under human care will ordinarily have little opportunity to discharge its normal escape reaction. Under such circumstances, the slightest disturbance or warning call from another will set off an intense panic response. It is as though the failure to discharge this escape response over a period of time had resulted in the "damming up" (Lorenz' term, as well as Freud's) of its energy so that there was a greater readiness to respond. Similarly, when an instinctive act has not been performed recently, it will be triggered by less and less specific releasing stimuli. Thus, with the passage of time, cruder and cruder clay models will suffice as adequate releasers for an act which, shortly after its performance, will respond only to the most typical natural triggers. "Within certain limits," says Tinbergen (in his definitive textbook, *The Study of Instinct*), "there is a correlation between the intensity of the liminal stimulus and the length of time that has elapsed after the last feeding or the last coition, as the case may be." Lorenz says that performance of an instinctual act "pumps out" its action-specific energy.

Second, when a sufficient period of time has elapsed without opportunity for discharge, the instinctual act may suddenly "go off" without any trigger whatever. Such an unreleased act is called a "vacuum reaction," since the reaction occurs *in vacuo,* so to speak. For example, Lorenz has described the movements of catching and ingesting insects among captive starlings in the absence of insects. Tinbergen observed typical courtship activities in isolated stickle-backs. The theory is that an excessive accumulation of action-specific energy explodes through its normal discharge channels without waiting for an appropriate trigger.

Third, when a given set of circumstances tends to evoke an instinctual act and simultaneously to inhibit it, the act itself is not performed but usually a different and irrelevant act is substituted. This phenomenon is called a "displacement reaction." Here, theory says that the accumulated impetus presses for discharge, and if its appropriate channel is obstructed, it achieves release through another. Lorenz goes even further in the construction of an energetic system. He describes a certain retardation in response and in termination of response, as "initial friction" and "inertia of reaction," respectively (Lorenz, 1937, 1939, 1952; Lorenz and Tinbergen, 1938).

Tinbergen (1951) takes up Lorenz' notion of action specific energy and develops it further. He enumerates and illustrates the motivating factors which arise internally and states that they create a "readiness" to act. The readiness is triggered into action when a specific configuration "releases" it. The internal factors include priming by hormones, somatic stimuli, and intrinsic activity within the central nervous system. Hormones seem to pertain chiefly to the motivation of the reproductive instincts (Beach, 1948). Internal somatic stimuli create motivation relative to nutritive and hygienic needs. Intrinsic nervous activity seems to suffice for the generation of locomotive impulses, and, I suspect, other simple tool activities. Whereas Lorenz emphasized the energetic impulse residing in each type of instinctual act, Tinbergen gives more attention to what he calls the "hierarchical organization" of instincts. A general, superordinate instinctual tendency is primed, yet its impulse is not forthwith transmitted to neural centers impelling specific acts. Such transmission is blocked—except for appetitive acts, that is, acts that search out opportunities for discharge. Thus, when the reproductive drive (the superordinate instinctual tendency, in this case) of a male fish is stimulated, it migrates to a suitable milieu but does not build a nest, fight intruders, or court a mate (subordinate activities) until it encounters a proper opportunity. Meanwhile, it merely swims around "looking for" such an opportunity. When an appropriate configuration appears, for example, an intruding male, the fighting subdrive receives motivation from the superordinate reproductive center. Even at this level, however, the performance of the intruder acts as a sign stimulus to release only one or a few of the several methods of fighting available. Tinbergen's system is more elaborate than that of Lorenz; it deals with sources, channels, and sinks of motivation, and with blocks and releasers. It seems to provide a better model for the analysis of motivation in the sense that it relates the performance of specific instinctual acts to the strength of a general instinctual tendency. It is therefore more closely comparable to the energy concept of psychoanalytic theory.

Thorpe, in his splendid monograph, *Learning and Instinct in Animals,* reviews the history of the drive concept in psychology and ethology, and agrees with many of the views of both Lorenz and Tinbergen. However, he considers the latter's concept of an elaborate hierarchy of mutually influencing networks somewhat too mechanistic. It fails to account, he says, for the progressive sharpening, the increase in the precise specificity of releasers deriving from experience. He cannot subscribe to the ideal of a system which drives a sequence of acts from a superordinate center. The consummatory act must also contribute to the drive, as Lorenz' term, "action specific energy," suggests. Thorpe proposes the term, "specific action potential." In my opinion, the questions that Thorpe raises are legitimate, but they can be answered by attributing the drive force, the instinctual energy, to the superordinate center of the instinct, and the attraction exerted by successfully consummated acts to a subjective lure of the nature of an affect. Such a two-pronged theory of motivation is implicit in psychoanalytic theory as well.

I have included this brief review of ethologic theories of motivation merely to demonstrate their similarity to homologous constructs in psychoanalytic theory. While the resemblance is striking, it is not surprising, for the phenomena which they are devised to account for are essentially the same, namely, internal origin of motivation, extinction of drive with consummation, decrease of threshold with frustration, and displaceability of impulse. Further comparison of ethologic and psychoanalytic concepts may be found in my paper, "The Biological Basis of Human Behavior." Because these hypothetical motivating entities are essentially the same, and because, in my opinion, most of the effective psychopharmaceutic agents function by increasing or decreasing the amount of instinctual energy available, I should suggest that animal screening and testing of new agents by drug manufacturers could profit by assessing their effects on the instinctual behavior of the experimental subjects. The kind of study I have in mind, while it may not pertain directly to the question of instinctual energy, is exemplified by that of Hess (1957) who examined the effects of chlorpromazine, meprobamate, and pentobarbital on imprinting in birds. Tranquilizing drugs have been found to retard the learning of conditioned responses and to impair their performance. It has been inferred that the drugs obtund the animal's perceptual or affective sensitivity to unconditioned and conditioned stimuli. I believe that the same observations can be accounted for as the result of a diminution in the intensity of the motivation of the unconditioned behavior. The observations themselves do not favor one rather than the other theory. I should guess that the effect of a drug on the intensity of an animal's reproductive drive, in its natural milieu, would provide a better estimate of its ability to control mental illness than its effect on conditioned escape from electric shock in a small cage. The testing problem is difficult because one cannot reproduce in animals the mental illnesses that the chemicals are expected to alleviate in humans. Nevertheless, close observation of the influence of these drugs upon the several kinds of instinctual behavior, administered, as they are to humans, in small amounts over weeks and months, may teach us not only about the drugs but about mental illness too, or at least about its homologues—if there are any—in animals. (Since we have learned how to precipitate the various mental illnesses in humans by the administration of tranquilizers and energizers, it will be interesting and useful from a pharmacologic point of view to examine the behavioral states induced by similar procedures in animals.)

PRACTICAL APPLICATION

Freud introduced the idea of a psychic energy as an explanatory concept in his attempt to understand and account for the phenomena of normal behavior and mental illness. In more recent literature, the same kind of approach has been extended and amplified. I believe that we are now in a position to utilize the concept in clinical diagnostic and therapeutic work.

In the next portion of this chapter I shall investigate some of the anatomic and physiologic correlates of psychic energy fluctuations. Although at this early stage many of my specific conclusions may be incorrect, it is important to establish that psychic energy changes accompany and are accompanied by many diverse alterations of body state. Some of these are significant because they can be used as clinical indicators. Others require attention because they constitute disturbing side effects of drug administration. Still others serve as connecting links between psychic function and somatic illness. Some will have theoretic interest only.

When I began to observe the effects of the drugs we now call tranquilizers upon patients in analysis, it occurred to me that the clinical changes could all be accounted for as the result of variations in the ego's supply of libido. This inference was in accord with Freud's suggestion of 1937 to the effect that when chemical agents capable of influencing the course of mental illness are discovered, their action will be exerted upon the energies of the psyche (Freud, 1940a). I found that the administration of tranquilizers and their withdrawal, and similarly the administration of energizers and their withdrawal, produced a consistent sequence of changes in the mode of ego function. The sequence of changes was actually predictable. Further, effects induced by tranquilizers were reversed by energizers, ego function traversing the same sequential path with only the direction changed to its opposite. I concluded that ego function varies sensitively with the amount of psychic energy available to it. For numerous reasons, to be discussed fully below, I think it is libido, rather than total energy, which is the relevant variable. In Chapter III I shall discuss the actual variations in ego function.

If the mode of ego function is determined by the ego's libido content, then perceptible ego function can be used to indicate the level of the ego's libido supply. I have suggested a method for estimating ego libido content, in Chapter III. When this method is applied in the course of daily psychoanalytic work, the analyst can detect variations not only in the patient's dynamic status but also in his energetic status. It will then be apparent that alterations in clinical behavior are determined both by dynamics and by energetics; moreover, that dynamics and energetics influence each other consistently. For example, one day, quite abruptly, a patient reports that she has become depressed. She cannot understand why. She says that she "feels unattractive," had difficulty sleeping the previous night, and had neither appetite nor sexual desire. In the analytic session she shows considerably more self-observation than usual, and is especially concerned with feelings of guilt and unhappiness. The dynamics of the change proved rather obscure and were not disclosed by the material of the session. I have, however, learned to recognize these phenomena as components of the syndrome of ego impoverishment. They are determined primarily by the loss of libido and are fairly nonspecific with respect to dynamic cause. That is, they are consistent from patient to patient with relatively little variation, and in any given patient the entire syndrome may be brought about by any of the usual causes of libido depletion, not all of which are related dynamically, or by the administration of a tranquilizer. If they do not subside spontaneously, they can be reversed by the action of an energizer. In the case of the patient just described (D. N. O.), I knew that the most common cause of depletion was object loss. At the time, she was planning a vacation trip to the West Coast with her husband, and departure was scheduled for just three days hence. The object loss, in this instance, was the anticipated separation from me. Since she was only recently in remission from severe catatonic psychosis, and was still maintained on drugs, I did not wish to disturb her fragile equilibrium nor to change the ratio of drugs which had been established only after an arduous balancing procedure. Therefore, I advised her to cancel the trip. The next day, the "depression," that is, the symptoms of ego impoverishment, had resolved completely. I wish to demonstrate here that certain clinical syndromes can be understood and handled more readily as the consequences of variation in ego libido supply, than as the consequences of the dynamic changes which have produced the energy change. This situation may be encountered in neurotics as well as psychotics. An awareness of the clinical syndromes and alterations of ego function associated with oscillations in energy supply rather than with specific dynamic constellations often clarifies puzzling phenomena. No doubt the reader will have many questions about the foregoing illustration. Most of these will be considered subsequently.

It is important, interesting, and perhaps surprising to note that an increase of motivation arises not only from an increase in the libido content of the ego, but also from a threatening or incipient decrease. This fact makes the estimation of libido level a difficult and subtle problem.

Following the discussion of variations in ego function that are effected by changes in the ego's libido level, we shall turn, in Chapter IV, to the energetics of mental illness. There will be found a recapitulation of classical theory of the pathogenesis of illness, emphasizing energetics. I shall introduce the suggestion that depletion of the ego occurs as a normal corrective maneuver when the libido level is threatening to rise too high. This hypothesis may account for the fact that in many instances mental illness starts with a syndrome of libido plethora and then passes to a syndrome of impoverishment. As a result of the discussion of pathogenesis, we shall be able to formulate the basic principles of psychiatric drug therapy. Further, we shall see how drug therapy may be used synergistically with psychoanalysis or psychotherapy.

The pathogenesis and course of specific mental illnesses will be considered next. We shall find that in several diseases, at least two distinct, though superficially similar, syndromes may be distinguished, one occurring in a state of libido plethora, one in a state of depletion. In other words, some of the variety of clinical syndromes found in specific neurotic or psychotic disease entities may be ascribed to alterations in the ego's libido content. It will be observed, for example, that the phobias, obsessions, and conversions occurring in a state of plethora differ from those occurring in a state of depletion. This principle will be useful for avoiding errors in drug prescription. Unfortunately, after ego breakdown has occurred, as in schizophrenia, the plethora and depletion syndromes are often difficult to distinguish, and therapy becomes correspondingly subtle. The principles of libido estimation, drug therapy, and the mode of combining drugs with psychological therapy are illustrated in two detailed case reports: one, a patient with neurotic illness, and the second, a patient with psychotic illness (chapters V and VI, respectively).

After having considered the clinical observations, elaboration of the theory, and practical applications, we shall be in a position to permit ourselves an intellectual luxury, that is, an exploratory extension of these concepts to the phenomena of group living, including group morale and religious organization. This projection will be based upon clinical observations of the effect of variations of the individual's libido level on his behavior with respect to others, and upon conjectures about the influence of group morale on the individual's libido content.

In summary, what we shall undertake to study in this work is:

(1) The influence of fluctuations of the ego's content of libido upon the ego's mode of function.

(2) The estimation of the ego's libido content from observable aspects of ego function.

(3) The usefulness of libido estimation in following a patient's therapeutic course.

(4) The interplay between dynamics and energetics.

(5) The role of libido fluctuation in the pathogenesis of mental illness.

(6) The usefulness of libido estimation in determining when drug therapy is indicated, and how it is to be pursued.

(7) How drug therapy and psychotherapy can be effectively combined.

(8) The application of the libido concept to problems of social living.

ANATOMIC AND PHYSIOLOGIC CORRELATES

Energy, the basal ganglia, and the drugs

In 1954, I attempted to guess, from the neuroanatomic and neurophysiologic data then available, which structures of the brain might be concerned with the psychologic functions we know in psychoanalytic metapsychology (Ostow, 1954, 1955, a and b). I found it reasonable to assign to the premotor frontal regions of the human brain the "function of devising and energizing derivatives of instinctual drives and unconscious fantasies, and of regulating the rate and sequence in which unconscious fantasies determine day to day behavior." I took note of the fact that the dorsomedial nucleus of the thalamus, which in the human projects to the premotor frontal region, in lower mammals projects to the striatal nuclei. The idea that the premotor frontal region of the brain possessed a motor energizing function could be inferred from the supposition that in the course of evolutionary development it seemed to take over some functions of the striatum.

Two years later, Kline and I, writing on the "Psychic Action of Reserpine and Chlorpromazine," called attention to the fact that both of these substances, although different in molecular structure, shared the psychic effect of tranquilization and a physiologic effect of inducing the Parkinsonian syndrome. We inferred, as others have too, that these drugs probably exerted their influence upon the basal ganglia. We suggested that some part of the basal ganglia complex, probably the globus pallidus, could be considered the source of instinctual energy; I still consider this a good hypothesis. If it is not the basal ganglia themselves, at least it is some structure that activates them directly.

It is reasonable to assign the function of generating instinctual impetus to the most archaic motor structure of the central nervous system. Among vertebrates, the striatal complex is the most archaic motor structure above the level of "the final common path," the specific motor nuclei (Kappers, Huber, Crosby, 1936, p. 1482ff.). The paleostriatum is represented in man by the globus pallidus. Starting early in the phylogenetic series, a neostriatum makes its appearance. It receives fibers from the thalamus and the cortex, and projects to the paleostriatum. In mammals, the neostriatum includes the putamen, the caudate nucleus, the amygdaloid complex, and the claustrum. The globus pallidus projects via the ansa lenticularis to the subthalamic nuclei and other midbrain motor centers. It would seem that the paleostriatum is concerned with the initiation of impulse, while its action is modulated by the structures of the neostriatum, which, in turn, are informed by the thalamus and the cortex.

Lesions of the globus pallidus, pathologic or experimental, result in the Parkinsonian syndrome, of which inertia is a prominent part. Although most neurologists and neurosurgeons who deal with Parkinsonism are interested in alleviating the tremor and rigidity, the inertia is generally just as distressing to the patient, or more so. It is more than simply an akinesia: it seems to be an impairment in motivation (Schwab *et al.*, 1959). Lesions of the putamen and caudate nucleus cause overactivity (Davis, 1955, 1958). If an animal rendered overactive by such a lesion then has both pallida removed, he becomes underactive and retains imposed postures (Mettler, 1948, p. 422f.). Suppression of the electrical activity of the cortex, obtained by stimulation of one of the cortical "suppressor strips," is mediated by the caudate nucleus. A lesion of the latter, however, does not suffice to interfere with the associated suppression of motor activity (McCulloch, 1944). Unfortunately, experimental observations on the effects of stimulation or extirpation of these structures have been limited to their acute effects, or their effects upon the integrity of locomotive and other motor performances, rather than upon instinctual behavior. The difficulty cannot be ascribed entirely to a lack of interest in instinctual activities; unfortunately, behavior regulation is so delicately balanced that any injury to the brain disrupts it grossly, so that it would seem virtually impossible to demonstrate small, specific defects in the patterns of appetitive or consummatory behavior sequences associated with small, specific lesions. I believe, however, that the tranquilizing drugs, given in small doses over long periods of time, can be used to create functional deficits of the basal ganglia and consequent focused effects on behavior.

It is interesting to note that the amygdaloid complex, or at least its basolateral, nonolfactory portion, is a part of the neostriatum, and hence presumably participates in the latter's regulatory inhibition of the globus pallidus. Since there is reason to suppose that the function of the anterior part of the temporal lobe, including the amygdaloid nucleus, is apperceptive evaluation of the presenting environment (Ostow, 1955, a and b), one wonders whether the amygdaloid complex may be the link whereby the rhinencephalic system can exert an inhibitory influence upon instinctual motivation.

About ten years ago, the brilliant experimental work of French, Magoun, and their associates demonstrated the existence, within the reticulated substance of the core of the midbrain and in portions of the thalamus, of a mechanism which, when stimulated, causes behavioral alerting and desynchronization of the electrical activity of the cortex. This interesting mechanism has engaged the fancy of psychiatrists and neurophysiologists, some of whom have ascribed to it functions of consciousness, of awareness, of apperception, and so on. Naturally, there have been attempts to demonstrate that the newer drugs exert their definitive influence upon this system. While no one can doubt the accuracy of the initial observations and the importance of the reticular activating system in the psychophysiological economy, I find no experimental evidence that its function is anything other than an alerting one. The behavioral changes it evokes are arousal of a sleeping animal and alerting of a resting one. More than that cannot be claimed for it. These changes are always elicited by stimulation. To my knowledge the system has never been shown experimentally to exert a continuing tonic influence, or to be self-activated. The properties of the reticular activating system are not the properties of the hypothetical source of instinctual energy, so that I cannot view it as a serious candidate for that role. Moreover, there are some reliable students of neuropharmacology who have studied the influence of some of the newer agents on the activating system and conclude that such action cannot be considered responsible for their therapeutic effect (Killam and Killam, 1960).

This is about as much as we can say in direct support of the hypothesis that instinctual energy is generated within or close to the basal ganglia. However, we can adduce additional support for two other hypotheses which, taken together, strengthen the former. First, the tranquilizing and energizing drugs achieve their therapeutic and occasionally pathogenic effects by decreasing and increasing, respectively, the level of instinctual energy in the psyche—that is, the level of psychic energy. Second, the tranquilizing and energizing drugs exert their definitive influence upon the basal ganglia. The evidence for the first of these subsidiary propositions is indirect. I am not aware of any studies of the effect of these drugs upon specific instinctual drives. Moreover, those animal studies that we have deal with the acute effects of the drugs rather than with the chronic effects, which are the therapeutic ones. The studies we do have, however, show that the tranquilizers produce a clear tendency to a decrease of total behavioral activity, both spontaneous and induced. For example, the rate of spontaneous locomotor activity of rats is reduced by tranquilizers (Irwin, 1960), and the fighting response of Siamese fighting fish is arrested (Walaszek and Abood, 1956). The tranquilizers also impair performance of conditioned responses (Wikler, 1957, p. 251ff.). With some specific exceptions, the tranquilizing drugs decrease vital functions such as respiratory rate, blood pressure, and body temperature, while the energizing drugs increase them. One important exception to this rule is that all of the known energizing drugs tend to decrease blood pressure.

Finally, turning our attention from the instinctual energy of animals to the psychic energy of humans, we can, if we accept some of Freud's suggestions, find further support for this thesis. Freud proposed (1911c, 1917e): (1) that melancholia was accompanied by "impoverishment" of the ego, that is, by a loss of its libido supply; (2) that mania was accompanied by a surfeit of libido; and (3) that paranoia was preceded by increase of libido due to damming up. Let us recall now that the tranquilizing drugs, which alleviate mania and paranoia, act—according to our view—to decrease the libido content of the ego, and that the anti-depressant drugs, which relieve melancholia, have, in our opinion, been correctly termed "energizers," because they increase the libido content of the ego. While none of these arguments is conclusive, their concordance is impressive.

What evidence have we that the tranquilizing and energizing drugs achieve their effects by their action upon the basal ganglia? The most cogent argument is the fact that all three chemically distinct types of tranquilizers—the phenothiazines, reserpine, and tetrabenazine—produce extrapyramidal side effects and, in general, the more potent a substance is as a tranquilizer, the more likely it is to produce these side effects. Thus far, it has proved impossible to dissociate a true tranquilizing action from a propensity to evoke extrapyramidal symptoms. The energizers, on the other hand, do not evoke signs of extrapyramidal disorder except in the case of imipramine, and amitryptiline, which resemble a phenothiazine in structure. Because their effects are not exactly opposed to each other, it is possible in some instances to administer a tranquilizer and an energizer at the same time without cancelling their respective therapeutic actions. We shall discuss the indications for, and the results of, this combined therapy below. Nevertheless, there is some reason to believe that even the hydrazine energizers influence basal ganglia function. Saunders (1959), for example, summarizes the points we have made, and adds the observation that monoamine oxidase, which is inhibited by the hydrazines and some other energizers (e.g., procaine; Bucci and Saunders, 1960), has been found to be elevated in the lenticular nucleus and serum of schizophrenics.

To recapitulate briefly, I have tried to adduce evidence in support of the following three propositions:

(1) The basal ganglia are concerned with the generation or distribution of instinctual energy.

(2) Tranquilizing and energizing drugs act upon the basal ganglia.

(3) Tranquilizing drugs act to decrease the amount of instinctual energy available to the ego; energizing drugs act to increase it.

Extrapyramidal Drug Effects and Spontaneous Manifestations of Disease

The striking resemblance between the extrapyramidal manifestations of basal ganglia disease and some of the symptoms of mental illness has been commented on in the past; for a decade after the 1916 epidemic of encephalitis, it was the subject of much study and speculation (F. H. Lewy, A. Jakob, and S. E. Jelliffe, all quoted by Tislow et al., 1960; Rosner, 1942). This interesting comparison has again achieved currency with the finding that these same manifestations are elicited by the drugs which possess both therapeutic and pathogenic potential in mental illness.

The symptoms of extrapyramidal disorder occurring during treatment with a tranquilizing drug are often frightening or distressing to the patient, and almost equally so to the psychiatrist—hence they have been termed "toxic" effects. Yet the evidence seems to indicate that, although they are effects in the sense that they are other than the desired therapeutic effect, actually they are only motor accompaniments of the total psychophysiologic change we are seeking to produce. They are an intrinsic part of the drug action, although we would prefer to obtain only the psychologic change and avoid the physical. We can do this either by keeping doses relatively low, or by counteracting the motor changes with anti-Parkinsonian drugs, such as benztropine methansulfonate (Cogentin) or procyclidine hydrochloride (Kemadrin).

Can we infer a specific relation between the extrapyramidal manifestations and the psychic events which accompany them? Consider first the individual basal ganglia syndromes that are elicited by the tranquilizers, and the sequence in which they are likely to occur. Within hours or days of the first administration of a potent tranquilizer, an acute dystonia may appear. We see torticollis,

jaw displacement, body twist, tongue protrusion, biting, oculogyric spasm, limb cramps, dysphagia, and dysarthria. These are
often accompanied by profuse sweating and a facial expression
of distress. Such phenomena suggest hysterical movements and
paralyses, which consist of aversive gestures, and also some of the
attitudes of tense, negativistic catatonia. In both catatonia and certain symptoms of hysteria, the physical and mental disengagement
from the world of reality is not only symbolized but achieved
through these gestures and attitudes. In the same group, I would
include cases of drug-induced "catatonia." May (1959) has described two schizophrenic patients who exhibited cataleptic states
similar to genuine catatonia only *after* tranquilizers had been given.
The catalepsy subsided when medication was discontinued and replaced by Cogentin.

This occurrence is reminiscent of the catalepsy induced in animals by phenothiazine drugs (Tislow *et al.,* 1960). Tislow remarks
that "it would appear somewhat of a paradox that a compound
which produces catalepsy in animals should be useful in the
treatment of catatonic patients." A patient of mine changed from
an inert, relaxed catatonic to a tense, negativistic catatonic under
the influence of a hydrazine energizer. At this point, 5 mg. of intramuscular Trilafon produced some relaxation. A second dose
eighteen hours later was followed after four hours by a resumption
of the tense catatonia, but this time with tongue protrusion. This
attack was alleviated within minutes by intramuscular sodium amytal. A third injection of Trilafon given two hours thereafter was
succeeded by a resumption of the catatonia six hours later, with
tongue and lip biting. This also responded to amytal. I dwell upon
this point because I believe it may elucidate the drug-induced
phenomenon of early dystonia. Specifically, here is a situation
where a drug given to reduce an excess of ego libido reproduces or
accentuates the spontaneous manifestations of libido plethora even
before it has had much opportunity to reduce its level. One may
guess that hysterical spasms and cataleptic resistance are the motor components of archaic forms of aversion to a threatening stimulus. From a psychoanalytic point of view, they are defenses against
the emergence of repressed erotic wishes toward a love object.
That being the case, we may surmise that the drug acts to attenuate
the disease by reinforcing and imitating natural defenses. Thus, the
first stage in draining the ego of excess libido is turning away from

the object that arouses it, or—in the case of schizophrenia—from the entire animate world.

The patient I have mentioned, who responded to Trilafon with tense, negativistic catatonia, began her illness in the following manner. She had suspected that she was being poisoned. While eating breakfast with her husband in a hotel room, she suddenly felt a spasm in her throat and jaw and tenseness in her shoulder muscles, and ran out of the room, scantily dressed, shouting, "Save me! He's going to kill me!" On the basis of this hysterical type of behavior in schizophrenia, I anticipated that this was funda-mentally a catatonic illness. Here the defense against the threaten-ing love object was muscular and oral aversion and then flight. Treatment with tranquilizers relieved her anxiety and desperation at first, but then either induced, or failed to prevent, a regression into inert catatonia. In the tense catatonic state which came about after the administration of Niamid, there was a negativistic defiance of all influence, and the mouth was held tightly shut. The same was true during the relapses induced by the Trilafon, except that here the tongue protruded so that it was injured by the teeth. Dur-ing the phase of hysterical behavior—that is, before the onset of the extreme muscular reactions—this patient would often complain of cramps in her neck and shoulders. These were doubtless the minor antecedents of the subsequent major spasms. But neck and shoulder cramps are relatively often encountered in the defensive phenomena of hysterics and paranoid schizophrenics, for exam-ple, in the cases of K. N. X. (see Chapter V) and R. L. X. When an energizing drug is given to a hysteric or schizophrenic, muscular cramps follow frequently. In fact, the occurrence of muscular cramps is often cited as a side effect of treatment with the hydra-zine energizers. It is difficult to avoid the inference that both the minor and major muscular reactions were expressions of defensive aversion, and the innate motor patterns of defensive aversion are what the tranquilizers may reproduce as dystonic spasms before they reduce the pathogenic libido plethora.

When a course of tranquilizing medication has proceeded for a few weeks—sometimes for just a few days—a restlessness appears. The patient fidgets and twitches; he must rise from his seat and pace. This symptom has become known as akathisia, a term intro-duced by Wilson to denote the urgent restlessness and distressing need to move occurring in paralysis agitans and postencephalitic

Parkinsonism. Here, again, the drug effect resembles not only a symptom of basal ganglia disease but also a symptom of mental illness, for these phenomena are similar to the agitation common to melancholic depression, especially as the disease is waxing in intensity. I am inclined to infer that akathisia is an automatic response to the progressive decrease of ego libido which occurs in the disease process. It probably has a function in the redistribution of energies, and may represent an effort either to dissipate energies or to retrieve them. In the first instance, the energies to be dissipated may be libido which is to be excluded from the ego. That is, the akathisia may resemble the fidgeting which normally occurs when an individual voluntarily restricts physical movements in the interest of concentration on a mental task. After a shorter or longer period of suspension of physical activity, a restlessness breaks through. The fidgeting and restlessness seem, therefore, to be efforts to drain off harmlessly the impulse to physical movement that would otherwise intrude into the mental activity. Another possibility is that the akathisia serves to dissipate harmlessly the energies of the death instinct, which are roused to action by the psychic pain of depression, and which are undiluted now due to the dearth of libido. Commonly, the agitation of incipient depression issues in a violent act, such as smashing a window pane. Or contrariwise, the akathisia may represent an effort to mobilize the emergency forces of the ego to combat the painful depletion. We know that physical activity as well as the maintenance of an erect posture exert an arousing, alerting influence on tonic ego functions. At present, I have no data which would permit me to choose among these possibilities, nor can I determine whether the drug-induced akathisia is a similar defensive effort to assist or resist the depleting effect of the drug, or whether, like the early dystonias and muscular spasms, it is a neurologic response to the drug itself, a paradigm which corresponds to but is not the same as the akathisia of agitated depression. It may be the first in some patients and the second in others. In the course of melancholia, the phase of akathisia comes to an end when the depletion process has come to an end, ego libido remaining at a low level and the melancholia changing from agitated to inert. It can also be terminated by the administration of an energizer, at least in those cases which have not been induced by medication.

There are three common forms of disorder: dystonias, akathisia, and Parkinsonism. I have listed these in the sequence in which they are likely to appear: dystonias within the first four or five days of treatment with a tranquilizing drug; akathisia within one to three weeks; Parkinsonism after two to four weeks. Of course, the rapidity of onset depends upon the potency of the preparation used and the dose; what is more, not every patient develops all of these symptoms. In fact, half of the patients, or more, will develop none.

Finally, a full Parkinsonian syndrome will occur in as many as half the patients treated with tranquilizers if the treatment lasts long enough. After weeks or months of medication, inertia, rigidity, tremor, dissolution of erect posture, loss of associated movements, blank relaxed facial expression, drooling, and cessation of blinking may occur. The same inertia, loss of vigor, blankness of facies, absence of blinking, and flexor prevalence in posture, characterize profound melancholia and inert forms of catatonia. In all three instances, I believe that the manifestations are to be ascribed to profound loss of ego libido. This is apparent in the common lack of animation, psychic and physical retardation, and muscular relaxation. The features appearing in Parkinsonism which are absent from melancholia and inert catatonia may be regarded as motor equivalents, components, aspects, or caricatures of libido depletion. One might wonder once more whether these are merely the response to the drug-induced depletion, or whether they are a neurologically induced paradigmatic prototype of the response. Since the motor aspects of Parkinsonism are so much more extreme than the motor phenomena of melancholia, we must favor the latter view.

All of these extrapyramidal syndromes can be terminated or alleviated by one of the anti-Parkinson drugs, and the dystonias can also be relieved by parenteral barbiturate, or by intravenous caffeine. However, I have seen no data on the influence that a hydrazine energizer could have upon them. Since it would tend to exaggerate the libido plethora, I should expect it to facilitate spontaneous defenses and thus sensitize the patient to the dystonic influences of the tranquilizers. For example, before she received the energizer, my patient did not respond to tranquilizers with muscular spasm. Since energizers would oppose the libido depletion that I believe is directly responsible for the akathisia, I would expect these drugs to attenuate, retard, or prevent it. Energizers limit the libido depletion that tranquilizers bring about, and of which Parkinsonism is, in my opinion, only the motor component. Whether the energizers could also resolve the latter, I cannot guess. If they do, it would be interesting to investigate their effect upon spontaneous Parkinsonism.

The problem is not a simple one, for we have to take into account the fact that although behaviorally the energizers and the tranquilizers oppose each other, chemically the monoamine oxidase inhibitors potentiate the action of many drugs which act upon the central nervous system. My patient, L. N. S., required 400 mg. of Niamid daily to recover from a depletion syndrome which presented as a paranoid and catatonic schizophrenia. She seemed to be quite well after about three weeks of this high dosage. On the second day of her recovery, I noticed some twitching of her right arm and an excessive tendency to use it in gesturing. Her mouth, too, seemed excessively active. The next day she was in a state of mute catatonia. When I added 40 mg. of Mellaril to her daily medication, the catatonia resolved and she returned to a nonpsychotic state, but began to show motor Parkinsonism. Here Parkinsonism supervened in the absence of depletion, so that it was plainly a neural response to the phenothiazine. It is worth noting that 40 mg. of Mellaril is a very low dose of a compound which is relatively benign with respect to the evocation of motor side effects. Evidently its propensity to induce these effects was greatly augmented by the accompanying monoamine oxidase inhibitor.

I realize that in this discussion I have wandered far from clinical data into speculation. But if these speculations help us, even as a mnemonic, to organize in our minds the diverse data, and if they lead us to profitable investigations, they will have earned the attention we are giving them. Here I have been following up one of Freud's (1926d, p. 93) suggestions, namely, that the motor components of affective states are abbreviated precipitates of phylogenetically archaic responses to traumatic events, much as an hysterical symptom is an abbreviated version of a trauma which was once important in the individual's history. On the basis of the motor accompaniments of the action of the tranquilizers, I am proposing that spontaneous natural defensive attempts to reduce a libido plethora are executed in two phases: first, a turning away from the tempting, but unattainable, object; and second, a direct effect upon libido supply. Such aversion from a source of pain consists only of a physical turning away in the case of lower animals. The spasms induced by the tranquilizers may represent the aversive, ejective, or resistive movements and attitudes persisting from lower forms into human life, which are largely, but not completely, replaced in the human by psychic disengagement from the object (such as one sees in hysteria and, more catastrophically, in schizophrenia). Akathisia is a motor response to the loss of libido from the ego. It often accompanies the psychic agitation which supervenes in early depletion, but the neural pattern itself can be elicited by tranquilizing drugs. The neural pattern may be seen as an innate defensive response to loss of instinctual energy, upon which, in humans, psychic restlessness and clinging are superimposed. Finally, Parkinsonism may be the motor component of some state of profound depletion which occurs naturally in lower animals.

Frequency of Blinking

Spontaneous rapid blinking is one of those everyday phenomena that are for the most part neglected, although obviously, in some obscure way, closely tied to some aspect of the psychic life or of mentation. Blinking has received some attention from psychologists who have considered it an indicator of difficulty of vision (Ponder and Kennedy, 1928; Luckiesh and Moss, 1942) or of difficulty in problem solving (Clites, 1935). Its easy susceptibility to measurement and its broad fluctuation with subtle changes in attitude intrigued me fifteen years ago, and I published some observations (1945) which, unfortunately, did little to elucidate its nature. I was able to show that psychotics, as a group, blink at a less uniform rate than recovered psychotics and nonpsychotic patients; my sample consisted largely of young hospitalized schizophrenics. I was not able to find any simple monotonic relation between rate of blinking and other subjective or objective manifestations of mental illness, such as visible affect, autism, compliance, responsiveness of reflexes, facial mobility, and general mobility. Estimates of some of these variables, however, showed distinct maxima or minima at intermediate rates of blinking. From this fact, I guessed that the frequency of blinking must be determined by at least two independent variables. I speculated that the physiologic function of blinking might be the facilitation of ocular blood flow by milking ocular veins, and that its frequency was automatically increased in the presence of a need to sharpen apperceptive and conceptual definition.

At about the same time, Sir Arthur Hall, a British opthalmologist, published a detailed paper in which he considered blinking as a biological phenomenon (Hall, 1945). He divided blinking into four varieties: (1) voluntary blinking; (2) reflex or automatic blinking, that is, blinking in reaction to a threat; (3) the spontaneous blinking of daily life; and (4) blinking of "technique," that is, blinking associated with punctuation during reading aloud. His chief interest, like ours, is the function of spontaneous blinking (Group 3). He cites Blount, who observed that the frequency of blinking among carnivora averages less than two per minute; among herbivora, ten and one-half per minute; and among arboreal primates, about twenty-four per minute, which is the same rate as for humans. Hall offered the interesting hypothesis that the purpose of such spontaneous blinking is to interrupt a "fixation reflex" which would otherwise hold the gaze of the animal fixed at a single target and make it difficult for him to turn to a new percept. Such a mechanism would be important for vulnerable herbivora to permit ready response to indications of danger. He suggests that the increased rate of blinking with "nervousness, emotion, or excitement" among humans is also a response to something feared—not a real, immediate danger, but an ancestral, unknown fear, the intensity of which varies with the individual. His idea, in short, is that defensive vigilance requires a frequent arrest of fixation so that there will be a readiness to turn one's attention elsewhere. One would infer, then, that the frequency of blinking varies directly with the degree of vigilance—and also, a point he did not make, with the intensity of fixation. Translating this into dynamic terminology, we should say that frequent blinking occurs when there is a need to interrupt attachment to an object. It would signify both intense attraction to the object and a simultaneous need to break away.

Since we know that the frequency of blinking is severely decreased in Parkinsonism, and since I have considered the possibility that the Parkinsonian syndrome induced by the tranquilizing drugs might be the motor prototype of ego depletion, it occurred to me that blinking might indicate the level of ego libido supply. For this reason, I undertook to count the frequency of blinking among my analytic patients. The method is simple enough. At the beginning of each session, when the patient has settled down, and while he is speaking, I set a stop watch going and stop it after I have counted twenty blinks. The counting time required is generally less than a minute. When the patient blinks infrequently, I count only ten blinks and in some cases just seven or five, so that the entire procedure distracts me for only a fraction of a minute. The counting can be carried out from behind the couch entirely without the patient's knowledge. It is somewhat more difficult to count blinks vis-à-vis, for patients tend to become uncomfortable if one stares at their eyes too steadily. Because the time required for twenty blinks varies from a minimum of nine seconds to three minutes or more, and because a difference of, say, five seconds represents a 50 per cent increase at the lower level and a negligible increase at the upper end, I have devised arbitrary logarithmic intervals which cover the entire range of usual variation. With such a scale, each step upward represents a constant percentage increase in frequency.

TABLE 1. *Scale of Blink Frequency*

SCALE POSITION	TIME REQUIRED FOR 20 BLINKS (IN SECONDS)
0	155
1	116
2	87
3	65
4	49
5	37
6	28
7	21
8	16
9	12
10	9

Using such an eleven-point scale rather than the actual number of seconds accomplishes two things. First, it minimizes the influence of small chance variations. Second, it records equivalent percentage changes rather than absolute changes: each scale interval represents an increase of one-third in frequency of blinking. Counts falling between two fixed points are assigned to the closer point. (More precisely, one should interpolate by dividing the intervals between each two successive points in a ratio of 3:4. There is no objection to this, but such precision is not required by the nature of the data.)

Is the blinking rate throughout a fifty-minute session so steady that a single count will be representative? In many patients, it remains well within a range of one-third from its lowest to its highest values within a single session. For these patients, the rate remains remarkably steady from day to day throughout the analysis. Let me illustrate by giving the rates (stated as scale numbers) for such a patient, counted on the first day of each month during two-and-one-half years of analysis: 6, 5, 7, 6, 7, 7, 7, 5, 5, 7, 5, 5, 6, 6, 5, 6, 8, 6, 6, 8, 8, 6, 6, 8, 5, 7. This series represents a very high degree of steadiness. The patient (C. J.) is compulsive, methodical, and reliable. A similar series in the case of a patient whose blink rate is extremely variable follows: 5, 7, 6, 6, 3, 4, 5, 3, 5, 5, 4, 2, 5, 3, 4, 5, 2, 6, 0, 3, 3. He is a withdrawn, dreamy, often depressed person, who has at infrequent intervals exhibited some traces of schizophrenic-type thinking. We should remember that as much as one-third fluctuation from a hypothetical mean can be tolerated within the same scale interval, and that one scale interval deviation on either side of the mean would cover a difference in absolute blink rate of more than 100 per cent. For example, assume that the characteristic rate for a given session is 5, and let us grant that a count of 4 may mean 3, 4, or 5, and that a count of 6 may mean 5, 6, or 7. Then we will understand that a true hypothetical mean of 5 may be indicated by actual counts of 4, 5, or 6. Now the number of seconds for twenty blinks is 49 for position 4, and 28 for position 6. In fact, when we consider interpolation, we will call a period of 55 seconds position 4, and 25 seconds position 6. Thus we shall be able to tolerate a change in absolute rate of two to one before we consider that a difference is significant. If, then, we acknowledge that any scale position is to be understood as that, plus or minus one, and if we look for consistent trends in a series of counts without giving too much attention to an individual value, we shall find that we are dealing with a useful variable.

Do these counts have diagnostic value? Can they be correlated with diagnosis? No, they cannot. Neither extreme of the blink frequency range, nor its center, can be considered characteristic of any diagnostic grouping. Can we make any superficial distinction between frequent blinkers and infrequent blinkers? Only a gross generalization. For the most part, the frequent blinkers, those whose counts are consistently 8, 9, or 10, are active, alert, quick, and continually striving. Of course, much of their activity may be neurotic waste motion, but I suppose this would be especially true of patients in analysis. Patients whose counts are consistently less than 5 seem to be less active, more inert, less striving. That is not to say that they are not ambitious, or that they are less effectual or more content; it is only that there is less intensity to their activity. A count of o is unusual in the absence of distinct ego depletion, but it cannot be considered pathognomonic of severe mental illness. The second patient I mentioned above occasionally showed such infrequent blinking without exhibiting more distinctly pathologic signs than on other days.

Note that the blinking rate fluctuates considerably from time to time during the day for any given individual. Reading aloud or listening to music is accompanied by considerable slowing of the rate. Problem solving or attempting to comprehend a difficult situation raises the rate. Even during the analytic session there are periods of rapid blinking lasting a few seconds, and other periods when blinking is suspended for a while. These tend to average out so that by counting for thirty to sixty seconds, a characteristic rate is secured, but the fact is that the blinks are often bunched. More consistent results are obtained if one counts only while the patient is speaking. I have not been able to discern the specific psychic events, such as memory, imagery, calculation, and recitation, which correlate with this bunching. One reason may be that I hesitate to permit myself to be distracted from the analytic material itself for more than a few moments. The problem remains open.

Now let us return to our principle concern: Does the frequency of blinking correlate with ego libido content? In order to answer this question, we must have not only a measure of blink frequency but also a measure of ego libido content. I know of no direct measure of ego libido content, but we can make either of two auxiliary assumptions which will permit us to continue with our investigation. We may assume that: (1) tranquilizers decrease, and energizers increase, ego libido content; and (2) there are characteristics of ego function which can be utilized as indicators of libido content. Actually, as we shall see in the next chapter, I have devised psychologic criteria which I believe can be used to assess libido content. Now, while these two assumptions are conceptually distinct, the fact is that I have always used psychologic criteria to estimate libido content since I have been administering these drugs, so that the observations have been concurrent. Moreover, I have yet to find one instance where the change in ego libido that was anticipated by the use of the chemical failed to register on the psychologic scale. Therefore, there is no practical loss in examining the problem while making both assumptions. We can, if we wish, first ascertain whether changes in blink frequency correlate with ego libido changes brought about by drug administration, using the latter as the independent variable, and then whether they correlate with ego libido changes that come about spontaneously as a result of intrinsic pathogenic or reparative forces.

Patient Q. S. T. is a thirty-four-year-old woman first treated in analysis in 1948 for acute paranoia; now she is in once-a-week therapy with mild to moderate anxieties and periods of depression. On March 9, 1960, she gave birth to a daughter, and when I next saw her on March 15, she had a severe post-partum melancholia with fears of harming the baby. I prescribed for her 60 mg. of Librium a day, together with 200 mg. of Niamid. The druggist mistakenly delivered 25 mg. tablets of Niamid instead of 100 mg. tablets as ordered, so that she was receiving only 50 mg. daily. Her symptoms improved immediately with the Librium, but the fundamental melancholia remained unchanged. As we shall see below, I estimate ego libido content by reference to an eleven-point scale, which ranges from 0 to 10. On this scale, positions 0 through 3 describe states in which the ego depletion is pathologic; 4 is low normal; 7 is high normal. On March 15, this patient's ego libido level had descended to 2; on March 19, it was 5; on March 26, it was 3. Blink frequency, which for her usually registered 5 to 7 with infrequent excursions to 4 and 8, remained 7, 7, and 6 on these three days. On April 2, however, with the ego libido level still at 2 or 3, the blink frequency level had decreased to 2, a value hitherto unrecorded for her in the three years that I had been observing blink frequency. On that day I discovered the error in the medication dose, and she began to take 200 mg. of Niamid a day. On April 16, the ego libido level was still 3, and the blink frequency now 3. A week later, the ego libido value remained 3 but there were signs of recovery, and the blink frequency value had ascended to 5. By April 30, the ego libido level had returned to 5, and the blink frequency to 8. Subsequent events are interesting but not too illuminating for this problem. In this case, the blink frequency did not respond very promptly to the onset of libido depletion, but three weeks later it did decrease to unusual levels. It returned to normal values together with, or perhaps slightly in advance of, clinical criteria of ego libido content.

Here is a much more clear-cut example. A fifty-five-year-old married man came to see me after two months of moderately severe melancholic depression. He had previously been in analytic treatment and had received Marsilid for a similar depression. I gave him Niamid and started to see him three times a week. Figure 1 shows his progress as measured by ego libido indicators, and also blink frequency value and medication dose. (It will be noted that for some days, particularly during periods of transition, two numbers are given for ego libido. The higher value refers to the patient's object relations and the lower to narcissistic libido. This double assessment will be discussed in the next chapter.) The first day on which the energy value rose above the pathologic level of 3 to 4 was October 2. But at the previous session, that of September 30, the blink frequency had risen sharply from 0 to 5, and on that day, the patient had offered that some improvement might have occurred. On October 2 he said he was definitely better. Here again a sharp increase in blink frequency anticipated clinical recovery. Because the patient resisted analysis seriously (he had terminated treatment after seven months on a previous occasion), I began to cut down the medication, reducing the dose of Niamid from 200 mg. daily to 150 mg. on October 21, and then decreasing it further by 50 mg. steps each of two successive weeks. On November 20, after two weeks on a daily dose of only 50 mg., the first signs of ego depletion appeared. On November 27, the ego libido value fell to 3, and the blink frequency fell to 3 for the first time since the onset of recovery. I raised the dose to 100 mg. on November 25. Blink frequency values of 4, 3, and 2 were prevalent until December 18, when they suddenly gave way to a value of 6. On this day the patient said he felt better, and an indication of significant object libido appeared for the first time since the beginning of the relapse. Thereafter there were no further indications of ego depletion, and blink frequency values remained at 4, 5, or 6.

The correlation in this case is particularly impressive. Such cases are not the rule, but I doubt that they are too rare. The fact that they do exist demonstrates that there is a basic relation between blink frequency on the one hand, and ego libido on the other, whether the latter is manipulated by drug administration or estimated by psychologic criteria. The infrequency of such clear demonstrations implies that this basic relation is often obscured by the dependence of blink frequency upon one or more additional variables. I suspect that at least one of these other factors is what might be termed psychic distance from the object. Given a high content

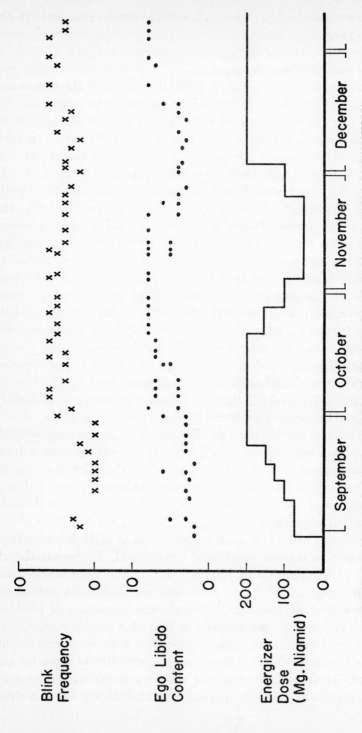

FIGURE 1. EGO LIBIDO LEVEL AND BLINK FREQUENCY IN RECOVERY FROM MELANCHOLIA

of libido within the ego, there is a strong tendency to cathect object images and to pursue objects. Many people, however, especially neurotics, try to attenuate the intense feelings evoked by strong object relations, by maintaining a certain intrapsychic distance, that is, a barrier between the self-image and the object image. In some individuals, hysterics and catatonics in particular, this inner barrier creates a sense of detachment. What I am suggesting is that the blink frequency is a function of at least two separate variables, ego libido content and psychic distance from the object. For example, I treated one inert, depressed catatonic patient, M. T. (mentioned above) with Niamid because I considered the inertia and other characteristics indicative of ego depletion. Gradually the depression was replaced with hebetude; she said she felt "wonderful." With this change, blink frequency increased from 20 in 300 seconds to 20 in 150 seconds. Within two days, however, the hebetude suddenly gave way to a tense, negativistic, rigid catalepsy. At this point, the patient seemed not to blink at all. She was given 5 mg. of Trilafon intramuscularly. By the next day, the negativistic catalepsy turned to hebetude once again, and blink frequency rose to 20 in 92 seconds. I infer that while the increase in ego energy tended to drive the blink frequency up, its influence was opposed by the catatonic detachment which was intensified by the energy increase itself. When the Trilafon cut down the energy level slightly and resolved the tense negativism, blink frequency rose again.

To what use can we put this observation? Can we employ blink frequency as a criterion by which we may choose between a tranquilizer and an energizer as the appropriate drug for any specific point? Certainly not as the sole criterion. In the first place, a simple determination of ego energy is the foremost, but again not the only consideration in selecting medication. Second, the factor of object distance may so affect the blink frequency as to make it misleading. For example, in the last mentioned instance, M. T., despite the almost complete cessation of blinking during the negativistic catalepsy, the drug indicated was a tranquilizer, which did indeed resolve the condition, and simultaneously the frequency of blinking increased. A less extreme instance is that of a young man, C. O., who sustained a mild depression associated with some ego depletion (the libido level was reduced to 3) immediately upon his engagement. This condition was not serious enough to justify drug therapy, especially since the patient was in analysis. Yet if a drug were to be given, let us say if he had first turned for treatment at this point to a psychiatrist who preferred drug therapy to psycho- therapy, the drug of choice would be an energizer. Yet his blink frequency, normally 8, 9, or 10, did not depart from that range dur- ing his depression. In other words, a tranquilizing drug would have been indicated by this high frequency blinking. We shall see, as we proceed, that the modulation of primary tendencies by second- ary ones makes drug therapy a subtle and delicate art, requiring in some cases little less perspicacity and dynamic comprehension than good, intense psychotherapy does.

It is true that in many cases where the blink frequency is ex- treme, it may serve as a cue for drug selection. It is more useful, though, as an accessory clinical datum in following the course of a given patient during therapy. I have found it especially valuable for those patients who display sharp breaks with reality or vigorous energetic shifts, for example, schizophrenics either in relapse or in remission. I have one patient, X. N. Z. (see Chapter VI) who is of- ten on the brink of paranoia. When the psychotic process seems to be gaining the upper hand, insight derived from current and past analytic work may encourage an abandonment of the pathogenic object relation with an accompanying ego depletion. I have watched this sequence of pathologic drive intensification followed by ego depletion on many occasions. With each intensification of drive, the blink frequency provides a helpful accessory clinical observa- ascended to 5 or 6, and when depletion supervened, fell to 0 or 1. Often the change in blink frequency anticipated the energetic change by a day. In this particular case, I have found the blink fre- quency useful in following the course of daily progress; quite dra- matically, blink frequency at the beginning of a session has usually predicted correctly the ego libido content characterizing the psycho- logic material that followed. Such cases are probably not too com- mon, but for these, as for the group who show extreme deviation of blink frequency corresponding to extreme deviations of ego libido, the blink frequency, which normally fluctuates between 2 and 4, tion.

Ego Strength

The problem of ego strength is an especially difficult chapter in psychoanalytic metapsychology which we shall not be able to avoid. Here I shall anticipate our discussion of it by referring to an interesting study which, in my opinion, may offer a physiologic measure of one of the factors that comprise the complex function we speak of as ego strength. Shagass and his associates tested the resistance of normal brain function to intravenous sodium amytal (Shagass and Naiman, 1955; Shagass *et al.*, 1956). They measured the amount of amytal an individual could tolerate before his speech became slurred and fast activity appeared in frontal electroencephalographic leads—both purely physiologic, as opposed to psychologic, criteria. This "sedation threshold" was found to vary directly with several measures of tension among patients diagnostically classified "psychoneurosis" or "pseudoneurotic schizophrenia." Unequivocal schizophrenics, however, showed a considerably lower sedation threshold than this predominantly psychoneurotic group. In other words, this test had disclosed a kind of vulnerability of brain function in schizophrenics that is not present in psychoneurotic patients. Further study revealed that similar weakness existed in patients with "psychotic depression" and depressed patients who seemed basically hysterical. It was absent, according to the same study, from patients considered to have "neurotic depression" and anxiety state. The criteria for a diagnosis of psychotic depression employed in this investigation were: psychomotor retardation, agitation, delusions, hallucinations, mutism, and negativism. Thus this group included both melancholics and patients with schizophrenic depression.

I cite these studies here because experience has taught me that the conditions for which Shagass and his associates have found low sedation thresholds—namely, melancholia, schizophrenic depression, hysterical depression, and schizophrenia—respond well to psychic energizers and badly to tranquilizers. (This statement is restricted to certain schizophrenics; others require primary treatment with tranquilizers. The distinctions between them will be considered further on.) On the other hand, patients with high sedation thresholds—namely, "tense" neurotics, neurotic depressives, and anxious neurotics in many instances respond better to tranquilizers than to energizers. These statements should not be considered indications for treatment. Treatment of hysterics and "depressed" catatonics with energizers must be carefully regulated and possibly supplemented with modulating doses of tranquilizers as well; conversely, if "tense" neurotics are given tranquilizers, these should be prescribed in small amounts, sometimes with low supporting doses of energizers. Fuller discussions of these points will appear later. From my observations with the clinical use of these pharmaceutic agents, I had concluded that in melancholia and depleted forms of catatonia, and to a lesser degree in the depressions of hysterics, ego function suffers due to its loss of libido. In certain other forms of neurosis, in paranoia, and in incipient paranoid schizophrenia, the ego is surfeited with libido. It seems to me that it is in just those cases where the ego is weakened by depletion that Shagass has detected a low sedation threshold. The correspondence between the findings of these two different approaches is impressive, and they must be considered mutually confirmatory.

Psychosomatic Considerations

In this section I shall discuss some physiologic and pathologic somatic correlates of energy states and changes. Unfortunately, since most of my observations were made in analytic therapy and I could not permit myself the examination procedures required to establish psychosomatic correlations, I have few data to contribute in this area. I offer this section more as a call for information rather than as a presentation of findings.

In an investigation of possible differences in autonomic reactivity in a population of mental patients, Funkenstein *et al.* (1952) studied subjects with high blood pressure. An intramuscular injection of mecholyl reduced the pressure in each instance. It proved possible, however, to separate two distinct groups on the basis of extent and duration of the pressure reduction so induced. Almost all of the patients with "manic-depressive" and involutional psychoses were to be found in Group A, which responded with substantial decreases in systolic pressure persisting for a specified observation period or longer. One-third of the schizophrenics also fell into this category, but the remaining two-thirds fell into Group B; that is, they exhibited small, brief pressure reduction. Pending more detailed clinical studies, it is possible to suppose that patients in Group A suffer ego depletion, while those in Group B do not.

Cohen and Silverman and their associates at Duke University have shown ingenuity and careful thought in their investigation of somatopsychic correlations among normals. One of their studies (1959) seems relevant here. Of 109 normal college students, eleven were selected for study on the basis of their response to two tests which were designed to distinguish between those whose behavior seemed to be determined principally by external cues, and their counterparts, whose behavior was determined principally by internal cues. Six of these eleven were the most extreme of the "field reactors," while the remaining five were the most extreme of the "body reactors." On the basis of psychologic criteria which we shall adduce in the next chapter, we may infer that the "field reactors" are individuals operating with a high, although probably normal level of ego libido, while the "body reactors" possess a low, although also normal, ego libido content. The "field reactors" as a group showed more spontaneous fluctuations of the GSR (galvanic skin response) per unit time than did the "body reactors." (A previous study by Silverman, Cohen, *et al.* had demonstrated that frequency of spontaneous fluctuation of the GSR varied with the level of alertness or conscious excitation.) The urinary excretory rate of the catecholamines, adrenaline and noradrenaline, was slightly higher for the body as opposed to the field group, but the difference was small and of doubtful significance. Other functions such as pulse rate and respiratory rate were not distinctly different for the two groups.

Considering the profound effects of stress upon mental state, the converse influence of mental state upon the response to stress, and finally the capacity of the 17-hydroxy corticosteroids to produce depression or excitation, one would expect to find some significant relations between ego libido level and various aspects of an individual's response to stress. Barbeau (1960) has found an unidentified substance probably related to the catecholamines, not normally excreted, in the urine of patients with basal ganglia disease. Selye (1956) suggests that some steroids may possess tranquilizing action. I have had no experience with patients receiving steroid hormones during analysis, and I have not kept up with the now voluminous literature on steroids. If we take the observations of Rome and Braceland (1952) on psychological effects of steroid therapy as the basis for our discussion, however, we find that the administration of ACTH or cortisone tends to produce effects similar to the administration of psychic energizers, namely, a feeling of well-being, overactivity, garrulousness, insomnia, mood elevation, and the intemperateness of hypomania. Some patients show not the simple increase in libido but the appearance of various neurotic symptom complexes, such as anxiety, phobias, and obsessions. This, too, resembles the action of the energizers, for not infrequently they will resolve a melancholia only to replace it by a neurosis or by schizophrenia. Psychotic reactions were also observed by Rome and Braceland. So far, I know of no argument to refute the supposition that the therapeutic administration of one of these steroid hormones results in an increase in the patient's ego libido content. Of course, we may reasonably question whether the increase is not merely the spontaneous rebound of a patient depleted by organic illness, and now liberated. Or it may be the replenishment of a depleted adrenal, by the administration of the steroid hormones, that causes the appearance of increased ego libido. However, the ubiquitousness of the effect among large groups of patients, its intensity, and its promptness of onset—in many instances even before the physical manifestations of the disease have begun to resolve—make it likely that the effect is pharmacologic rather than simply physiologic.

However, there is a difference between the actions of these hormones and of the energizers that is of theoretic significance. While an energizer may precipitate neurosis or schizophrenia, it never brings about a melancholic type of depression or an apathetic form of schizophrenia. The reason is that the latter two conditions result from energy depletion. In the natural course of events, melancholia may follow mania and neurosis, and apathetic schizophrenia may follow paranoia or excited schizophrenia, because a withdrawal of libido from the ego is a mode of defense against libido plethora disorders. Such a withdrawal is precluded by the administration of an energizer. The steroids, on the other hand, not infrequently induce profound melancholia. In this respect, the conditions they create resemble the course of natural recovery from a mild to moderate ego depletion syndrome, namely, repletion of the ego, followed occasionally by overswing to hypomania, neurosis, or schizophrenia, which, if sufficiently severe, may correct itself with a counterswing back to melancholia or a depleted form of schizophrenia. I can see two possible explanations. One is that the psychic effect of the steroids is actually not pharmacologic but that it merely relieves the individual of the enervating weight of physical illness. Another is that the administration of large doses of these hormones suppresses the function of their normal source, the adrenal cortex by influencing its pituitary controlling mechanism, and thereby artificially creates a deficit of a different hormonal substance which is not replaced by the therapy. Such phenomena are well known in endocrinologic therapeutics, and this hypothesis finds some support from the fact that mild to severe melancholic depressions are almost invariable accompaniments of steroid administration in amounts sufficient to produce Cushing's syndrome. In any case, the data reported by Rome and Braceland justify the generalization that the administration of cortisone or ACTH to patients with somatic diseases requiring them is followed by an increase in the libido content of the ego, often producing neurosis or psychosis; if enough of the substance is given over a long period of time, a decrease of libido will ensue, frequently of sufficient magnitude to induce melancholia. Other steroids may exhibit different patterns of action (Lemere, 1957).

In a recent study, Eyster (1960) has described the psychic effects of the administration of cortisone and ACTH. In small doses these agents often induce a feeling of well-being, increased alertness, renewed interests, and a greater capacity for emotional relations. Sometimes these effects, which resemble the effects of energizers, are followed by anxiety, restlessness, irritability, difficulty in concentration, depression, and feelings of unreality. As a group these are suggestive of depletion. This apparently constitutes a critical difference between the energizing action of steroids and the drugs which we employ as therapeutic energizers. The former exert an energizing effect only while their body content is increasing. Apparently, when the body level is constant the energizing action disappears and may be replaced by depletion. Consistent with this concept is the observation that withdrawal of steroid medication is likely to cause severe depression and affective detachment. In other words, withdrawal not merely removes the energizing influence but acts positively to produce depletion. The psychic energizers, on the other hand, retain their energizing effect so long as their blood level is maintained; a decrease in the blood level is followed merely by a loss of the energizing action and effects but not by a rebound into depletion. When large doses of steroids are administered, psychoses may be precipitated.

A related problem has come to my attention in connection with the use of hydrazine energizers. I have, on a number of occasions, confirmed the observation of others that treatment with these drugs may produce trunk or generalized body edema. The question arises whether the edema is a specific toxic effect of these chemical substances, or whether it is a physiologic concomitant of their action, namely, the forced increase of ego libido content. It has been suggested to me (H. R.) that the edema might be a rebound phe-

nomenon caused by the improved nutritional status which fo
the return of the patient's appetite with the administration of
energizer. Water retention would come about for two reasons. First,
with increased food intake, salt would be ingested and retained.
Second, the general replenishment of all organ systems would increase the adrenal's production of Compound F, which acts to retain water. One might relate the phenomenon to the periodic mood
changes which accompany the sequential retention and release of
fluid during the menstrual cycles of many women. Study of these
changes might throw light upon the former, but such studies are
difficult to make in analysis where the expression of even trivial
interests by the analyst may interfere with the progress of the
therapy. I have recently had the opportunity to make an observation which was consistent with my hypothesis. A forty-three-year-
old woman (R. L. X.), who had been on various tranquilizers and
energizers, and combinations of the two, continuously for three
years, and who had previously shown a tendency to accumulate
edema fluid when taking energizers, seemed at one point to be becoming depressed. There were indications of progressive ego depletion, so I gradually increased the dose of the energizing drug
(Niamid). The depression was slow in responding, but she did
begin to accumulate fluid rapidly. Diuretics failed to eliminate
this fluid, as did an antialdosterone steroid, spironolactone (Aldac-
tone). So insensitive was the edema to these measures that the
internist who was treating her suspected it was fat, rather than
fluid, which she had accumulated. Nevertheless, when I complemented the increase in energizer by a decrease in the tranquilizing
drug (Thorazine) that she had been taking together with it for
more than a year, there was an abrupt and profuse urinary elimi-
nation of fluid. Each stepwise reduction of Thorazine was followed
by a similar loss of edema fluid. I think one reasonable explanation
might be that the edema is generated in the attempt, whether
spontaneous or induced, to raise libido level within the ego. The
mechanism by which this effect is induced probably involves steroid
hormones. Mirsky reports an increase in plasma concentration of
anti-diuretic substance in response to painful stimuli (Mirsky et
al., 1953).

A similar but more obvious relation obtains between body per-
spiration and the effort to raise ego libido level (Ostow, 1960d).
It is commonly observed that while taking energizing drugs of

whatever chemical nature, many patients report profuse sweating. This is apt to be more pronounced at night than during the day, and characteristically affects head, posterior neck, and posterior trunk, although it may be generalized. Such excess sweating is often cited as a side effect of the energizers. I have noted that some patients with mild to moderate melancholic depressions (ego depletion) suffer from this profuse sweating during their entire illness. Others who were first seen after the onset of the depression reported profuse sweating for months and even years before the clinical syndrome appeared. This sweating generally stops when the patient has recovered, even though he may still be taking the drug. I have seen these phenomena often enough to conclude that the nocturnal body sweats accompany efforts to raise ego libido level, whether these efforts are spontaneous or are induced by energizing drugs.

If this is the case, then one wonders whether the drenching body sweats or "night sweats" of chronic diseases such as tuberculosis or Hodgkin's disease, of the crisis of pneumonia, and of surgical shock, may similarly accompany efforts to replete an impoverished ego. The same may be true of hypoglycemia; we know that one mechanism of the diaphoresis of acute hypoglycemia is the secretion of epinephrine. Carrying the analogy one step further, one may consider the possibility that if aspirin induces sweating, then part of its action may be ego repleting. The therapeutic aspect of this hypothesis remains to be tested. In a small number of cases, I have found that two aspirin tablets bring some temporary relief to patients with mild ego depletion.

In view of these observations on edema and sweating, I have considered speculatively the possibility that the attempt to combat ego depletion is accompanied by the transfer of fluid out of intracellular and into extracellular compartments.

Another interesting and unexpected correlate of ego depletion is headache. In fully developed melancholia, one seldom encounters headache as a complaint. Nevertheless, headache is a common complaint among analytic patients; I have found that it generally occurs simultaneously with a decrease in ego libido. For example, I mentioned in the discussion of blink frequency patient X. N. Z., who exhibited recurrently a building up of ego libido levels to the brink of paranoia or paranoid schizophrenia. The episodes of libido accumulation were terminated by abrupt depletion, signaled not only by depressive distress and decrease in blink frequency, along with

psychologic changes, but in many instances also by hea
headache continued as long as the downward libido te
Two phobic patients each complained of distressing
tions other than pain. They spoke of a sensation of "s
"spin out," "dizziness," or "a veil." These corresponded to deren...
attempts to detach themselves from love objects. The intrapsychic
detachment was usually followed by a sense of loneliness and isolation and a feeling of depression. In both instances, there was mild
to moderate ego depletion at this point, accompanied by headache.
These situations lead us to consider whether it is individuals whose
libido is hysterically displaced from genitals to head who are especially prone to develop headache of this type. This, of course, brings
us to the subject of hypochondria, a discussion of which we must
defer. It cannot be mere coincidence, however, that all three patients
I have mentioned in this connection also suffered recurrent hypochondriacal fears of becoming insane.

What kind of headache did these three patients suffer? Each of
them referred to it as "migraine." One patient had a simple generalized headache. A second usually experienced visual sensations
such as veils, film, waviness, blurred vision, and flickering spots at
the time of onset of the headache, but she often had the same sensations at other occasions without headache. Nor was any specific
visual field affected, and the headache was certainly not a true
hemicrania. The third patient, in remission from schizophrenia,
described a hemicrania with flickering lights at the onset of the
headache, but these were not restricted to any portion of the
visual field. It was interesting to see how, in the dreams of the
destruction of the world which ushered in the sequence of detachment, headache, and depression, the threat to the world was represented by ominous lights and luminous explosions in the sky.
Still a fourth patient, a compulsive, developed classical hemicrania,
with nausea and visual defect in the contralateral field, in association with moderate depletion depressions. In short, the evidence
does not permit us to draw any conclusions about the nature of the
headache, or more specifically about its relation to migraine, but
I do think that the association of headache and incipient depletion
can be considered fairly reliable. I suspect that the degree to which
the headache resembles a full migraine depends upon the constitutional susceptibility of the patient. In all four, the headache
yielded grudgingly, if at all, to aspirin.

A recent report from the Headache Clinic at Montefiore Hospital, New York City (Kimball *et al.*, 1960), supports my hypothesis. Reserpine, a tranquilizer, induced typical migraine in nine out of ten migraine subjects after a single intramuscular injection. Conversely, the prophylactic administration of phenelzine, an energizer, markedly reduced the frequency and severity of migraine.

It has been observed that patients with cardiac pain seem to suffer less when given one of the hydrazine energizers. The mechanism of this fairly consistent effect is obscure. There is no evidence that it depends upon an improvement in cardiac circulation. I think that the mechanism may be psychic. As we shall note in the next chapter, a state of libido plethora is characterized by an interest in the objects of the external world and by a disinterest in sensations arising internally. In fact, there seems to be an increase in the threshold for body and ego sensations and a decrease in the threshold of affective response to perceived images. Hence the psychic energizers seem to exert an analgesic effect.

In closing this section, I should like to suggest that an investigation of the ego libido status of patients with known psychosomatic diseases, such as peptic ulcer, colitis, hypertension, and allergies, may yield correlations of theoretic and therapeutic significance.

Sleep

This is another subject about which I have little to offer beyond speculation only meagerly supported by fact. Yet I think it is worth recording the possibility that the phenomena of sleep may influence decisively the generation and distribution of instinctual and psychic energies.

Sleep is still almost entirely *terra incognita* to science. Tinbergen speaks of sleep as an instinct (Tinbergen, 1951). Freud, too, speaks of an "instinct to sleep," which is psychically expressed as an instinct to return to the mother's womb (Nunberg, 1955, p. 11). Despite our great interest in the nature of mental activity during sleep, there are no facts and even little speculation about the function of sleep. Nunberg lists sleep among the defenses, since it represents a negation, a rejection of the real world. Federn specifically supposes that in sleep instinctual energies are regenerated (Federn, 1952). This is the position which I, too, have tentatively begun to adopt. In my office, a bird cage stands opposite me, tenanted at various times by one or two chaffinches or a pair of Chinese nightingales. Under constant observation, these birds show a distinct activity cycle. They awaken each morning and chirp, fly about, preen themselves, and drink vigorously, with but brief rest periods all day. As evening approaches, the rate of activity slows distinctly and the rest periods lengthen. At night they sit quietly and fall asleep, to awaken again in the morning in full vigor. It is difficult to escape the impression that the vigor which they display in the morning is the fruit of the night's sleep. Of course, in humans the cycle is not nearly so evident for many reasons, most of which would be included in the simple statement that the human ego is far more complex than the bird's.

Students of the physiology of sleep have learned the importance of distinguishing between the recuperative powers of rest and the restorative function of sleep. The former relates to the fact that many organ systems of the body can perform satisfactorily for only a limited period of time. Continued activity results in impaired performance, and full recovery requires temporary cessation or diminution of activity, or "rest." The need for rest and its effectiveness are easily observed and measured. The restorative function of sleep, however, is something above and beyond the concurrent rest provided to the entire organism. Its objective detection, measurement, and differentiation from the effect of rest have been difficult, if not impossible. The essential element in this restorative function of sleep is, I believe, the regeneration of instinctual energies and the psychic energies to which they give rise.

Recent studies of sleep by Aserinsky, Dement, and Kleitman have done much to elucidate the physiologic course of sleep—or, at least, it seems to be much by contrast with our previous ignorance (Aserinsky and Kleitman, 1955; Dement and Kleitman, 1957; Dement, 1960). By observing eye movements and recording the electroencephalogram during sleep, they have been able to ascertain that a full night's sleep for the normal adult consists of four to seven cycles. The cycle is defined by a progressive decrease of EEG frequencies to a low of 1 to 2 per second high voltage activity, from an initial period of high voltage fast waves and 12 to 14 per second spindles. Following a variable interval of slow activity, the frequencies increase again to 3 to 4 per second, then 5 to 6, as amplitude diminishes. As this higher frequency appears, it becomes associated with spindles and low voltage fast activity, 15 and more per second.

This period of increased frequencies follows about an hour or more of slower activity, and itself lasts about half an hour. During the fast period following the disappearance of spindles, there are vigorous eye movements, and if the subject is awakened at this time he will almost invariably recall dreaming. During the period of slower frequencies, on the other hand, eye movements are absent, and an awakened subject will recall no dreams.

While this discovery represents a fundamental advance in our understanding of sleep, it tells us nothing new of its physiologic nature or biologic role. Neither the psychoanalytic theory of the psychology of dreaming nor my suggestion concerning the biologic function of regeneration of instinctual energies is rendered obsolete. We need assume merely that energy regeneration occurs during the period of minimal cortical and diencephalic activity, when frequencies are slowest and voltages highest; that only a limited amount of energy can be regenerated in the id before an overflow into the ego takes place; that dreaming is the manifestation of the ego driven solely by id pressures, but lacking much of its own characteristic organization and activity, including access to motility and the ego supplement. These assumptions are reasonable, and they lead to Freud's original hypothesis that the function of the dream is to preserve sleep, that is, to protect the ego from being prematurely activated by the surges of energy generated in the id (Freud, 1900a). Spontaneous awakening normally occurs during the high frequency, low voltage phase, the phase in which dreaming occurs.

Dement and Fisher (1960) have been conducting a series of well-conceived and meticulously executed studies of the effects of interfering with sleep. They have awakened subjects night after night in one phase or another of sleep; they have suppressed some aspects of the cycles with drugs; and they have used sedatives to protract sleep. Such studies promise to yield significant information concerning the biology and physiology of sleep. I must dissent, however, from one of the first inferences they have drawn from their data. They claim to have demonstrated a "need to dream." This is inferred from the observation that subjects who have been awakened night after night during the phase of fast, low voltage activity, and so prevented from dreaming, show a marked rise, once they are again permitted uninterrupted sleep, in the proportion of time spent in the high frequency dream phase. By inspecting their data, however, one can ascertain that the proportion of time spent in very low frequency activity also rises. What they have done essentially, in my opinion, is to deprive the subject of adequate sleep, and what they have observed is the effect of such deprivation on the cyclic characteristics of subsequent sleep. They deny having deprived their subjects of sleep because the number of hours spent "sleeping" has not changed significantly. The time spent in the phase of cortical and diencephalic inactivity, however, is much abbreviated by their interference techniques, and if, as I assume, it is during this phase that instinctual energies are regenerated, then it follows that their procedure severely encroaches upon the restorative effect of sleep. Moreover, they concede that their experimentation results in the same influence upon waking behavior as if their subjects had been deprived of sleep.

What can the effects of sleep deprivation tell us about the function of sleep? The experiment has been done many times, but the results vary with the specific conditions. What is clear and undeniable is that ego function becomes progressively and severely impaired (Brauchi and West, 1959). It is my view that the impairment of the ego function results from the dearth of energy which is effected by sleep deprivation. This might be considered simply a *post hoc* hypothesis, but it is supported by an observation of Dement and Fisher (1960). Their subjects, after sufficient sleep deprivation, showed a bulimia, sometimes with marked weight gain. One of their subjects renewed an old alcoholism. I shall call attention below to the fact that addictions to food and intoxicants are frequent responses to ego libido depletion.

The relevance of the subject of sleep to our principal concern is not entirely theoretical. It arises largely from the fact that disturbance of sleep is a common manifestation of mental illness, and from the observation that the tranquilizing and energizing drugs themselves strongly influence sleep. One of the earliest symptoms of both mania and melancholia is early awakening. In the former case, the patient rises with a feeling of vigor and refreshment; in the latter, with a feeling of enervation and fatigue. Insomnia is also a side effect of both the energizers and the tranquilizers. (The sedative effect of the chlorpromazine series of phenothiazines and of reserpine is entirely incidental and unrelated to their tranquilizing effect. The prochlorperazine series do not show this sedative action, although they are the more potent tranquilizers.) The data which would permit us to understand the causes and effects of sleep disturbance in mental illness and in treatment with tranquilizers and energizers are not yet available to us. Not all melancholics suffer from insomnia. There are some who awaken with unusual difficulty, and left uninterrupted, would sleep for unusually protracted periods of time. It will be helpful to compare these two groups with respect to other clinical characteristics as well. The techniques of Dement and Fisher for studying the course of sleep will do much to elucidate sleep disturbances and the effects of tranquilizing and energizing drugs.

The commonest disturbance of sleep pattern encountered in depleted patients consists of an abrupt awakening some time in the early morning, or after no more than one or two hours of sleep. The patient often remembers a dream from which he awoke, and this dream generally expresses a wish for nourishment (expressed either directly or in defense). In many instances the patient will go to the kitchen and eat. Other patients will awaken retching and vomiting. The former group of individuals will gain weight, and the latter group will lose weight. Which pattern obtains depends upon whether the oral drive is merely strong enough to demand gratification, or so strong that it invokes antagonistic defensive measures. We are discussing depleted patients and we know that these patients express vigorous oral drives in their general behavior. It is apparently their resurgent orality which awakens them either to insist upon some more realistic form of gratification, or to prevent even hallucinatory gratification.

What can be the meaning of this sleep-dream cycle? In its earliest weeks the infant sleeps almost round the clock. When he begins to pass time awake, sleep is still distributed fairly evenly during the entire twenty-four hours. As waking intervals become longer, sleep is confined to restricted periods. Typically, the child is fed, sleeps, and awakens crying for food. He is stilled by being fed, remains awake for some time, is fed again, and then falls asleep. The length of time he can remain awake is a measure of the energy he has accumulated during sleep. It may well be that the several cycles of an adult night's sleep consist of the agglomoration of what was in the infant a series of discrete sleep periods. Such a hypothesis can easily be checked, and should be. In that case the nocturnal awakening of the depleted patient merely recapitulates the infantile mode of sleeping. Both awaken because they need to be fed before they can sleep more. Apparently the regeneration of instinctual energies and the repletion of the ego, if that is what sleep does, requires some fuel, some chemical or neural energies which are directly supplied to the infant as food and which the depleted patient seeks to obtain symbolically by eating. In normal adult sleep this fuel is obtained without complete awakening. Perhaps the physiologic changes which accompany the arousal to the first phase of sleep in which dreaming occurs, or the physiologic effects of the dream hallucination serve to provide the instinct regenerating mechanism with the raw material it requires. Withholding this fuel may be the mechanism by which depletion is accomplished.

Fisher (1962) reports that an obese patient had an elevated dream time (over 30 per cent, as opposed to the normal value of 20 per cent). A depressed patient had a similarly elevated dream time. Since these were probably both depleted individuals, we may infer that the elevated dream time arose from the difficulty of obtaining adequate fuel for instinct regeneration. He also reports a patient whom he considered "probably borderline or potentially psychotic" and whose dream time during the first five months of psychotherapy fluctuated between 27 per cent and 30 per cent. This man abruptly developed an acute paranoid psychosis with delusions and hallucination. He was given 20 mg. of Stelazine and 10 mg. of Artane. On the first night on this regime, the patient's dream time rose to 59.5 per cent. His first dream period, which lasted two and a half hours, came on within a few minutes after he fell asleep, whereas the dream phase normally appears only after one to one and a half hours of sleeping. On the next night the dream time fell to 30 per cent. The dose was halved to 10 mg. of Stelazine, and the dream time rose again to 45.5 per cent. With restoration of the initial dose, the dream time fell again to 30 per cent and the patient improved clinically.

Since the patient improved with Stelazine, we may infer that the acute episode was a plethora psychosis. Apparently in this state of plethora the dream time doubled. I can account for this only by supposing that the generation of libidinal plethora generally increases the demand for fuel supplies, which is expressed by an increase in the time spent in the dream phase of sleep. This one observation requires confirmation. If it stands, then we may conclude that the plethora state requires a high dream time to obtain the fuel sufficient to meet the increased rate of libidinal regeneration.

The depleted patient requires a high dream time, on the other hand, because only a small amount of fuel is forthcoming during the dream phase of sleep.

Fisher suggests that per cent dream time is proportional to the instinctual discharge pressure which prevails during sleep. I prefer to think that per cent dream time is a measure of the amount of fuel required for the regeneration of instinctual energies during sleep, or perhaps of the effort required.

One of my patients, who is in analysis for treatment of a studying block, is often on the verge of libido depletion due to the repression of erotic tendencies, the great demands of his work, and a relative dearth of sleep. The sleep deficiency builds up during the school week, and generally is partially made up over the weekend. I have observed a tendency for the blink frequency to diminish progressively each week from Monday to Friday. These are the daily blink frequencies (in my inverse logarithmic scale) from Monday through Friday, averaged for forty weeks: 4.68, 4.40, 4.28, 4.05, 3.84. This observation, I believe, supports my contention that a function of sleep is the regeneration of instinctual energies.

It is my impression that the work of energizing and tranquilizing drugs, but especially the former, is done during sleep. An increment or reduction in dosage of these drugs is generally reflected in behavior only after the patient has slept. In other words, if one doubles on any specific day the dose of energizer given to a patient, one will never see behavior alteration until the next morning, following the night's sleep. I have wondered whether the action of the drug is mediated by its influence on the regeneration and redistribution of energies that occurs during sleep.

One often observes that patients who are forced to defend themselves against a high libido pressure, turn forcibly away from the object by falling asleep. The need to sleep seems to be automatic and irresistible, and the picture that follows is often that of narcolepsy. Patients who do not show this phenomenon otherwise, may do so under the influence of an energizing drug. This maneuver is self-limited, however, for the defensive sleep itself serves to increase the ego libido level, and the latter evokes even more extreme defenses.

NON-PSYCHOLOGIC METHODS OF
INFLUENCING EGO LIBIDO CONTENT

The principle non-psychologic method of influencing the libido content of the ego with which we shall be concerned is the administration of energizing and tranquilizing substances. I wish to note here that certain other procedures and events, therapeutic, experimental, and spontaneous also affect ego libido.

While the libido content of the ego does not rise proportionately with the availability of potential chemical energies to the brain, obviously it must be limited by them. Accordingly, any interference with the brain's supply of energy-yielding metabolites must result in a diminution of ego libido. If ego function collapses abruptly, the specific effect of depletion may not be discernible, but a mild, protracted metabolic disturbance will disclose the depletion syndrome. The hours of hypoglycemia which are induced during insulin treatment for schizophrenia must have a tranquilizing effect similar to that induced by the tranquilizing drugs. One is led to speculate about the possibility that the oral hypoglycemic agents might be used effectively to produce ego depletion (Ljungberg, 1958). The ancient remedy of repeated blood-letting may have been useful in the treatment of some instances of mental illness by virtue of its enervating effect upon the ego. The occasional yielding of mental illness to a debilitating physical illness must be attributed to the operation of the same principle.

Sleep deprivation, as was noted above, is an effective means of depleting the ego. As a practical therapeutic measure, it has two serious drawbacks. In the first place, it is so arduous that it would be difficult to elicit sufficient cooperation from disturbed patients. One may perhaps regard the usual insomnia of mania and incipient schizophrenia as spontaneous reparative attempts to decrease libido pressure. Whether induced or spontaneous, however, a second drawback to the use of sleep deprivation as a therapeutic measure arises from the dissociation of ego function which it brings about.

Dissociation of ego function is a phenomenon which I have largely neglected thus far, but we must finally examine it. The ego may be considered to contain: (1) an archaic nucleus which is essentially an agent of the id—that is, its job is to secure gratification of instinctual needs as promptly and directly as possible; and (2) a phylogenetically newer supplement which is concerned with deferring and attenuating instinctual gratification in compliance with the demands of reality and the superego (Ostow, 1959, a, e). The energies of the id are directly transmitted to the ego nucleus. The ego supplement must be supported by id energies, too, but its energy supply seems to be especially vulnerable, so that under certain circumstances it is depleted sooner or to a relatively greater degree than the ego nucleus. The dissociation of ego functions which ensues has some characteristic properties which we shall have to deal with extensively below. Hallucinations and specific kinds of delusions are chief among them. Under the influence of sleep deprivation, this dissociation occurs so that one generally sees a confused, delirium-like state rather than a tranquil one.

Having introduced the concept of dissociation of ego function, we are in a position to take up briefly the now complex subject of sensory deprivation. The studies of Heron, Hebb, Vernon, Lilly, and others are well known. (Bexton, Heron, and Scott, 1954; Hebb, 1954; Lilly, 1956, 1956a; Vernon and Hoffman, 1956). Essentially they have demonstrated that when a subject is isolated from sources of perceptible information for periods of hours or days, ego function becomes impaired. His fantasies become imagery and then hallucinations. Delusions appear. Reality testing weakens. Time sense is distorted. The individual develops an urge to move about. When he is again exposed to perceptible stimuli, they seem especially intense or unfamiliar or distorted in shape and size. These changes have turned out to be entirely reversible, but Bressler and his associates have indicated that neurotic behavior may be precipitated which, in a few instances, has persisted for some time (Bressler *et al.*, 1959).

How can we relate this phenomenon to psychic energetics? From classical psychoanalytic theory we know that the loss of the love object causes a damming up of libido, at times to the point of creating anxiety. Moreover, since the existence of the object and the relation to it are established only via the channels of perception, "the absence of perception becomes a loss of object" (Nunberg, 1955, p. 198). We may expect, then, that sensory deprivation will bring about an intensification of object libido.

From clinical observation, we know that a reduction in the inflow of sensory stimuli results in an impairment of ego function. Visual hallucinations in delirium are promoted by darkness and discouraged by light. The same is true of the visual hallucinations of schizophrenia (Bleuler, 1950, p. 103). Ophthalmologists have repeatedly observed that many patients, both of whose eyes have been bandaged after one has been operated—and this is especially true in the case of cataract extraction—are apt to develop a delirium (Chamlin; Linn, *et al.*, 1953; Ziskind, 1958).

In experimental sensory isolation, we bring about a virtual loss of object with consequent accumulation of libido pressure and, at the same time, an impairment of the function of the ego supplement. The combination can readily account for all the abnormal phenomena that have been encountered. Sensory isolation has recently been proposed as a therapeutic measure (Gibby *et al.*, 1960). It seems to me that the only likely candidates for such treatment would be patients with low libido levels, such as melancholics and depressed catatonics, whose egos are already depleted and functioning badly. If the libido level can be raised by isolation, the procedure might be helpful.

Assuming that our explanation is correct, then we should expect that individuals operating with a high ego libido level would be affected more seriously by sensory isolation than those at a low libido level. The experiments of Cohen *et al.* (1959) confirm this supposition. Both field-oriented and body-oriented subjects—that is, subjects with high and low levels of ego libido, respectively— exhibited a distinct diminution in touch threshold. This diminution was the effect of the need of the ego supplement for support by percepts. The former group, however, described more subjective distress as a result of two hours of sensory isolation than the latter. It was apparently the exaggerated discrepancy between the increased ego nucleus libido and the impaired function of the ego supplement that was responsible for this distress. Moreover, the imagery of the field group was more vivid, and their projections were more compelling. The frequency of spontaneous fluctuation of GSR (galvanic skin response, a measure of central excitation) was initially higher for the field group than for the body group. It remained high in the field group for almost the entire isolation period, dropping only at the end; for the body group, it fell promptly to low levels and remained low for the duration of isolation. The ratio of activity between the two groups was 7:7 at the outset, but rose as high as 10:1 at one point. Additional confirmation is provided in another isolation study performed by Solomon (1957), Mendelson (1960), and their associates at Harvard. They found that subjects able to tolerate the isolation procedure longest were those who expressed their discomfort in somatic terms. In Cohen's study (1959), the body-oriented group expressed their fantasies in somatic terms; we shall see that concern with body sensations is an indicator of low ego libido level. In other words, we find that those subjects who entered the experiment at a relatively low ego libido level were best able to withstand the isolation experience.

An interesting study by Petrie *et al.* (1958) is relevant to this discussion. These investigators have examined an aspect of perception which they call "satiability." This term denotes the rapidity with which a percept seems to lose its specific characteristics. For example, the sooner a subject becomes unaware of the size of an object grasped steadily in his hand, the higher his level of satiability. Two factors can be seen to play a role in determining satiability. First, a subject with a high libido level will pursue objects avidly and will rapidly lose interest in already available percepts; he will be readily satiable. Melancholics, on the other hand, are intolerant of impinging objects. Second, the work of Cohen and his associates has disclosed that body-oriented individuals are sharper in their evaluation of tactile stimuli and are, therefore, presumably less satiable. The body-oriented group is the low libido group. It follows from both considerations that satiability will vary directly with libido level. Petrie and his group have found that tolerance to pain is directly related to satiability, hence to libido level. This is different from what one would have anticipated, since we know that tranquilizers reduce the effectiveness of conditioned noxious stimuli in motivating escape behavior. This inconsistency will have to be resolved by studies differentiating between subjective tolerance of pain and behavioral response to pain; between intensity of pain and persistence of response; and, further, among sensitivities to the various types of pain. Cohen *et al.* have found no consistent relation of pain threshold to field vs. body orientation. As we shall see in the next chapter, the individual under the influence of a high ego libido level is relatively more interested in the environment than in sensations arising in his own body. Conversely, when the ego libido level is low, body sensations overshadow percepts arising outside. Sensitivity to pain follows sensitivity to body sensation.

Hence the energizers seem to have an analgesic influence, while patients who are depleted appear hypersensitive to pain. These statements accord with Petrie's findings. More relevant to our interest at this point is Petrie's finding that "sensory deprivation tolerance is negatively related to satiability." On the basis of the relation we have suggested between satiability and libido level, we can interpret this finding to mean that subjects with high libido level are relatively intolerant to sensory isolation. This is the same conclusion inferred from other data.

Among the subjects of Cohen's experiment, it was observed that the body-oriented group excreted more epinephrine and norepinephrine in the urine than the field-oriented group, and that the rate of excretion of both substances increased during sensory isolation so that the initial difference between the two increased in the course of the experimental procedure. The ratio between the excretory rates of the two substances either before or during sensory isolation bore no evident relation to the distinction between body and field orientation and, therefore, presumably to energy state. Similarly, in the study reported by Mendelson et al. (1960), there was no correlation between the excretory rate of these two substances and any behavior indicator which might give a clue to energy state. They confirmed the findings of Cohen and his group to the effect that the excretory rate of both substances increased during sensory isolation. Cohen also found that the excretory rate of adrenaline increased with the degree of subjective discomfort, but similarly without direct reference to body versus field orientation.

We may conclude that an individual's response to sensory isolation depends upon two energetic factors: first, the initial level of libido; and second, the susceptibility of the ego supplement to breakdown incident upon the loss of its own special, tonic energy supply. The libido content of the ego supplement is determined primarily by the level of libido available to the ego as a whole, but it is also sensitive to other, secondary, modulating dynamic influences (which we will consider later) and, as we have seen, to the presence of meaningful percepts.

What are the energetic aspects of ECT? Since electric shock is a potent therapy for melancholia and for some cases of schizophrenia, one wonders whether the treatment affects the ego's libido supply directly, as the psychopharmaceutics do, or whether it acts in an entirely different way so that the resultant energy changes are incidental. If melancholia alone responded to the method, I should infer that its effect was simply to increase ego libido. The fact that many schizophrenics also respond has made me hesitant to draw such a conclusion. However, the data presented by Shagass (1955, 1956), and Funkenstein (1952) and their respective associates, lend credibility to the idea that no matter what the diagnosis, it is those patients with low libido levels who respond to electric shock therapy. I base this statement upon the relation we have suggested between a low "sedation threshold," as determined by Shagass, and low ego libido; and upon the relation between susceptibility to the hypotensive effect of mecholyl, as determined by Funkenstein, and low ego libido. Funkenstein demonstrated that the schizophrenics who improved with ECT were the minority who fell into the mecholyl-susceptible group together with the melancholics. The majority of schizophrenics, however (two-thirds of the entire group) who resisted mecholyl, resisted the therapeutic potency of ECT as well. He also showed that following treatment, mecholyl susceptibility decreased. These data tend to support the idea that the therapeutic efficacy of ECT depends upon its capacity, by whatever means, to increase the ego's content of libido. This statement must be qualified in one important respect. While electric shock is not a good therapy for either mania or paranoia, some patients treated with it do recover, provided enough is given. If even a few patients with increased libido, such as manics and paranoids, improve with ECT, we shall have to conclude that although the first effect of electric shock is to increase ego libido, given in large enough doses and over sufficiently long periods of time, it can decrease libido too. The comparison with cortisone and ACTH suggests itself here, and we may even consider the possibility that electric shock achieves its therapeutic effect by altering rates of steroid secretion. We should also remember that some patients who are clinically paranoiacs, paranoid schizophrenics, or even manics, suffer depletion and are responsive only to energizers. We shall discuss this further in Chapter IV.

A recent experience demonstrates, I believe, that electric shock treatment exerts a therapeutic influence upon ego function other than changing the overall libido supply. A catatonic patient (D. N. O.) had been treated with ECT during a previous episode of illness to no avail. During her third attack, she received thirty-nine shocks within a period of two weeks. She recovered, but relapsed again after about two weeks. Two more series of treatments each brought about a remission which endured no more than a few days. At this point I was asked to see her. It took three months to arrive at a precisely balanced formula combining energizing and tranquilizing medication. When this balance had been achieved, she was not disturbed, cared for herself, participated actively in diverting activities such as painting and dancing, but would not speak and would not agree to visit with her husband. Here I ordered ECT started. She had two treatments, one on Thursday and one on Saturday. Sunday morning she woke up in complete remission and has remained well for more than a year now, with the support of the medication and daily psychoanalytic sessions. It is difficult to describe just what the ECT accomplished. The level of ego libido was determined by the medication and was apparently not much affected by the shocks. One might say that the shocks effected a redistribution of energies within the ego, but unless the meaning of this redistribution can be specified, such a statement is not too helpful. Clearly the medication was the effective, therapeutic agent, but the ECT in a relatively small dose evidently performed a significant function. It did something to the ego which made external reality relatively less intolerable.

CHAPTER III

Psychologic

Estimation of

Libido Level

IN THIS CHAPTER we shall study the psychologic manifestations of ego libido level, and note how they can be used as indicators. In view of the varying usages of energy and libido terms, let me clarify my own terminology. In the first place it is my impression that only libido, the energy of Eros, is the independent determinant of mental health or illness.* Following Freud's hypothesis, I shall include in the libido concept erotic energies directed toward objects, erotic energies directed toward the self, and the energies of the ego supplement which are not directly involved in erotic gratification but rather in the synthetic, constructive comprehension of the real world and in its mastery. These last, Freud called "desexualized libido." The aggressive energies of the death instincts can be treated, for our purposes, as exerting no spontaneous discharge pressure, but rather as providing a potential which can be released by the appropriate trigger. The erotic instincts seek opportunities for discharge, create them if they are not available, and probably hallucinate them when they cannot be created. Except to

* Some of the manifestations of mental illnesses are determined immediately by an excess of death instinct energies—for example, suicide and murder. Similarly, hysteria and catatonia represent a turning away from the world of reality, the one in a minor, the other in a major, sense. However, in most instances of neurosis and psychosis, it is either a plethora or a dearth of libido which evokes the excess of death instinct potential. Traumatic neurosis is a possible exception to this generalization.

72

the extent that they have become fused with, and are carried by, the erotic instincts, the aggressive instincts affect behavior only when they are evoked by appropriate external or internal sources of distress.

Second, when I speak of energy, I shall refer only to that energy residing and functioning with the ego. We assume that all energy is generated in the id and achieves its effect by seeking discharge through the executive agency of the ego. At what point in the psychic apparatus instinctual energy becomes psychic energy is not known. We assume, too, that since the superego is the precipitate of the earliest love relations, it is energized by the id, whence it achieves its power to confer both libidinal gratification and masochistic punishment. Nevertheless, since in our work with our patients we observe only the actions of the ego and speak only to it, we cannot know directly anything of id or superego energies. The energies whose effects we can see directly are the energies of the ego (Freud, 1940a). Hence I have used the term "ego libido," by which I mean the ego's content of libido. For the sake of brevity, I shall omit the necessary limitation in the discussion hereafter, and shall speak of "libido."

Third, energy is not an independent fluid substance secreted into the psychic apparatus and seeking outflow channels. Energy is in every case an aspect of an instinctual drive; it is the impetus whereby the drive exerts its influence upon behavior. In using the energy concept for describing the vicissitudes of individual impulses and fantasies, we take for granted its origin in specific instinctual drives. For certain purposes, however, we may conveniently speak of the total energy content of the ego. Since the energies of an instinct that has been frustrated tend to pass over and add to the motivation of other instincts, we impute to energy a fluid quality. In a sense, then, when any instinct is obstructed, its energies are available to others, so that whatever its specific origin, libidinal energy creates a general discharge pressure. Also, when the energetic endowment of an instinct becomes pathologically increased, in "seeking discharge" (1) it overrides the defenses specifically mobilized against it; (2) it facilitates the discharge of other instincts; (3) it undoes the dynamic equilibria of forces and counterforces in the ego and the id; and so (4), it alters many aspects of ego function. Similar considerations apply to states of libido deficit, when not merely one instinctual drive is deprived of its energy but all libido which might possibly be transferred to it from other sources is drained from the ego, leaving the latter generally impoverished. For these reasons, Freud, in discussing the energetics of states of mourning, melancholia, schizophrenia, paranoia, intense love, and even less extreme affective constellations, such as the humorous attitude, found it helpful to speak of the vicissitudes of the total free libido content of the ego.

Fourth, in my discussions of energy shifts, displacements, increases, and decreases, I shall attempt to create no more hypotheses than can be supported by, or at least related to, the facts. This policy will leave many theoretical questions unanswered. They could doubtless be answered by invoking some ingenuity, but a multiplication of *ad hoc* hypotheses contributes nothing to our understanding and is likely to hinder investigation by concealing ignorance. For example, Freud attempted to suggest mechanisms whereby the ego becomes impoverished. In states of mourning, he said the libido is entirely absorbed by the work of dissolving ties with the lost object (1917e). In melancholia, he attributed the impoverishment of the ego to the "binding" of the libido at the site in the ego where the representation of the lost object exists and causes pain. States of generalized ego inhibition come about, he said (1926d, p. 90), when libido is withdrawn from the ego. I doubt that he was satisfied with any of these proposed mechanisms, for he never developed them further. For our purposes, fortunately, it will suffice to restrict our interest to problems of accumulation, loss, and redistribution, and we shall not be hindered by being unable to spell out actual mechanisms.

Another area of imprecision in psychic energetics is our concept of quantity. In dealing with energy or energy-like entities, we generally attempt to distinguish amount, potential, and distribution between free and bound or degraded states. Freud made an effort to deal with fluctuations in amount of available psychic energy by appealing to the thermodynamic concepts of bound and free. I find it difficult to set up operational criteria by which one could define quantity, potential, and degradation in the area of psychic energetics. The most I have been able to do with any confidence is to recognize changes of quantity, the forces that give them rise, the defenses against them, and the dynamic changes that they bring about.

Some of my colleagues have had difficulty with the semantics of such statements as: a tranquilizer decreases the libido content of the ego. Since a tranquilizer is a chemical substance, and libido and ego are hypothetical constructs, it is incorrect, they argue, to speak of one in an operational relation to the other. The difficulty is only an apparent one, for the statement in question can be read as a contraction for the semantically correct but longer statement: a tranquilizer alters brain function in such a way that a change in psychic function comes about which could be described psychologically as the manifestation of a decrease in ego libido.

Fifth, it is necessary to distinguish between the libidinal energy which is contained within the ego and which presses the latter to seek out opportunities for instinctual gratification and to proceed to consummation, on the one hand, and that quantum of libido which is deflected from the main stream to support the tonic functions of the ego supplement, on the other. Since this sequestered portion of energy drives activities which are not primarily sexual, that is, apperception, recollection, and problem solving, Freud spoke of it as "sublimated" or "desexualized" libido. I have mentioned this distinction above, and we shall have occasion to develop it further. I can take this opportunity to call attention to it in the hope of preventing some confusion. Hereafter, I shall refer to this sublimated, "desexualized" energy which supports the tonic activities of ego function as "sublimated energy."

Now let us proceed to describe the psychologic characteristics of the ego in its various energy states. We can start by making two complementary assumptions, or rather by following out the logical consequences of two of Freud's assumptions. In *Mourning and Melancholia* (1917e), he proposed to regard melancholia* as a condition in which the ego is "impoverished," that is, depleted of libido. The justification for this assumption lies in the inertia of the melancholic, the retardation of thought and action, the absence of object libido, and at the same time, the reduction of self-esteem.

* The term *melancholia* does not appear in the Fourth Edition of the Standard Nomenclature. It is the classic term for depression accompanied by psychomotor retardation, pessimism, and self-condemnation, and is so used by Bleuler (1916, p. 119ff.) and by Freud. The condition may occur as an event in any neurosis or psychosis, that is, it is not restricted to so-called involutional conditions or manic-depressive psychosis. The arguments of this book regarding energetics highlight the necessity of distinguishing between a clinical state of depression without ego depletion, and one with ego depletion (Ostow, 1960c). I am here retaining the term *melancholia* with its classical meaning. It may be defined energetically as depression with severe and general ego depletion.

On the other hand, in mania, the ego, Freud said, is surfeited with libido, exhibiting overactivity, rapidity of thought and motion, intensified object pursuit, and exaggerated self-esteem.

Let us assume further that these two points, melancholia and mania, are the two ends of a continuum of ego states, each defined by a specific ego libido content. Although a number of possibilities can be seen in the various physiologic correlates of libido which we discussed in the previous chapter, no successful procedure for the direct or indirect determination of ego libido exists at this time. Moreover, since we are dealing with psychologic criteria, we will do well to adhere to a notation appropriate to them. Correlation with organic measures can be made later. Let us then arbitrarily divide the continuum of ego states into ten approximately equal segments, separated from each other by eleven positions numbered 0 to 10 in sequence. The state of the ego in melancholia will then be denoted by 0, and its state in mania by 10. It will be helpful to remember that it is not only in mania that the ego is surfeited with libido; a plethora of libido exists at the outbreak of an attack of paranoia and paranoid schizophrenia too (Freud, 1911c). In fact, no matter how the subsequent course of schizophrenia may differ from patient to patient, it is likely that at its onset—that is, before the narcissistic withdrawal—the energetic and dynamic state is the same in all cases. (Nunberg, 1955, p. 131). I shall call this condition "incipient" or "nascent" schizophrenia. On our scale, then, 10 denotes the ego state characteristic of mania and of nascent schizophrenia.

Even if one is willing to grant that melancholia is characterized by a dearth of libido available to the ego, and that mania and nascent schizophrenia are usually characterized by a plethora of libido, one may still challenge the assumption that between these two points there lies a single continuum that defines all other ego states and that can be traversed sequentially in either direction. I justify this assumption on the basis of two sets of observations. First, if one watches patients lapse into melancholia and then emerge from it, one notices that they pass through essentially the same sequence of states in either direction. Generally, the decline into melancholia is considerably faster than the recovery from it. Moreover, there are certain secondary modulations of the course, depending upon the direction of travel, which we shall take up in the next two chapters. But by and large, the path toward and away from illness is the same. Similar considerations apply to becoming ill and recovering from mania and nascent schizophrenia. (Once the schizophrenic process has passed beyond the incipient stage, recovery need no longer retrace the steps of pathogenesis) The second set of observations differs from the first only in the respect that the movements to and from the o to 10 positions are induced by pharmaceutic agents. One can administer a tranquilizer and drive a patient into melancholia, replace it with an energizer and force him out of it. Similarly, by giving an energizer, one may precipitate mania or nascent schizophrenia in some patients (neurosis in others), and by replacing the energizer with a tranquilizer one can draw the patient back to a normal status. Again, except for the secondary modulations noted above, the paths of illness and recovery are the same. We may fairly conclude that the passage between a mid-position and either extreme, or from one extreme to the other, whether spontaneous or induced, traverses and thereby defines a continuum of ego states such as we have assumed.

THE INDICATORS

Direct Functions of Libido Level

General attitude and behavior. If one were confronted simultaneously with two patients, one a melancholic, the other a manic, there would be no difficulty in distinguishing between the two even without a history or formal interview examination. The manic will be taut and erect, the melancholic relaxed and bent. The manic will move abruptly and quickly, the melancholic heavily and slowly. The manic will be voluble, the melancholic reticent. The manic will be alert and curious, the melancholic inert and indifferent. If not crossed or irritated, the manic will be friendly, the melancholic cool. The face of the manic will be expressive and fluid, of the melancholic droopy and blank. The manic's skin will be warm to the touch, the melancholic's cold. The manic will shake hands vigorously, the melancholic hardly at all. Corresponding contrasts characterize the subjective life of the two. The manic feels buoyant, energetic, vigorous, healthy, self-confident, invulnerable, and—except when he is angry—optimistic. The melancholic feels heavy, lethargic, fatigued, enervated, decrepit, unhealthy, cold, weak, and pessimistic. These two sets of easily recognized attributes, in extreme degree, characterize positions of 10 and 0 respectively. Intermediate positions will be accompanied by intermediate degrees of the same categories of attitude and behavior. Let me note again that this set of criteria and the others listed below apply to the schizophrenic only in the period preceding the crucial narcissistic withdrawal. After that point, dynamic forces alter the apparent behavior and secondary reductions of libido occur.

Pursuit of objects. At the zero position, there is an utter indifference to objects, indeed, an aversion to them. The melancholic wishes to be quite alone; any intrusion into his solitary awareness is painful, and he resents it. At the opposite end of the range, there is an intense interest in, and pursuit of, objects. It is so great that often one person cannot satisfy the patient's need for love, and he may seek out one object after another, or accumulate a group of objects. Intense object love such as we see in the upper two or three positions readily gives way to envy. We may attribute the envy to the fact that the object who is loved so intensely is endowed not only with the object libido available but also with narcissistic libido attached to the image of the self projected onto the object. The yielding even of narcissistic libido tends to deplete the ego, especially if the lost libido is not restored by return of the love. If the euphoriant upward pressure of libido should weaken, the loss will be attributed to the disappointing love object. The patient may also envy the person preferred by the disappointing object. Carried even further, disappointment and envy will lead to hatred and a wish to kill. It is important to understand that hatred is a continuing object relation in which the affective sign has changed from the plus of love to minus. It stands in contrast to the resentful indifference of the melancholic, who finds the companionship of everyone onerous. Pursuit of objects increases directly with libido scale position.

Affective sensitivity. It is something of a paradox that melancholics, who are also called depressives, do not cry, while manics who are disappointed or angry do. In fact, I have learned that when a melancholic starts to cry, he may well be on the way to recovery. The reason is that although melancholia may be ushered in by a state of sadness and is characterized by "depression" of activity, actually it is accompanied by a blunting or obliteration of affect. The melancholic feels no love, envy, or hate. He may be momentarily angry with an intruder into his self-imposed isolation, and annoyed with anyone who makes demands upon him, but these feelings subside as the irritant withdraws. He says that he is guilty and should be punished, but he makes no effort at reconciliation with those he thinks he has offended (Nunberg, 1926).

The one thing the melancholic does feel is the inner pain that overwhelms him and seems to exclude all other impressions from his ego. But I do not believe that his affective unresponsiveness is to be explained entirely by the blocking effect of this psychic pain. Even if the pain were absent, the affectlessness would still prevail. An affect appears only to label an object or opportunity as desirable, or desirable but prohibited or dangerous, in each case only with respect to currently active instinctual drives. When no pleasure-giving instincts are active—the situation which obtains in profound melancholia—there is no basis for any affective response to an object, at least none derived from erotic instincts. Since the destructive drives of the death instincts are not stripped of their energy as the erotic drives are, they retain their capacity to give rise to affective responses, the affective responses appropriate to them: anxiety and horror and depression. These are actually not the affects appropriate to the death instincts, so much as the protests of Eros against them. When Eros is attenuated, and the death instincts are undiluted or "defused," even these protests are weak. They are more clamorous in moderate than in profound melancholia, and resume for a while as the patient improves.

As one passes toward the high end of the ego libido range, instinctual drives become stronger and stronger, and the affects associated with their potential and actual gratification become more and more intense. Frustration may cause a painful intensification of the affect, and disappointment a humiliating sudden reduction. Frustration or disappointment is almost inevitable, for such individuals are insatiable. But even without these mishaps, the very intensity of the affect itself becomes too difficult to bear. It is under these circumstances that the manic's love changes to hate, and he runs from object to object; or the paranoiac attempts to get rid of his impulses by projecting them out and fleeing from the object; or the schizophrenic cuts himself off from inner and outer reality. In general, the degree of affective responsiveness varies directly with position on the libido range.

We should take note of the special properties of the feeling of guilt. Although affective sensitivity in general increases with an increase of libido, the latter also tends to render the ego subjectively less responsive to the demands of the superego. Hence the conscious "sense" of guilt diminishes with accumulation of ego libido. Toward the lower reaches of the normal range, the feeling of guilt is prevalent and pressing. As actual dearth ensues, verbal expressions of guilt become more and more common, but the absence of libido makes the ego unable to respond to the feeling of guilt in any effective way. The verbal protestations then become meaningless. We may say that libido plethora makes the ego sensitive to affects arising from external percepts, and that libido deficiency makes the ego sensitive to guilt which arises internally.

Self-observation. The nature and degree of self-awareness vary sensitively with the ego's libido content. I have adopted Nunberg's term *primary self-observation* (Nunberg 1955, p. 135ff.) to denote a simple, direct apperception of sensations entering the ego, whether they are the sensory concomitants of somatic processes or affective overtones of psychic processes. *Secondary self-observation,* then, is a somewhat detached, self-conscious awareness of the somatic and psychic processes themselves, as well as of the subjective responses to them. It includes observation of intrapsychic events, at least those that achieve consciousness, and observation of one's physical attributes and social circumstances. For example, feeling the pain of toothache or of object loss is primary self-observation. To reflect, "Now I am feeling this pain," is secondary self-observation. To feel worthless or powerful is primary self-observation; to wonder why one feels so worthless or powerful is secondary self-observation.

The critical self-observation of the superego is generally not conscious. It may become conscious in the self-accusation and self-degradation of melancholia, when the self-destructive instincts of the superego gain control over the ego and speak with its voice. It may also reach consciousness as a perception after it has been projected out. In other words, the superego is at times projected out upon the love object or anonymous observers, and the self-criticism of the superego is placed in the mouth of others. This type of self-observation which is attributed to others I have called *tertiary self-observation.* In its most extreme form, it appears as delusions of reference: being watched, spied upon, accused, and punished. In less pathologic form, it consists merely of concern with others' opinion of oneself.

In melancholia, that is, at the low end of the range, only primary self-observation prevails. The patient is unable to achieve any detached objectivity about himself. He is preoccupied with his feelings of pain, and it is only these feelings he can express. A characteristic remark is, "I'm not the man I was." He will often make statements that sound like secondary self-observation, such as, "I am a terrible person." These are actually not observations at all, though they may express sentiments of the superego; they are *post hoc* rationalizations of his feeling of guilt. Moreover, the lack of interest in objects makes self-observation almost the sole psychic activity of the melancholic. This primary self-observation effectively lowers the threshold for the perception of all body sensations, including pain. An increase in ego libido, therefore, has an analgesic effect. The state of libido deficiency makes the ego less sensitive to affects arising from the perception of external objects, and more sensitive to affects arising internally, namely, guilt.

As one ascends the range, the tendency toward projection as a means of object pursuit grows. At the upper end, the pursuit of objects becomes such a single-minded concern that there is almost no self-awareness. There is an increase in the threshold for body pain and feelings of guilt. The superego is projected out so that its self-observation appears as the unwelcome opinion of others. When criticism is offered by the current carrier of the superego, the patient feels it as a blow against his narcissism and responds with indignation and self-righteousness. Secondary self-observation statements, such as, "I am a powerful person," are promptly followed by an estimate of the impression that the powerful appearance makes upon others. Even narcissistic self-aggrandizement tends to seek the confirmatory support of object love.

Toward the center of the range, primary, secondary, and tertiary self-observation are all available to the ego and appear as needed by the current dynamic circumstances. Self-observation is a function of narcissism, and, as we shall note shortly, its quality depends upon the quality of the prevailing narcissism. When the ego is oriented toward object love, but still within the normal range, narcissism is minimal and so is self-observation. When internal or external obstacles obstruct object love, narcissism is facilitated and self-observation becomes more active.

Narcissism. Freud spoke of a primary narcissism and a secondary narcissism (Freud, 1941c). The former is assumed to be the psychic state of the infant before he has achieved the capacity to conceive of persons or love objects. He is aware only that certain percepts and certain activities are accompanied by characteristic feelings, pleasant or unpleasant. It seems likely that many of the vertebrates, especially the lower ones, are able to take cognizance only of inner sensations, despite the fact that they relate in instinctual performance to other individual organisms. These inner sensations are elicited in response to specific sign stimuli from the outside, or to the proprioceptive concomitants of their own activity. Similarly, the fact that the human infant participates in complex instinctual activities with the mother does not imply that it is aware of the mother's existence as an object. Its instinctual apparatus can perform accurately with nothing more in consciousness than the affective states aroused by sign stimuli and somatic sensory data.

As one descends the libido range, less and less libido is available for object relations, and what little libido is left is retained within the ego as narcissistic libido. The individual in profound melancholia takes cognizance of no external objects. The approach of an intruder creates an unpleasant sensation which seems to emanate from within. I have seen melancholic patients develop bowel cramps or nausea when visited by people they loved. It was as if the unwelcome visit created a sense of inner discomfort, whose apparent or virtual source they attempted to eject via the gastrointestinal musculature and orifices.

As the human infant develops—and to an extent this is true of certain higher birds and mammals as well—the ego acquires the capacity to acknowledge the existence of living creatures outside itself and to concede that these creatures are the carriers of the sign stimuli to which they have been responding. It comes to realize that the pleasant and unpleasant sensations heretofore associated with these "releasers" actually derive from certain performances carried on with the objects. And as it grows older it realizes, too, that these pleasure-giving objects cannot be held simply by the infant's emission of its own stimuli. The concepts of subject and object individuals are required. This development, however, takes place only under the insistent pressure of libidinal energy. When the pressure fails, as it does in melancholia, regression to primary narcissism occurs, and with it indifference to objects and regression of activity to magical, somatic actions like the bowel cramps which aim to eject an intruder.

As libido begins to flow into the depleted ego of the melancholic his psychic pain is alleviated, interest in objects develops, and, as if he were recapitulating the process of his own psychic development, he begins to acknowledge and deal with others and himself as individual, discrete human beings. Hence both the intensity and the quality of the narcissism change. When frustration of object love requires a resumption of narcissism, in the presence of an adequate libido supply, the self-love is the love of the self as an object, as a person, including one's character, personality, possessions, attitudes, and so on. In fact, as Freud points out (1914c), it is actually the ideal of the ego, the ego ideal which is loved, and the recognition that the real self falls short of the ideal is painful because it jeopardizes the narcissism.

As libido grows in the upper half of the range, the pursuit of objects becomes more and more intense, and even the fraction of libido reserved for self-love becomes depleted in favor of the object. The offering of love tends to empty the ego of free, usable libido, and libido can be retained or regenerated only when the love is returned. When an individual is intensely in love, he has no narcissistic libidinal reserves, and all of his available libido is devoted to expression and exhibition of love. His entire libidinal economy, so to speak, is tied up in this love affair, and if he is disappointed, or if he must repress the love, the remainder of the ego, including the ego supplement, is left without resources and an ego-depletion depression may ensue.

The vicissitudes of persistently accumulating libido encompass the entire gamut of neuroses and psychoses. In some instances, where the object is lost or abandoned, one form of narcissism or another ensues. In hysteria, for example, an alteration of body or mental function is substituted for an object relation. In hypochondria, an organ or system of organs is substituted for the genital, which, in turn, was hypercathected as a substitute for the cathexis of the object.

In certain predisposed individuals, the libido plethora can be dealt with only by a complete and catastrophic abandonment of the entire world of reality, the acute schizophrenic breakdown. There is a withdrawal into a primary narcissism, a reversion to the mode of function of the archaic ego. We may say, then, that primary narcissism occurs of necessity with libido depletion at the lower end of the range, and that it occurs as one mode of possible defense against a painfully intense object love at the upper end. Is there a difference in the primary narcissism that occurs under these two sets of conditions? At the lower end, the patient falls into the primary narcissism, one might say passively, simply out of dearth of libido. At the upper end, the primary narcissism is an active defense which requires a vigorous psychic effort to sustain. This psychic effort flows over into the musculature, so that one can see violent physical aversion in the negativistic catatonic. With the regression to narcissism, there must be a great increase in self-observation. Here we run into a paradox, for we noted above that the self-observation of the archaic ego, and therefore of the schizophrenic, can be only a primary self-observation. Yet we have said also that with an increase in ego libido, self-observation changes from primary to secondary, and often, to tertiary. If we listen to schizophrenics, we hear them talk not about their feelings but about delusionary changes on the surface of the body, or in the cosmos. We have learned (Freud, 1911c, 1914c) to interpret these as projections of intrapsychic changes. Now we have the solution to the paradox. The exaggerated self-observation of the excessively libidinized schizophrenic in a state of primary narcissism is indeed primary self-observation, but the report is projected out from the psychic interior onto the physical exterior, or onto the cosmos, both of which the patient considers external and alien to himself. The schizophrenic's intimacy with, and love of, the cosmos are expressions of his projected narcissism.

Self-regard. Self-regard, or self-esteem, and ego libido have a direct influence upon each other. An increase in one increases the other, and a decrease in one causes a decrease in the other. At the low end of the ego libido range, the dearth of libido—both object and narcissistic libido—results in a painful loss of self-regard. With the reacquisition of libido, narcissism becomes a less painful experience, more gratifying, and it raises self-regard. As the quantity of libido rises to the upper half of the range, more than enough libido for narcissistic purposes is available. The degree of self-regard, however, may vary from the self-abasement of the person in love to the megalomania and omnipotence of the manic or the schizophrenic. What determines the actual degree of self-regard is the distribution of libido between narcissism and object love. In other words, at the lower end of the range, self-regard is necessarily low because of the dearth of libido; at the upper end, there is adequate libido for self-regard, but the actual degree which prevails depends upon how much libido is withheld from object love and retained for narcissistic cathexis. We shall consider the influence of self-regard upon libido in a later chapter. The complete narcissism of incipient schizophrenia is usually painful so that even with a great plethora of libido, omnipotent megalomania gives way to hypochondria and self-condemnation with a consequent diminution of self-esteem.

Projection and identification. Projection and identification are two of the most primitive of the psychic mechanims. Ultimately, they consist, respectively, of moving an energic cathexis or charge from within the archaic nucleus of the ego to the image of an object located within the microcosmic replica of the world that is contained within the ego supplement, or vice versa. Both mechanisms are employed in dealings with love objects, projection increasing the distance between the ego and the object, and identification decreasing it. Both mechanisms are used for establishing a positive relation with an object as well as for terminating it. Projection, however, increases the distance from an object, and thus lends itself more readily to sustaining object relations, though in an attenuated state; while identification, though it decreases the distance from the object, lends itself more readily to severing relations with an object.

Consider the archaic ego of the infant. The only relation with an object which he can achieve is a primitive form of introjection. Stimuli which impinge upon the infant's exteroceptive organs can only create sensations whose source seems internal, since his ego has not yet the capacity to take cognizance of an external world. As the ego supplement develops and becomes filled with a catalogue of object images, the inner sensation which the perception of one of these objects generates is now attributed to the object itself—as though it were a property of the object rather than the subjective response of the ego (Freud, 1912-1913). At first the object is introjected; subsequently the sensation is projected. Introjective identification is the only kind of object relation that the archaic ego can sustain; in fact, it is not really an object relation at all, but a precursor of an object relation. The first authentic object relation can be established only with the development of the concept of an object, and then by projecting sensations onto the object, or, more precisely, onto its image.

At the low end of the libido range, the individual has no libido with which to cathect objects. The approach of a person who is normally loved and has a claim upon the love of the patient creates only pain, but, as I have noted above, the pain seems to emanate from an internal source, and the individual attempts literally to eliminate it by gastrointestinal contractions. Here, the introjection of the object, or identification with it, serves the purpose of ignoring or negating the existence of an external object. In other words, at the low end of the range, identification is used as a defense against object relations. As the patient's ego accumulates a little more libido, he becomes able to acknowledge the existence of external objects, though he still has little or no positive feeling for them. Under such circumstances, external objects continue painful to deal with, and they can easily be used as foils, either to accept blame for the patient's misery, or to have bestowed upon them the hypochondriacal, delusional diseases from which the patient seems to be suffering. In either case, projection is used both for the purpose of getting rid of the demanding object and, with him, of some painful aspect of the ego.

Toward the middle of the range, there is just about enough libido to cathect objects comfortably, but not sufficient to insure an uninterrupted libidinal relationship. Under these circumstances, identification can be employed as a technique to guarantee a continuing object relation, even if it should be necessary to give up the real object, and also as a technique to terminate an object relation. An example of this dual function is the partial identification of a mourner with the deceased, which occurs as an aid to the work of mourning. The use of identification to establish a libidinal relation is seen in the mutual identification of members of a group with each other, by virtue of which the group acquires a positive cohesive force.

In the middle of the range, both projection and identification are employed, separately or together. More often than not, both mechanisms occur simultaneously, and it is not always possible to distinguish them. A classical illustration is the case of one type of male homosexual who identifies with his mother in order to abrogate his libidinal tie to her, then projects himself upon a boy, often younger than himself, whom he loves as he wished his mother to love him. Another common instance is the woman who defends herself against her masochistic homosexual tie to her mother by identifying with her, projecting the image of herself upon her children, and then visiting upon them the same sadistic love that she expected from her mother.

The normal resolution of the Oedipus complex demonstrates the use of identification to fortify one object relation, and modify— though still retain—another. The boy identifies partially with his father and strengthens his love for him, simultaneously terminating his sensual desires for his mother but preserving the tender component of his love.

Toward the upper end of the libido scale, there is a centrifugal tension urging the energies of the ego outward onto objects. Therefore, identification is inappropriate and projection is encouraged. As we have seen above, the establishment of the simplest kind of true object relation requires the projection of the feeling of pleasure outward upon the object image, as though the pleasure were a gift of the object rather than an inner response. By means of projection, object love may be reinforced by narcissism. The mother's love for the baby, especially a male baby, is intensified by the superimposition, upon the object relation, of the mother's hitherto frustrated love or desire for her fantasied penis. A distinguished scientist, who was a paranoiac with megalomaniac fantasies, defended himself against object love with the aid of an intense narcissism. He was able to forego this narcissism only in his love for his son to whom he attributed his own greatness and even more. It was clear that his son carried the burden not only of his father's homosexual libido but of his father's narcissistic libido as well. The paranoid schizophrenic, who suffers because of his abandonment of reality, tries to recapture it without giving up his narcissism, by projecting his own psyche outwards upon the perceptible world, which then becomes nothing more than a screen for his image of himself (Freud, 1911c; Nunberg, 1955). In these instances, projection is used as a means of establishing or strengthening an object relation without simultaneously giving up narcissism.

Projection, at the upper end of the libido range, can be used entirely defensively. For example, the object of an unwelcome impulse may be considered a tempter; one may reinforce repression by avoiding the object who is considered responsible for the impulse. The well-known projection of the paranoiac and the paranoid schizophrenic accomplishes two things at the same time. Because the patient's exaggerated love for his homosexual object is so threatening to him, the perception of the object is associated with anxiety rather than with pleasure. Thus the affective "sign" of the relation is changed from plus to minus, and the patient feels hatred rather than love. If the defense goes no farther than this, the patient need only avoid the object. In this case, however, he would be left without an object, and would continue to suffer the painful urgency of accumulated libido. By projecting the hatred upon the object, and, in many cases, by condensing the projected critical superego with the object, he changes the object into a persecutor. Thus the patient first wards off consciousness of homosexual love for the object, and then converts it into a masochistic, punitive relation which can be retained with considerably less anxiety.

To summarize, the mechanism of redistributing libidinal energies between the archaic nucleus of the ego and the object images contained within the ego supplement is strongly influenced by the ego's content of libido. When the ego is depleted, there is a centripetal pull favoring identification; when the ego is filled, there is a centrifugal push favoring projection. Practically, where the ego is within the lowest third of the libido range, identification is encouraged, and serves primarily to eliminate object relations. Within the highest third of the libido range, projection is encouraged and is employed to establish, to reinforce, or to terminate object relations. In the middle third, projection and identification are both available for establishing and defending against object relations.

Outlook.   It is often remarkable to see how the patient's outlook for the future is radically changed by the administration of a tranquilizer or an energizer. The melancholic, whose thoughts are only pessimistic, becomes confident and even optimistic in the face of the very same set of circumstances, when libido level has been elevated. The manic, whose confidence is unbounded, becomes more realistic when treated with a tranquilizer, and if the reduction in libido goes too far, he becomes unreasonably pessimistic. Of course, the frustrated manic, the frightened schizophrenic, the detached hysteric, the panicky compulsive, all have negative outlooks toward the future despite high ego libido. This is the result of dynamic opposition to, and defense against, the instinctual wishes. Thus, when a melancholic is lifted out of his depleted state with an energizer, we generally see this optimistic self-confidence.

This may in turn soon be dissipated, however, when the revived libido encounters ego and superego anxieties and resistances.

The ego and other psychic structures. In melancholia, the exclusion of libido from the ego, by whatever means accomplished, renders the ego relatively insensitive to id demands. On the other hand, the superego, or at least that portion of it which is energized by the death instincts, makes itself felt and heard by taking credit for the suffering of the ego. One sometimes has the impression that, in the absence of any other potential for gratification, the ego submits masochistically to the punitive chastisement of the superego. Yet I make this statement with some reservations, for the maintenance and gratification of even a masochistic relation require some complement of libido. The feeling of guilt, the hallmark of superego pressure, seems to vary inversely with ego libido: it increases at low levels and vanishes at high levels. In melancholia, however, the verbal expressions of guilt are not accompanied by any acts of restitution. They are affective feelings, but have no motivating power.

In the upper reaches of the libido range, the ego is flooded by libido from the id and so is forced into the service of the id. It has relatively little resistance of its own and it seems to ignore whatever protests the superego offers. Feelings of guilt are almost unknown to the manic or nascent schizophrenia. Often, though, we see patients under the influence of high levels of libido, especially incipient schizophrenics, mutilate themselves, kill themselves, fall into some destructive trap of their own devising, or develop hypochondriacal delusions. While some of these incidents are doubtless efforts at defense against overstrong impulses, others seem to be punitive operations of the superego. So that while the superego is not rendered ineffective in states of high libido, it does its work silently. It may be that superego punishment is invoked by masochistic impulses.

Freud makes an interesting point in his paper on "Humour." At times, he says, the individual is able to identify with his superego and regard his own ego condescendingly, in a detached way, as an adult might regard a child. This is the humorous attitude, and it is essentially an instance of secondary narcissism, though the individual pretends to be detached from both the object and the narcissistic strivings of the ego nucleus. Obviously, such an attitude cannot be adopted when the ego is highly charged, nor when its charge is too painfully low. It represents an effort to rise above oneself by identifying with the parents. Participating in a religious service, or attending a meaningful event, such as a funeral or a wedding, is often able to achieve this identification with the superego and detachment from the ego.

U-Shaped Functions of Libido Level

All of the functions listed above vary with libido level in some direct relation: they increase, decrease, or change in some other consistent way with libido level. For example, the tendency to project, omitting the modulations due to dynamic influences, might be said to rise proportionately with ego libido. There are some other functions that also vary with object libido, but that achieve a maximum or minimum close to the center of the range, and minimal or maximal values, respectively, at both ends.

Objectivity in self-observation. We approached the subject of objectivity in self-observation earlier in this chapter. When the ego is intensely driven by object libido, it cannot achieve any objectivity in self-observation. Even when dynamic forces cause the libido to be reflected back upon the ego and so create an intense narcissistic cathexis, the exaggerated self-observation that follows is bent to the service of the narcissism. At the low end of the range, the psychic pain caused by the ego depletion, and the depletion itself, preclude secondary self-observation in favor of completely involved primary self-observation. If we consider objective self-observation as a unitary function, we see that it is maximal toward the center of the range, and that it falls away toward either extreme.

Shame. Shame is the affective response to wishes to exhibit oneself seductively to an object, and it often appears in the presence of pregenital wishes, in the execution of which the subject might be observed. It evokes a reactive wish to hide, to cover or to bury oneself, or to fall to the ground.

At the lowest extreme of libido supply, primary narcissism precludes any object relation, and no real criticism or censorship seems as realistic as the rebuke of the superego. In profound melancholia, there is a state of shamelessness, and in mild to moderate melancholia, a need to beg for help often overcomes what residual shame exists. At the upper extremes of the libido range, the superego which contains and enforces the code regulating shame is flouted and projected out. Hence manics and incipient schizophrenics are shameless and resent criticism from others, which is reminiscent of the voice of the critical superego. Shame, we must conclude, is an affective mechanism, which prevails toward the center of the libido range, but which is put out of action with movement toward either extreme.

Aggressiveness. In the introductory portion of this chapter, I stated my belief that whereas upward pressing erotic drives induce active searching for objects and opportunities, the death instincts, except to the extent that they are fused with, and carried by, erotic instincts, are entirely responsive—that is, they make no effort to create or find opportunities for discharge; they are elicited only by adequate cause. We assume that the essential trigger for the evocation of the death instincts is a trauma or the threat of a trauma (Freud, 1920g, 1926d). Now a depletion of the ego is as severe a trauma as the ego can sustain, and it creates a painful state. Hence, we must expect that with improverishment of the ego, the energies of the death instincts are evoked, and they occupy the ego undiluted by libido. It is their aim of destroying the source of the pain, or at least its apparent source, that creates the great suicidal tendency in melancholia.

Again, at the upper end of the libido range, the integrity of the ego is threatened by the plethora of libido. In fact, Freud considered the ultimate danger situation to be the possibility that the ego might be flooded with energy. This threat to the integrity of the ego evokes powerful destructive impulses, which take the forms of catatonic negativism, suicide, self-mutilation, and murder. Moreover, this prevalence of aggressiveness in the presence of extreme values of ego libido favors sadism and masochism in the choice of modes of libidinal gratification. This is not to say that the energies of the death instincts are absent when the ego is only moderately innervated. In the middle third of the range, destructiveness can be invoked when and to the degree that it is necessary. In the absence of a specific or dynamic threat, however, there is minimal aggressiveness. At either extreme of the range, on the other hand, the energetic state of the ego evokes the continued activity of the death instincts, both fused with libido at the upper end, as well as unfused at either.

Hypochondria. Let me add a comment about a symptom which seems to be especially sensitive to fluctuations of ego libido —hypochondria. Hypochondria is a manifestation of narcissistic cathexis of the image of an organ or organ system. Such narcissistic cathexes occur when repression has resulted in the withdrawal or partial deflection of libidinal cathexis from the object. If this narcissistic substitute for the object, and also for the genital of both subject and object, is only moderately cathected, sublimated or substitutive instinctual pleasure is obtained. If the strength of the cathexis grows, as it does in some neurotic or psychotic patients, the organ in question seems to become a source of discomfort or pain. Some schizophrenic patients may mutilate themselves in order to overcome this distress. One patient (R. L. X.) whose narcissism was concentrated in her attractive face and body, proceeded systematically to mutilate these, and to try to blind herself as well, refusing at the same time to acknowledge what she was doing. The anxiety associated with hypochondria may be ascribed to this flooding of the organ representation in the ego with libido drawn from the object. The organ may be selected on the basis of a previous experience which gave rise to guilt or anxiety, or it may be selected to establish an identification with the lost object or with the punitive superego figure.

But hypochondria also occurs in states of ego depletion. The patient complains that his guts have been eaten away, his head is empty, his body is decaying, and so on. Just as excessive cathexis of a part of the body image may be painful, so can depletion. In melancholia, complaints about body decay are part of the general misery and do not stand out as special threats. In states of libido plethora, however, an attempt is made to keep the excessive cathexis concentrated at the specific organ, so that the hypochondria seems to be the chief source of pain. A second difference between the two forms of hypochondria is that in the plethora state, the affected organ is generally located on the surface of the body, clearly visible, such as the eye or a specific organ with well-recognized functions, such as the heart; while in the depletion state there are only poorly defined references to the interior of the body.

A common form of hypochondria is "fear of losing one's mind." This is seen in dissociative states, including hysteria, anxiety hysteria, incipient catatonia, and paranoid schizophrenia. It is especially intense when the dissociation is reinforced by incipient ego depletion. We shall discuss this further.

Ego function. At the upper end of the libido range, the ego is usually unable to contain the extraordinary pressures which pour into it from the id. The pursuit and defense against objects, and the vicissitudes of the narcissism, first strain and then overcome the reality constraints of the ego supplement. As libido grows, one notices an increasing loss of objectivity, an irrational distribution of confidence and interest, and the emergence of delusional ideas, first as notions, then as opinions, and finally as unshakable convictions. If there is a schizophrenic break with reality, the world of object images is lost and the archaic ego nucleus begins once more to respond to sign stimuli. For example, limb movements become signals, a glance means spying, a gesture is a controlling influence.

If we listen to a patient sinking into a melancholia, we hear complaints of confusion, loss of memory, inability to make a decision, fear of "losing my mind." The patient is aware that thought processes are sluggish. He may try to describe the distress he feels as due to "numbness" in the head, "as if my head were empty." As the ego becomes progressively emptied, mental life seems to come to a standstill. Fantasies which expressed inner feelings now become crystallized as hypochondriacal delusions, which may occasionally be projected onto others. The feeling of guilt becomes a conviction of guilt. The fantasy of an inner demon, which represents the abandoned object, evolves into a delusion of harboring a devouring parasite. Analysts have speculated about whether the sublimated energies with which the ego supplement operates are derived from the main stream of libido or from an independent source. Observing a patient descend into melancholia, either spontaneously or under the influence of tranquilizing medication, leaves no doubt but that the entire ego is fed from the same libidinal source.

We must conclude, then, that the ego is able to function properly only within about the middle third of the libido range (actually from scale positions 4 to 8), and that deviation of libido to either side of this results in increasingly serious impairment of ego function.

THE SCALE

One serious hazard encountered in any effort to add anything to psychoanalytic or psychotherapeutic technique is the possibility that the innovation may impair the analysis by distracting the analyst from attending fully to the productions of the patient. It is difficult to conceive of an innovation whose value would be so great as to justify the diversion of the therapist's attention. Fortunately, the indicators which I have just enumerated are aspects of psychic function which are normally assessed during the treatment session, although seldom as systematically as this method would require. The additional effort which is demanded consists solely of noting, mentally or in writing, the assessment of each of these functions, and selecting the position on the libido scale to which they point.

Of course, it is understood that the state of the transference itself conveys much of the required data. For example, the degree of interest in objects is generally reflected in the intensity of the transference, curiosity about the therapist, insistent demands upon him, or attempts to influence him. Tertiary self-observation may be expressed as concern about the therapist's opinion of the patient. Projections and identifications with respect to the therapist are often indicated by the very first remarks made in each session.

I present here a relatively simple scale which I have been using during the past several years. It has a number of faults, some of which I shall point out, and I do not offer it as a fixed or final or even essential ingredient of this method of treatment with pharmaceutic agents. Despite its drawbacks, its simplicity recommends it. Nevertheless, I expect the accumulated experience of others, as well as my own, to disclose methods for improvement.

Scale of Ego Libido

POSITION	CRITERIA
0	Profound, inert melancholia or catatonia
1	Delusional melancholia
2	Vigorous self-condemnation and pessimism
3	Guilt, pessimism, and primary self-observation
4	Self-orientation, feeling of enervation
5	Showing no other indicators distinctly
6	Object orientation
7	Moderate object striving with optimism
8	Pronounced object striving, perhaps with anxiety or with tertiary self-observation
9	Ideas of reference, but with adequate reality testing
10	Delusional mania or schizophrenia

The most obvious difficulty with this scale is that it indiscriminately combines criteria which reflect the intensity of the libido charge of the ego—for example, degree of object striving—with criteria which depend entirely upon the toughness of the ego—for example, reality testing. We must acknowledge here that two factors determine whether a psychic conflict will issue in illness: the strength of the instinctual impulse and the strength of the ego which must contain it. Since it is likely that these, in turn, depend upon two quite separate physical substrates, we should not be surprised to find that the inheritance of mental illness is multifactorial, that is, that the appearance of mental illness in a given individual depends upon his inheritance of at least two separate predisposing defects, as well as complementary traumatic personal experience. *Ego strength* is a term used to denote the capacity of the ego. We should obtain different measures, however, depending upon which aspect of ego capacity we investigate. We can do no better at this point than to refer back to Nunberg's classic paper of 1942, *Ego Strength and Ego Weakness.* Should we adopt as a measure of ego strength the strength of the instinctual energies with which it is supplied, since a person with a vigorous ego will accomplish more than a person with little or no vigor? In that case, we would be faced with the paradox that the strong ego, by definition strongly innervated, is the more likely to break down, due to the intense pressure of these same instinctual energies. Nunberg considers assessing aspects of ego function, such as narcissism, responsiveness to threats of trauma, synthetic power, and readiness for defense. In each, he concludes, "it is not the maximum or minimum of cathectic energy of an ego function that decides the strength of an ego, but the optimum. In other words, an excess of cathectic energy impairs function just as does too little cathectic energy. Only a medium amount of cathexis, which we cannot measure, is favorable for the function of the organ." Our discussion above of the relation of ego functions to its libido content has led us to the same conclusion.

Nunberg concludes that we can consider the strength of the ego to be a measure of the strength of the instincts with which it can cope. "If we wish to estimate the strength or weakness of the ego, we must be able to measure the energies of the ego." Hence we might take comfort in the idea that the libido scale I have proposed is not actually a measure of the ego's supply of libido, but a measure of the relative amount of libido considered with respect to the strength of the ego. While this is a relative rather than an absolute measure, it is in one way more useful because it measures the actual pathogenic potential of the libido. Here again, though, we must acknowledge a serious limitation, for not all ego functions deteriorate simultaneously, nor is the sequence necessarily the same for different individuals. Some individuals will retain reality testing, for example, or objectivity in self-observation, only close to the center of the libido range. Others will tolerate a substantial deviation of libido from the center before any ego functions deteriorate. Some ego functions vary only gradually, though continuously, with changes in libido—self-observation, for example. Others, such as reality testing, may change abruptly with small alterations in libido at critical points. We may conclude that the strong ego, as opposed to the weak, will tolerate relatively broad deviations of libido supply, reflecting these changes in its mode of function within normal limits, but resisting pathologic breakdown.

Clinical observation alone discloses that some patients seem to shift in a mercurial way from ego states characteristic of depletion to ego states charactistic of plethora, and back. One would be inclined to suspect that the ego in question is a weak one, responding with little inertia to small influences. This suspicion can be confirmed by the administration of tranquilizers or energizers, for such individuals respond with unusually great sensitivity to relatively small doses and brief courses of these agents. In a sense, then, we may be developing a method to measure ego strength, and its converse, libidinal intensity, namely, by titrating with a tranquilizing or energizing drug from one ego state to another.

How closely would two different observers agree in estimating libido scale values? I have not actually checked this with any other individual, but I would find it difficult to see how two observers could differ by more than two scale positions, and I doubt that they would differ by more than one at the borderline of disease. Further, while differences betwen observers might make comparison of their findings difficult, this problem does not arise when an individual analyst or therapist employs the scale to follow the vicissitudes of his patient's illness.

Inspection of the scale will soon disclose to the reader that although it is symmetrical in form, the normal range is not centered about position 5. We expect to find normal individuals driven by some pressure of object libido, although at times, frustrations, failures, and disappointments may make us moody, self-preoccupied, and enervated. We should then consider position 4 within the range of normal fluctuation, but not 3—at least not for more than a few hours' or a day's duration. Again, we expect moderate object striving with a reasonable degree of optimism in normal individuals. When object striving becomes too intense, or is accompanied by anxiety or excessive self-observation, and lasts too long, we suspect disease. A person in love is an exception. Position 7 then becomes the upper limit of normality in most instances. To summarize, fluctuations between positions 4 and 7 may be considered normal; positions 3 to 8 raise the suspicion of disease; and 2 and 9 are definitely pathologic. On time charts of libido fluctuations, horizontal lines at positions equivalent to 3½ and 8½ form a channel which generally defines the limits within which ego function remains intact.

DISCORDANT FINDINGS

We have yet to resolve one of the most serious difficulties with this method of estimating ego libido. It often happens that a patient will show simultaneously indications of at least two different ego libido values. For example, a patient hospitalized after a melancholic suicide attempt and still evincing some of the indications of melancholia may accuse the nurses of making homosexual advances. This we should be inclined to assign values of both 2 and 10. A less extreme situation: a woman will feel enervated, wake up early with depressing thoughts, retch or vomit upon awakening (an early sign of melancholia), and yet look forward with combined pleasure and apprehension to an afternoon art class. Here we should wish to assign both value 2 or 3 and value 6 or 7.

How can we explain the occurrence of discordant findings? First, we should be surprised if an agency as complex as the ego, which contains within itself components from different phylogenetic ages, some of which derive their energy through various channels from others, were to respond to energy changes in a unitary fashion. The fact is that discordant findings are most commonly encountered at times when patients are shifting from one energy position to another. Generally, after the shift has been completed, and the several components of the ego permitted to re-establish an equilibrium with one another, findings again become concordant. With respect simply to notation, it will generally suffice to record the libido position in such instances by two numbers rather than one. Thus, by criteria associated with object striving, position 8 might be indicated, while criteria associated with self-observation and narcissism might simultaneously conform to the requirements of position 4. Libido state would then be recorded as 8-4. I have so far been able to discern two mechanisms making for the co-existence of findings characteristic of different ego states. I imagine there are others.

Splitting of the Ego

Freud used this term to denote the coexistence of logically inconsistent ego attitudes. One example he gave (1927e) was the perversion of fetishism, in which one part of the ego acknowledges the castration of women, and the other denies it. In hysteria and schizophrenia, the existence of an erotic impulse toward a given object is repressed. I have observed that following such a massive and abrupt exclusion of a major fraction of the total libido flux from the preconscious, signs of ego depletion appear, and in predisposed individuals this depletion may proceed to a full melancholia. We shall encounter examples of this in the report of patient K. N. X., to be presented in Chapter V. Another woman hysteric would become angry with her husband, turn away from him, and become overwhelmed by a profound enervation; she would awaken from sleep in drenching night sweats. A phobic man repressed his love for his mother and wife, and also his homosexual attachments to friends, in repeated hysterical withdrawals associated with feelings of detachment from reality, and depersonalization. On each occasion, the hysterical withdrawal was followed by a sense of ennui, fatigue, pessimism, primary self-observation, and guilt. It was only after I had made this observation that I understood the meaning of the following passage: "Loving in itself, insofar as it involves longing and deprivation, lowers self-esteem; whereas being loved, having one's love returned, and possessing the loved object, raises it once more. When libido is repressed, the erotic cathexis is felt as a severe depletion of the ego, the satisfaction of love is impossible, and the re-enrichment of the ego can be effected only by a withdrawal of libido from its objects" (Freud, 1914c).

At the beginning of an attempt to disengage from the object, the two tendencies may be observed simultaneously. The patient seems to be trying to place his libido elsewhere, upon another real object, a hysterically affected organ, or upon a fantasied object. Meanwhile, the depletion affects self-observation, self-regard, and often a variety of other ego functions. It is this simultaneous incipient enervation of the ego and search for a new object that is responsible for the discordant signs in such cases. If the object search should be successful or, on the other hand, if a full-blown melancholia should ensue, the findings will again become concordant. Often when melancholia is treated with an energizer, object libido will be renewed before other ego functions are re-innervated, and for a short time we may see the discordant picture of a melancholic patient who has active genital sexual desires.

I have observed that the complaint, "I'm afraid I'm losing my mind," is often made by patients who have just detached themselves hysterically from a love object, and sometimes by patients who are experiencing the sensations of progressive ego depletion. But when the hysterical detachment is promptly followed by ego depletion, this feeling of "losing one's mind" seems to be especially common. Both processes result in the loss of control over a portion of the ego, and it is apparently the awareness of this loss of control which creates the frightening impression. Incidentally, while this concern is not always followed by an actual psychotic breakdown, it often may be. It is striking to see how severe an anxiety this experience can create in patients who have experienced it innocuously many times before. One is reminded of the castration anxiety that accompanies depersonalization. In these cases, too, one often encounters material which indicates that the loss of ego control is interpreted as castration. A danger common to both the repression of a powerful libido flux and to castration is the danger of losing the love object, and this common threat may underlie the equivalence. Of course, we must not overlook the fact that often the fear of insanity is based upon masturbatory guilt. In these hysterical, phobic, and schizophrenic patients, physical approach and withdrawal from the object are often replaced by the admission of libidinal wishes into consciousness, and by their withdrawal. In other words, physical relations with the object are replaced by mental maneuvers. The head, or rather the brain, takes on the significance of a genital organ, and these patients, who for the most part have given up masturbation, derive sexual pleasure from their mental manipulations.

The fear of losing one's mind is also frequently associated with the fear of losing sphincter control or with losing the capacity to arrest sexual excitement. One hears patients describe a fear of losing contact with reality during orgasm. "I get that remote feeling," or, "I feel as if I'm slipping away." We see thus the close association of the several ego functions: control of consummatory discharge of instinctual impulses, including sphincter regulation; intellectual activity; the maintenance of object relations; and the sense of reality. The last has two distinct components. The primary process sense of reality is the affective feeling that something perceived is real. The secondary process sense of reality is the intellectual knowledge that it is real. In states of depersonalization and feelings of estrangement, the first is lost although the second persists. In the experience of hallucination, the first is retained but the second is lost. Any of these ego functions may be discarded by virtue of hysterical repression. With ego depletion, however, all tend to weaken and fail passively. It is probably this disruption of ego function which is the proximate cause of anxiety.

In many instances where strong object libido persists alongside a depleted ego supplement, hallucinations seem to be facilitated. Pieces of evidence from several different sources contribute to this impression. First, let me refer to a recent report of my own (1959e) of autoscopic hallucinations experienced by two patients. Two such instances occurred spontaneously early in the analysis of one patient. On both occasions there was mild incipient ego depletion. The third instance occurred only once in a patient I had known for ten years, and that was while she was taking a tranquilizing drug and complained of the enervation it was causing. Neither of these patients has ever been psychotic. When I observed these instances, I was aware of the ego depletion, but I was not impressed by the paradox of its co-existence with residual libido, because at that time I did not yet suspect the relation between hallucination and *partial* depletion of the ego. Upon re-reading the report now, I find that I was impressed then by the fact that both patients were given to hysterical dissociation, and that in both the autoscopic hallucination represented an effort by a persisting narcissism (which had replaced the persisting object libido) to cast out the unsatisfactory portion of the ego by means of death and rebirth. The three conditions for hallucination exhibited in these cases were: (1) partial ego depletion; (2) ego split; and (3) persisting object or narcissistic libido.

The second piece of evidence for this hypothesis is my observation of visual or auditory hallucinations appearing in several patients recovering from schizophrenic episodes (Ostow, 1960e). These had not been present before the start of the recovery process. In all instances but one, recovery was achieved by means of tranquilizing drugs; in one instance the patient recovered spontaneously. In each case, hallucinations appeared after the patient had become more placid and was achieving insight. In most instances, hallucinations were accompanied by indicators of ego dysfunction, here due to depletion—namely difficulty in thinking, "confusion," or headache. I concluded from that study that hallucinations occurred when the function of the ego supplement was so impaired that it could not contain the libidinal energies pressing outward from the ego nucleus. Sarwer-Foner and Ogle (1956) report two patients, a manic and a patient with character disorder, in whom chlorpromazine administration induced hallucinations, visual in one case, auditory in the other. Hallucinations had not been present before treatment, and ceased when the drug was discontinued. We must infer that the administration of tranquilizing drugs reduces ego libido, but seems to deplete the ego supplement of its sublimated energy before emptying the ego nucleus of its libido.

A third piece of evidence is derived from an experience with a catatonic patient (M. T.). I first saw her after an acute episode when she thought she was being poisoned by her husband and a doctor; she ran scantily clad through a hotel lobby shouting that her husband wished to murder her, felt "tightening" in the muscles of her throat, neck, and shoulders, and smelled gas. A combination of tranquilizers and energizers, concomitant with psychotherapy, produced enough recovery in two weeks to permit her to leave the hospital. The drug dosage was fairly heavy, amounting at one point to 64 mg. of Trilafon together with 200 mg. of Thorazine. At home she did well for about two weeks taking only tranquilizers, but soon she began to show confusion and perplexity, and complained of a feeling, "I'm not the girl I used to be," characteristic of ego depletion. Visual and olfactory hallucinations returned, as well as delusions. Despite a rapid, progressive withdrawal of tranquilizers, she lapsed within one week into an apathetic catatonia. It is my impression that the combined administration of tranquilizers and energizers and simultaneous psychotherapy produced the initial improvement, but the continued administration of tranquilizer unopposed by an energizer contributed to her relapse. The total situation is, however, not quite so simple. It is important, perhaps critically so, to note that her relapse began when her husband urged her to give up psychotherapy with me because I was "too young" and reminded her of himself. He thought she should see an older psychiatrist who would remind her of her father. She was obviously furious, her unconscious wish to kill him was strengthened, and his attitude lent credibility to her delusion that it was he who wished to kill her. At one point during the relapse, she again fled from the apartment and from him, begging help from strangers and accusing him of wishing to kill her. She came up to the hospital and called for me. Even if she were getting no drug at this time, such pressure would probably have been sufficient to cause a relapse. I believe, though, that with a small dose of tranquilizer and a small counterbalancing dose of energizer, she might have been able to tolerate his pressure without breaking down. The hallucinations returned during an interval when the ego supplement was enervated to a greater degree than the ego nucleus. There was no further evidence of hallucinations—although I cannot be certain they did not exist—when a complete apathetic, catatonic state developed.

Note that in all three situations, hallucinations occurred during a process of ego depletion, whether the process was tending from extreme plethora to normal, or from normal to depletion. In other words, it is not the absolute libido level which is to be correlated with hallucinations, but the temporary disequilibrium that accompanies the process of depletion. Moreover, we see that a tendency toward hysterical or schizophrenic splitting of the ego constitutes a specific kind of ego weakness which does not easily tolerate the rapid reduction of libido. Such patients, if treated with tranquilizing drugs, should be given small doses in the expectation of obtaining slow improvement. The catatonic patient, for example, in a state of tense excitement, will respond well to a tranquilizer; but if the medication is continued without reduction in dose, or without counterbalancing by small doses of an energizer, the original psychotic behavior inevitably returns. The reason is that further depletion impairs ego function, facilitates splitting, and the clinging that ensues becomes too disturbing for the impoverished ego to contain.

A fourth subject pertaining to the appearance of hallucinations with energetic disequilibrium of the ego, is delirium. The following case will illustrate its relevance. A sixty-nine-year old man developed paranoid delusions and ideas of reference, specifically that his wife was having an affair with their chauffeur. He was depressed and cried often. In addition, he suffered with slight to moderate Parkinsonism, for which he was taking 2 mg. of Artane t.i.d., and showed some mental signs of cerebral arteriosclerosis. I prescribed for him 10 mg. of Stelazine daily, a fairly high dose, and 25 mg. of Catron to be taken every second day. Within a week both the delusions and the depression seemed to have disappeared, but four days later the delusional ideas returned, or re-asserted themselves if they had merely been silent. I increased the dose of Stelazine to 15 mg. daily, and decreased the Catron to 6 mg. every two days. A few days later, the patient developed severe insomnia with nocturnal delirium, including vivid visual hallucinations and even more forceful paranoid delusions. I infer that the ego supplement, in this case, weakened by the cerebral arteriosclerosis, responded to the strong dose of tranquilizer much more than did the ego nucleus, which was highly charged by the energizer. Hallucinations and delirium issued from this disequilibrium.

This instance leads us to wonder whether the conditions for delirum may be injury to the ego supplement in the presence of high libidinal charge of the ego nucleus. If this is indeed so, then we can understand why tranquilizing drugs are able to dissipate not only alcoholic delirum, but even the delirium-like hallucinations induced by hallucinogenic drugs. It had been assumed that the clinical antagonism between tranquilizing drugs and hallucinogenic drugs was based upon opposite actions upon the same biochemical system. Our line of reasoning has led us to infer that their antagonism is based upon effects on two separate mechanisms balanced in physiologic equilibrium. The effect of the impairment of the ego supplement by the hallucinogenic drug is counterbalanced by the attenuation of the ego's libido charge wrought by the tranquilizer.

These remarks about the conditions which give rise to hallucination and delirium lead us to our fifth point, which is concerned with the hallucinations and other signs of ego disintegration that follow from sensory isolation. There are two related connecting links. First, there is the common clinical observation that the hallucination and confusion of delirium—and this may be true of some of the hallucinations of schizophrenia, too—are much exaggerated by darkness and quiet, and are better controlled in an illuminated, busy environment. Second, it has been noted that the action of hallucinogenic drugs is accentuated when the subject sits in a darkened room, or when his eyes are closed. In our earlier discussion of sensory isolation, it was suggested that the adverse effects could be explained by the disequilibrium between persisting ego libido and impaired function of the ego supplement. We cited evidence there that those subjects who started the experiment under the influence of a higher libido pressure, seemed to suffer more.

We may return at this point to the study of sensory isolation conducted by Cohen *et al.* (1959). In our previous discussion, we proposed that the group of subjects who tended to orient themselves in space by criteria based upon the perception of external cues likely represented a group with relatively high levels of ego libido, while their counterparts, who tended to orient themselves in space by criteria derived from internal cues, probably represented a group with relatively low levels of libido. We are now in a position to justify this assumption from other considerations introduced in our presentation of the indicators of libido level. High levels, we said, were characterized by a greater interest in the environment than in the self, by a greater interest in objects than in the ego, and by a greater tendency to project interest outward than to introject objects centripetally. If our arguments are correct, we should then expect, furthermore, the high libido, field-oriented group not only to suffer more distress during sensory isolation, as they do, but also to engage in less self-observation, to project more freely, to be more concerned in a delusional way with observers and persecutors, to be more certain of the reality of their delusions, and to be more given to visual and auditory imagery and hallucination, in contrast to the low libido, body-oriented group. And these were indeed the experimental findings. The low libido group, on the other hand, engaged in more self-observation and were more concerned with body feelings than the high libido group.

By what mechanism does sensory isolation weaken the function of the ego supplement? One possible explanation is that, deprived of the arousing effect of external stimuli, the ego supplement is no longer able to command its quota of energy from the ego nucleus. I have no evidence for this hypothesis; I suggest it because of the analogy to the depletion of the ego supplement which follows hysterical splitting of the ego. The generalization would be that when the ego is disengaged from the libidinal pressures that impinge upon it from the inside, or from the sensory stimuli impinging upon it from without, it tends to lose its energy supply. This hypothesis might be tested, or, what is more important, more data might be obtained by stabilizing ego energy in the experimental subject with small balancing doses of energizer and tranquilizer, and then observing the response to sensory isolation. It would be especially helpful to assess libido supply on the scale I have proposed, or some similar one—or better still, to record the state of all of the indicators at the various stages of the experiment.

It is not only sensory isolation which impairs the function of the ego supplement; recumbency does, too. Hypnagogic hallucinations occur, I believe, due to the imbalance resulting from persisting libido supply in the ego nucleus on the one hand, and the impairment of ego supplement function, on the other, due to the combined influence of sensory isolation, recumbency, and beginning sleep. Of course, in any discussion of the mechanism of hallucination, we come back to the problem of the dream. The observations of Dement and his co-workers tell us that dreaming occurs repeatedly during the night, in periods of twenty to forty minutes' duration, separated by intervals of an hour so so. Electrical activity is slowest and most synchronized during the time when dreaming is absent. This has led me to suspect that the "work" of sleep, the regeneration of instinctual energies, takes place during the period of cortical and diencephalic electrical slowing, which probably indicates the absence of intrinsic activity in these structures. The regeneration of a certain amount of energy tends to arouse the sleeping ego, and libido begins to flow once more into the ego nucleus. There it encounters a still inactive ego supplement and, in accordance with the hypothesis we are now considering, generates hallucinations. Apparently the hallucination has some discharging effect, for after a given amount of it, libido is again withdrawn from the ego nucleus and energy-regenerating sleep resumes. It would be interesting to examine the implications of this ebb-and-flow theory for the classical theory of dream psychology. I doubt that any change at all would be required.

Finally, we must mention the hallucinations and delirium produced by sleep deprivation. Since I believe that the function of sleep is to regenerate instinctual energy, I necessarily believe that the principle effect of sleep deprivation is reduction of libido level. I attribute the hallucinations and delirium to the disequilibrium that usually occurs, when libido is being reduced, between the more susceptible energy content of the ego supplement and the reduced, but still relatively high, libido content of the ego nucleus.

Can we say anything, based upon these considerations, of the nature of hallucinations, their psychologic or physiologic mechanism? I'm afraid that I can do no more than to refer the reader back to Freud's paper, "*A Metapsychological Supplement to the Theory of Dreams*" (1917d). There he cites two conditions for the occurrence of hallucinations. First, sleep or mental illness produces a topographic regression of the ego whereby the instinctual impulse seeks discharge, not by action but by reversing its course and stimulating the perceptual apparatus from within. Second, a withdrawal of energetic cathexis from the system Cs (Consciousness) will abrogate the faculty of reality testing and render stimuli from within the psyche equivalent to those from without. This is, of course, a metapsychologic description rather than an explanation. For the moment we have nothing better.

Clinging

There are two circumstances under which a person tends to cling: first, when threatened with the loss of the love object, and second, when threatened with the loss of ego libido. As we have seen above, these two dangers are related in several ways. If there is a loss of libido, then the object is also necessarily lost, for libido is required to sustain an object relation. On the other hand, we have observed that if a love object is lost, or if a major segment of the total libido flux is invested in an impulse which is repressed, the rest of the ego is likely to be depleted. In addition to the fact that each of these two events tends to create conditions eliciting the other, it is important to note that both have the same ultimate meaning, namely, a loss of love.

It is my impression, though, that as between the two, the loss of the object is less dangerous than the loss of libido. First, a lost object can always be replaced. If it cannot be replaced immediately, a re-investment of the stream of libido in the ego will bring

about a satisfying narcissism, which will permit a temporary ob-
jectlessness. Second, ego depletion has a tendency, once started, to
advance rapidly in a vicious circle: loss of libido → lowering of self-
esteem → further loss of libido → further diminution of self-esteem,
and so on. Third, loss of object with retained libido does not preclude
replacing the object with another or with narcissism; loss of libido,
on the other hand, precludes object seeking. My impression, however, is based not upon this theoretical reasoning but upon observation. It has seemed to me that when I have observed clinging,
there has been a danger of libido loss. When the libido loss was
reversed, the clinging stopped and the patient recovered, often via
the path of strengthened narcissism and then renewed object seeking. It often appeared that when adequate libido was available,
the patient could handle the problem created by the object loss.

When libido continued to decline, despite the efforts at clinging, anxiety sometimes developed. Like all anxiety, this might be attached to a specific fear—for example, a fear of becoming insane,
of falling ill, of dying. It might be attached to specific circumstances
—for example, a fear of traveling, a fear of being alone. Or it might
be "free floating," that is, a nameless dread. In his discussion of anxiety, Freud (1926d) proposed that the general condition for anxiety was helplessness in the presence of an actual trauma. In
some forms of neurosis, the helplessness which evokes the anxiety
is the flooding of the ego by a plethora of energy from the id. This
is doubtless one of the chief precipitants of neurotic and psychotic
defenses. But if the danger of flooding a well-innervated ego can
generate anxiety, should not the helplessness of an ego already
partially depleted, in the face of persisting libido plethora in the ego
nucleus, also be adequate cause for anxiety? Such anxiety is seen
in hysterics, in phobics, and in schizophrenics following ego-splitting
detachment from the object or from major segments of reality.
Moreover, I suspect that since a general ego impoverishment will
render the ego helpless, at least against the demands of reality if
not against the now quiescent internal demands, it too will give
rise to anxiety, at least until impoverishment has progressed so far
that the anxiety mechanism has been put out of action.

Although libido loss is more dangerous to the psychic economy
than object loss, and can generate anxiety, it does have a certain
value, which may be considered the biologic "purpose" or function
of the mechanism. If an individual has sustained a severe loss and

requires the lost object in order to permit the discharge of instinctual impetus, then the ego is liable to be flooded and crippled
by the now dammed-up and more intense libido supply. Consider,
for example, patient X. N. Z. (see also Chapter VI). Before she
came for treatment, her defense against intensified conflict about
her erotic impulses toward her husband and children was to turn
away from them and seek extramarital gratification, meanwhile projecting her infidelity and homosexual love for women upon her
husband. She recovered with the aid of a tranquilizing drug (experiencing visual hallucinations during the recovery process) and
psychoanalysis was begun. Under analytic scrutiny, there were
many other occasions when accumulated libido pressure, as high
as 9 and occasionally to 10 on the libido scale, threatened to override the reality testing of the ego and to create psychosis. Psychotic
breakdown occurred only twice. On all other occasions, the loss by
detachment of the love objects, plus the analytic insight which she
had gained and with which she was confronted at the time, acted
to reduce libido pressure to normal range. It was at such times that
her characteristic signs of ego depletion became evident: fatigue,
early awakening, confusion, headache, and infrequent blinking. In
this case, we can see that ego depletion acted as a kind of defense,
a countervailing force, protecting the ego against the explosive
force of the rapidly accumulating ego libido. From this and similar
observations, I infer that ego depletion is a salutary defensive mechanism when an object has been lost or discarded, but like other defensive mechanisms, it can get out of hand and thus lead into a state of
melancholia. Generally, ego depletion which accurately corrects
ego plethora is accompanied by a sense of relief and comfort. If
the depletion is too rapid and creates a temporary disequilibrium
by emptying the ego supplement faster than it attenuates the
libido of the ego nucleus, the feeling of subjective distress may be
exaggerated and anxiety may appear. Again, if the depletion goes
too far, it evokes first anxiety and then the general misery associated with melancholia.

To summarize: clinging occurs when ego depletion, due to
natural defensive mechanisms or other causes, develops too rapidly
or excessively, or when, in a phobic individual who has experienced
it before, it merely theatens to recur. The resultant helplessness of
the ego in the face of instinctual or environmental demands gives
rise to anxiety, which is the trigger that releases the clinging tend-

ency. What are the manifestations of clinging, and how does it produce discordant indications of the state of ego function? Clinging occurs only so long as there is sufficient ego libido available to activate the anxiety mechanism in response to progressive ego depletion. Since the energies of the death instincts do not seem to be compromised by the depletion mechanism—or, if they are, it is to a much lesser degree than libido—the clinging response to depletion anxiety generally mobilizes these, fuses with them, and so renders the clinging not only libidinal but also destructive. The intensified object relations which accompany clinging are generally inappropriate to the ego state as determined by its libido content, and so result in discordant findings. Typically, we may see increased object striving, sometimes even with projection, in the presence of such indications of depletion as fatigue, enervation, morning insomnia, pessimism, guilt, primary self-observation, and so on.

That the agitated, ambivalent clinging is a defensive response to the threat of progressive depletion, rather than the effect of the depletion itself, is supported by the following observations I have made on several occasions. When it has seemed to me that a patient's excitement, whether psychotic or not, represented agitated clinging, I have administered an energizing drug. Often, within a matter of days or of one or two weeks, the excitement has ceased and given way to a state of depletion. With continued medication, finally the depletion, too, has given way, this time to a state of clinical normality. With continuing medication, in some instances a state of plethora anxiety or excitement has been induced, and a resumption of normality has been achieved only after reduction of the energizing medication or the addition of a tranquilizer. Apparently, even before the drug was able to exert sufficient energizing influence to undo the depletion which had already occurred, it was yet capable of terminating the threat of further depletion and thus to terminate the clinging agitation.

One may compare this sequence of events with the phenomena of the early stages of starvation. Hunger occurs when food is totally withheld, but it persists only a very few days. If food is given, the hunger is terminated at once even though the metabolic deficit has not been fully compensated. On the other hand, if starvation continues, the hunger disappears, because it represents a state of active craving which the depleted metabolic energy reserves are unable to sustain.

I am aware of three chief modalities of clinging: to people, to nourishing substances or experiences, such as food or sleep, and to intoxicating drugs which anesthetize the ego against the pain.

Hostile clinging to people is especially characteristic of children, who are depressed by loss of, or rejection by, a parent. Their nagging, exasperating tenacity represents the fear of losing the parent once more, as well as angry punishment for the pain of the loss. Not infrequently children will react this way to a divorce. But hostile clinging is seen in adults too. Such patients, constantly on the brink of depletion, often try to use psychotherapy or analysis for support. They demand more and more time and affection from the analyst or the therapist, at the same time resisting the analytic process itself. If the analyst refuses to comply, the patient may slip into melancholia. On the other hand, if he should comply, there would be no analysis. It is necessary to gauge just how much frustration the patient can tolerate and to impose that much upon him. One might try to fix a termination date for, say, six months or a year hence, but that is a hazardous maneuver in such a case, because when the time comes and there is no possibility of turning back, there may occur a melancholic breakdown or suicidal blackmail. I think that in the case of such patients, the administration of an energizer might relieve the fear of depletion and urge the patient back into the object relations he has abandoned.

An object relation established and sustained by this clinging defense against depletion resembles the anaclitic relation of the infant to the mother. It is a relation in which love and sustenance are demanded but nothing is offered. The entire existence of the relation depends upon the simultaneous gratification of repletion needs by the object. Such a clinging love nevertheless creates the impression of an object relation, and causes discordance of libido scale indications, since it occurs along with signs of incipient depletion. This kind of object love can be called anaclitic love, and the libido involved seems to be primarily pregenital.

Patients who protract analysis indefinitely and demand more and more time of the analyst are sometimes said to be "addicted" to analysis. This seems to be an apt term, for the clinging to nourishment, better called craving, is a kind of addiction. Its most common form, perhaps, is bulimia or hyperphagia. This, I suspect, is one of the most common causes of obesity. Such patients have an actual addiction to food which they are unable to overcome unaided, in the manner of the alcoholic. They may eat all foods indiscriminately or have specific cravings, for example, for milk or for candy. They may eat all day or only when they feel the onset of depletion. The bed-time snack often has an addictive quality. I have seen the habit develop with mild melancholic depression and disappear when the depression is relieved. Some people who give up smoking take to eating more, as though the smoking had served the purpose of a repleting addiction. Fat men are supposed to be jolly. It is my impression that their obesity is due to a food addiction required by impending depletion, and that their joviality is a denial of depression.

This same addiction to food which defends against incipient depletion is, I believe, responsible for the striking weight gains which often accompany the use of tranquilizing drugs. One woman who remained free of psychotic manifestations for years with the aid of small daily doses of tranquilizers was, nevertheless, disturbed by obesity due to uncontrollable appetite. I was finally able to solve this problem by giving small daily doses of Deaner, a mild energizer, which were not sufficient to undo the anti-psychotic effect of the tranquilizer, but were apparently enough to dissipate the feeling of depletion.

Earlier in this chapter the relation of hallucination to ego depletion was discussed. We concluded that hallucination was especially apt to occur when the ego supplement was impaired in function, generally by incipient depletion, while the libido charge of the ego nucleus remained relatively high. If the level of the sublimated energy of the ego supplement is absolutely, as well as relatively, low, we should expect to find some evidence of clinging or addiction in the patient's behavior, or even in the content of the hallucination. For example, the initial delusions of the catatonic woman (M. T.) whom I have already described were delusions of being poisoned, and that fact, I see in retrospect, should have made me anticipate that, despite the presence of delusions, the absolute libido level was low. Hence the flight from her husband was a defense against anaclitic clinging, probably associated with fantasies or acts of fellatio. I had suspected the latter detail and subsequently the suspicion was confirmed. It should not be forgotten, though, that oral wishes and defenses against them occur also in states of libido plethora. The clinical differentiation between a libidinally intense object relation and an anaclitic, clinging relation is difficult. Yet, when psychopharmaceutic agents are to be used it is a crucial distinction to make, for the former condition requires a tranquilizer, and the latter, an energizer. At times only a therapeutic trial, dangerous as it is, can distinguish.

Let me cite two more illustrations of the relation obtaining among hallucination, ego depletion, and food craving. Forrer (1960) gave several examples of benign auditory and visual hallucinations, that is, hallucinations occurring in individuals without evident mental illness. In each case, the hallucination occurred in association with a mild craving for food or drink, and further, the subject's associations to the content of the hallucination had to do with food and drink. Dement and Fisher (1960) observed that subjects whose sleep was interrupted after a single full electroencephalographic and eye movement cycle on each of several consecutive nights began to overeat, and one subject who had previously been alcoholic resumed his addiction. I have mentioned that it is my impression that the procedure which Dement and Fisher called dream deprivation was actually sleep deprivation. The latter causes ego depletion due to failure of normal libido regeneration, and I believe the subsequent bulimia and alcoholism are to be attributed to this depletion. It is difficult, too, to ignore the possibility that in ascribing a fundamental oral wish to every dream hallucination, Lewin (1950) has apprehended the existence of a sense of depletion in the partially awakened dream ego.

Related to this issue in some way is a phenomenon I observe in patients whose ego libido is being sustained by energizing medication. They will awaken abruptly sometime during the night, generally with no recollection of a dream, and proceed to search in other rooms, in closets, or in possible hiding places for someone or something, or they may get something to eat or to drink, or they may both search and eat. Then they will return to bed and fall asleep again after a shorter or longer interval. Since they are seeking a person, and are often satisfied by real or symbolic nourishment, it is likely that they are looking for mother so that they may be fed. If this is so, then we may infer that it is a signal of depletion which motivates them. The phenomenon invites comparison with the two related attitudes of melancholics and manics, respectively. The former will awaken at night or in early morning and lie in bed ruminating over a feeling of miserable emptiness and horrid, biting, often cannibalistic fantasies. These often induce nausea. By contrast, manics will awaken early in the morning and busily pursue one or another promise of gratification, other than reunion with the principal love object. I suspect that the awaking occurs in each case at the termination of the period of slow electrical activity when, normally, the phase of dreaming would occur. The ensuing activity is determined by the regeneration and redistribution of energies that have occurred or failed to occur during the period of slow activity. Melancholics awaken hungry because no repletion has taken place, and they are horrified by the fantasies created by the unopposed and undiluted death instincts. Manics awaken with a vigorous drive to find substitute objects. Patients who are clinging because of threatened depletion awaken with nightmares of a frightening intruder, who represents the loved but disappointing object. Patients who are recovering from a state of depletion awaken with enough libido to seek mother.

I find that sleep is disturbed in patients who are resisting depletion. Apparently some phenomena are characteristic more of the depletion-resisting state than of either plethora or depletion itself. These include clinging in its various manifestations, nocturnal sweating, retention of fluid, and oral drives. An increment in sleep disturbance is reported by patients who are lapsing into depletion either as a result of dynamic pressures or excessive tranquilization, and also by patients in pronounced depletion who are being treated with energizers. In fact the onset of the sleep disturbance or the nocturnal sweating may be used as an indication of the fact that the energizer has begun to take hold, even before the clinical picture betrays improvement.

In the light of the remarks I have made about sleep in the previous chapter and in this, we can make some guesses about the meaning of these sleep disturbances. Sleep seems to proceed normally in these patients for at least sixty to ninety minutes. Spontaneous awakening seems to occur, then, at the time when dreaming would normally occur. In fact, spontaneous awakening may follow a disturbing dream and often the patient obtains something to eat at this time. I have compared the role of dreaming in the adult sleep cycle to the role of feeding in the infant sleep cycle. It is as though only a certain amount of libido regenerating sleep can proceed without refreshment of some substrate supplies. In the infant, these supplies are provided by actual feeding. In the adult, the dream process—including its characteristic and pronounced physiologic changes—seems to accomplish the same function. One is led to wonder, then, whether the wish expressed in the dream proper may perhaps always be the oral or anal need which is required to support the libido generating process. The fact that the wish often takes a genital form, even in its unconscious version, need not prevent our imputing a primarily pregenital motive to it. This is no more than an interesting speculation which can be tested.

Sleep disturbance in patients with serious libido deviation disorders may reflect, then, dysfunction of the sleep mechanism. An increased per cent of dream time in plethora disorders may be required by the need to support an abnormally high libido level. Psychogenic depletion may be effected, to a certain extent at least, by a block in the dream-nourishment mechanism. So that it is only when this mechanism is tested, after the initial phase of regenerative sleep, that awakening occurs together with a hypertrophied oral appetite. The different ways in which this mechanism may become disordered, and the specific influences upon it of the different psychodynamic mechanisms and the different varieties of chemical agents, remain to be studied, both in the clinic and in the laboratory. These studies will contribute, I believe, not only to practical techniques of drug administration, but also to our understanding of the processes of pathogenesis.

That alcoholism and possibly other forms of drug addiction are related to depression was suggested by Rado (1933), by Federn (1952), and by Fenichel (1945). From my limited experience, I have the impression that it is not so much the painful affect of depression that drug addiction defends against, as the ego depletion that accompanies the melancholic type of depression. Alcohol and other intoxicants serve the function of antagonizing ego depletion in three ways. First, they serve as anesthetics which deaden the ego pain due to depletion. Second, they are symbolic nutriments and thus function as food. Third, the consumption of alcohol often leads to companionship with other drinkers, and greater enjoyment of this companionship than the ego could otherwise experience. It is interesting that of the three modalities of clinging in the service of ego repletion, the most real is the clinging to the love object, for that really achieves a gratifying love relation. Eating and drinking, while they accomplish the intake of materials that may have actual nutritional value, do not really contribute directly to the libido supply of the ego; their contribution is entirely symbolic. It may well be that in infancy the level of instinctual energy is immediately determined by the blood sugar level, and therefore feeding raises the libido level promptly. The hungry infant's clamoring for food, then, may be considered the prototype of the agitated clinging of the depleted adult. Supplying food to the former and an energizing drug to the latter stills the clamor. With the intake of food, and the sleep that follows, the infant begins to generate the instinctual and psychic energy which eventually leads him to develop object relations. It is also true that if ego depletion in an adult is caused by hypoglycemia, feeding will replenish the ego. Since most ego depletion, however, is due to object loss or abandonment, or other psychologic cause, the consumption of food can have, at best, only symbolic value. Intoxicants do better, for they actually provide, in addition to the sensations which gratify oral instincts, relief from psychic pain.

In this connection it will be interesting to ascertain whether there is a relation betwen ego libido and blood sugar level in the diabetic. Kaplan and co-workers have reported recently (1960) that the administration of an energizing drug (imipramine) to diabetics decreased the glycosuria as the patient improved; and conversely, when the drug was withdrawn, glycosuria increased as the patient relapsed. This situation should be clarified by further investigation. Meanwhile, I should guess that the hyperglycemia in some diabetics may be a miscarried automatic effort to correct libido depletion. If this is so, we should expect its reduction to follow either the administration of an energizer that would undo the depletion, or the administration of large doses of tranquilizer which would overcome this defensive effort. Corresponding alterations in the glucose tolerance curve might be encountered under similar circumstances among nondiabetics.

Because addictions represent defenses against threatening or ongoing ego depletion, they can be alleviated by the administration of energizing drugs. If necessary, small doses of these, prescribed as long as required during analysis or therapy, can keep the patient relatively free from addiction while the conflict responsible for the depletion is analyzed. Patients do not become addicted to true energizers, because these really elevate the libido level, which remains high for days after the drug has been withdrawn. Further, with revived libido supply, the patient regains his self-confidence and self-esteem and is often eager to give up the drug in order to demonstrate his renewed feeling of invulnerability. If he relapses shortly, he is more realistic about giving up the drug the next time.

I believe that there are other cases of addiction where the danger is simply the threat of object loss without the accompanying threat of depletion. I have not treated such patients, but I assume that these situations may exist since I have known other types of clinging to occur in the presence of a threat of object loss alone. Such patients would respond well to tranquilizers and poorly to energizers. It would not be surprising if addiction were used, at different times in the same patient, to defend both against the threat of object loss in the face of libido plethora and against the threat of ego depletion. I have noticed that patients tend to use the same defenses against the threat of object loss and the threat of depletion.

In a paper on depression (Ostow, 1960c) I drew attention to the marked contrast between the state of addictive clinging and the state of melancholia which ensues after addiction has failed. In the former, there is a general centripetal tendency. The patient is impelled to engulf and retain as much as he can in every way. He eats and drinks too much. He clings to love objects tenaciously. There is frequently a tendency to constipation. In the state of melancholia, there is a general centrifugal flow. The patient suffers nausea and anorexia. He does not eat, he retches and vomits. He rejects companionship. He feels that parts of his body are falling away. He feels empty and poor. I believe that the transition between object love and object rejection would be more gradual, were it not for the defensive clinging effort in which there is an emergency mobilization of greater energies than the libido state would justify. This intensified energy supply becomes even stronger by virtue of the fusion with the energies of the death instinct. When the emergency effort finally collapses, the transition to the functional state characteristic of the low libido level seems abrupt indeed. It may be strange to speak of a state which can persist for years as a state of emergency mobilization. Yet patients in such a state are notoriously unstable, and I suspect that when we have the proper chemical correlations worked out, we shall find that they are actually under continued stress.

I have recently encountered, in my own practice and in the experiences of some of my colleagues, instances of promiscuity, homosexuality, and sado-masochistic perversion which were relieved by the administration of energizers. I could assume that in these instances the pathologic activity was clinging and anaclitic in nature. Whether similar perverse activities would occur in these individuals under intense libido pressure cannot be foretold. The phenomenon requires further study.

CHAPTER IV

Use of Pharmaceutic

Agents in Therapy

THEORETICAL CONSIDERATIONS: THE PATHOGENESIS OF MENTAL ILLNESS

THE PROPER USE of the psychopharmaceutic agents requires a sound knowledge of the pathogenesis of mental illness. Efficient causes are dynamic and energetic. Formal causes are essentially genetic (that is, they are determined by the individual's psychic development); material causes lie within the constitutional endowment of the individual. With respect to dynamics, I have no additions to make to classic psychoanalytic formulations; I can do no better than to refer the reader to Freud's papers or, for systematic presentation, to Nunberg's text, *Principles of Psychoanalysis* (especially Chapter VIII, "The Processes of Defense," and Chapter IX, "The Process of Illness"), and to Fenichel's, *The Psychoanalytic Theory of Neurosis.* I should like to complement these dynamic accounts of pathogenesis with certain energetic considerations which constitute the theoretical basis for the sound use of psychopharmaceutic agents and for their coordination with psychoanalytic and psychotherapeutic work.

The pathogenesis of a mental illness, says Nunberg, can be divided into two elements: the primary element is the conflict, and the secondary, the process of symptom formation. Under what circumstances does a conflict appear? When, as a result of an increase in instinct strength or impairment of ego function, the ego fails to contain the instinctual impulses which it cannot admit to consciousness and to gratification. Instinctual strength may increase as a result of externally imposed frustration, of physiological development—for example, puberty—of exposure to temptation or seduction, or of incomplete gratification. Ego weakness may develop as a result of physical illness or exhaustion, sensory isolation or intoxication, or loss of ego libido for reasons such as disappointment or failure.

Conflict arises when the ego cannot permit a relatively powerful instinctual impulse to reach consciousness or achieve gratification. Why should the discharge of an instinct be inhibited? There are two principal groups of obstacles. One applies especially, though not exclusively, to the pregenital impulses. There seems to be some intrinsic, inherited danger in the full gratification of sexual instincts. The pregenital impulses threaten the ego, which responds with anxiety, and at some point in early childhood, the ego excludes these impulses by means of primal repression. When subsequently these same pregenital instincts are reactivated, notably at puberty, the repression is repeated. The second group applies especially to genital impulses and arises from the identification which resolves the Oedipus complex and establishes the basis for the superego. In adult neuroses, at least, the primary instinctual conflict arises with the revival of the Oedipus complex and the superego's opposition to the forbidden sexual impulses. Often in neurosis, conflict at the genital level compels instinctual regression. Pregenital impulses are thus revived, and their repression must once again be renewed.

How does neurotic symptom formation alleviate the conflict between impulse and ego? Unresolved conflict endangers the integrity of the ego, and the ego responds to this threat with anxiety. The latter is a painful experience and activates certain primitive mechanisms for dealing with threats—namely, defenses. Several of these defenses combine with the disturbing impulse itself, often with a need for punishment contributed by the aroused superego, to form an irrational behavior complex, the symptom. The symptom then compromises between the conflicting demands of id and ego by simultaneously satisfying both, if only partially. To the id it offers some instinctual gratification; in the name of the ego it prevents full gratification; and often the superego, too, is satisfied by the patient's suffering. Although this neurotic solution mitigates the conflict between id and ego, the symptom itself creates a new conflict between ego and reality.

To summarize: when the relative strength of a hitherto well-controlled unconscious instinctual impulse vis-à-vis the ego grows beyond a given point, it evokes anxiety. The latter, in turn, evokes primary-process defenses with which the pathogenic wish combines to form a symptom. We conclude that the pathogenic potential of an instinctual impulse is ultimately its strength relative to the hitherto adequate ego controls. In psychoanalysis, and in analytic-type psychotherapy whose goal is cure by insight, the processes of abreaction, interpretation, making conscious unconscious connections, and working through, attenuate the acuteness of the conflict and the need for symptom formation. In the supportive, gratifying type of psychotherapy, some relief is afforded by partial or symbolic gratification of the instinct, by reassurance of the ego against anxiety, and by placating the superego.

If drugs alone are to be used to help the patient, there are two possible approaches. When the symptoms are forming, and before they have been crystallized, anesthetizing the ego against anxiety may abate the urgency of the situation and defer the need for symptom formation. Barbiturates with relatively short durations of action, such as amytal, were formerly employed for this purpose in acute situations, and phenobarbital in somewhat less acute situations. At present, meprobamate and other new, synthetic, ego-anesthetizing agents seem to have an anxiety-alleviating effect at least as great as the older drugs, with the advantage of relatively less sedative action, less cumulative toxicity, and less subsequent "hangover." The limitation of such treatment is that its influence lasts only as long as each dose of drug; no contribution is made toward resolving the conflict, and the deleterious effect of the conflict on general behavior, love, and social relations, on work and on sublimations, is not checked.

At the risk of seeming tiresome, I must again emphasize that I do not recommend attempting to manage mental illness of any sort with pharmaceutic agents alone, except when the exigencies of the situation offer no other recourse. From a theoretical point of view, however, it is helpful to examine the effects of drugs upon a mental illness. To return to our argument, if we were going to try to treat neurosis or psychosis at its incipience, tranquilizing drugs would be more useful than the ego anesthetics. The tranquilizers would offer more than mere relief of subjective distress and interruption of the evolution of symptoms; they would actually attenuate the pathogenic conflict. Of course such action could not prevent a second and third exacerbation of the conflict, but if it was a specific and nonrecurrent event that activated the conflict initially—for example, a trauma or an unusually strong temptation—treatment with a tranquilizer might give the patient relief for a considerable period of time. It must be obvious that by weakening the libidinal drive behind an instinctual impulse and so resolving the conflict, the drug also precludes any kind of lasting resolution of the conflict by insight therapy. Hence, when dealing with a neurosis not severe enough to cripple total performance, and when the benefit of psychotherapeutic working through of the problem is desired, tranquilizing drugs are actually contraindicated.

Often we find that the process of symptom formation does not continue indefinitely; moreover, some symptoms after a brief period subside apparently of themselves. What has happened? Could it be that in the symptomatic behavior, or perhaps even in the process of symptom formation itself, the disturbing impulse was exhausted? This may occur in some instances, especially when the impulse has not grown to immoderate proportions and when the defensive manuever functions more as an ego syntonic sublimation than as an ego-alien, distressing symptom. A second spontaneous healing mechanism may come into play when more serious and persistent libido accumulations develop.

I should like to present this corrective phenomenon in three ways. First let me describe what actually happens. Under certain circumstances, we observe the rapid development of what I have referred to as the libido depletion syndrome. Its manifestations may be those of the defensive clinging and addiction we discussed in the previous chapter, or its evolution may be so rapid that it bypasses this stage entirely, or it may pass briefly through the clinging stage. Then the definitive depletion syndrome emerges. The patient begins to complain of confusion, indecisiveness, fatigue, boredom, early morning waking, insomnia, anorexia, then guilt, pessimism, nausea, feelings of emptiness, and if it goes further, severe self-criticism, self-degradation, a wish to die, and a suicidal urge. Such patients wish to be relieved of all of their responsibilities and often ask to be taken to a hospital. When this happens, all pre-existing neurotic or psychotic symptoms seem to disappear.

Under what circumstances does this depletion syndrome occur? We are familiar with it, of course, in mourning, and after the loss of a love object in any other way, through separation, rejection, disappointment, and so on. In all of these instances, the intensity of the manifestations may be mild, moderate, or severe. We consider the reaction a normal one so long as it is not immoderate in degree. The libido depletion syndrome may also follow a narcissistic loss, such as illness, mutilation, aging, business or professional failure, and adverse criticism. Here, too, we consider such a response not unnatural, especially if it is mild and short lived. There is a third set of circumstances under which this phenomenon may appear, and that is as an intercurrent event in any mental illness. It succeeds mania so frequently and its manifestations are so directly contrary to mania, that we consider an alternation between mania and melancholia to constitute a disease entity. It may appear in schizophrenia as schizophrenic melancholia, or in some forms of catatonia. It is not uncommon in conversion or anxiety hysteria or in obsessive-compulsive neurosis. We shall discuss depletion in each of these specific instances below. To summarize, a libido depletion syndrome, either in the form of anaclitic clinging or in its definitive form, often appears following the loss of a love object, following a narcissistic loss, or in the course of neurosis or psychosis. The syndrome is frequently accompanied by the affect of depression, especially in mild to moderate forms of definitive depletion, but the affect may be denied, as it generally is in the clinging phase, or it may be absent, as in profound melancholia. When the affect is present, the whole, complex, affect-and-depletion syndrome may be referred to as "a depression."

Second, having described the phenomena, we wonder whether we can understand them as having any meaning, any function, any "purpose" within the disease process itself. It is my impression that depletion does have a function, namely, the prevention or attenuation of neurosis or psychosis. I believe that object loss frustrates object instincts and that narcissistic insult frustrates narcissistic impulses. Frustration is an adequate precipitant of pathogenic conflict because it causes damming up of libido and more desperate efforts toward instinctual discharge. In the absence of any corrective measure, the initial object loss or narcissistic insult is therefore liable to be followed by the initiation of a pathologic process leading to neurotic or psychotic symptom formation. What I am suggesting is that the ego impoverishment is just such a corrective effort to arrest the pathogenesis of illness. Consider the gambler. Faced with a small loss, he will simply increase his stakes so as to make up for the loss in the next win. Persistent losses make him desperate and he risks more and more. When his resources are exhausted, he is likely to suffer a "reactive depression" which deters him from further adventure while it lasts. The sooner in the cycle the depression syndrome comes into play, the less will he have lost before stopping, and the less severe the reaction is likely to be.

A young man who had hitherto displayed temperamental stability and good character was jilted one day by his girl friend. He went to her house in the middle of the night, awakened her and her parents, threatened violently to kill her, then returned home and pounded the walls with his fists until they bled. The next day he was appropriately depressed, remorseful, retarded, self-critical, and pessimistic. Had the depletion come sooner, he would have been spared the hysterical fury.

A woman had deferred marriage until her early thirties, hoping for an extraordinarily attractive and romantic husband. She considered that she had found the right man when she married, but ten years later it was clear that he had disappointed her in almost every way. She developed a severe, suicidal melancholia. After two years, during which her illness made her husband miserable, forcing him to take care of the housework and children as well as attend to his job and to expend more than he earned on medical care, she was referred to me because her psychiatrist had suggested lobotomy. After four weeks on Catron, her melancholia subsided. She felt well and denied knowing the cause of her illness. That the cause continued to operate became clear when attempts to withdraw the drug were followed promptly by relapses. Then she began to show apparently unprovoked hysterical outbursts, punching and scratching her husband and berating him for being such a failure. It was clear that the drug had relieved her of her melancholia, but in so doing, had forced her to confront her disappointment and fury with her husband and herself. The fury was expressed in brief hysterical attacks; between attacks she blandly denied the validity of the words and actions which she expressed during her outbursts.

This defensive depletion may miscarry in the sense that the desperate, aggressive clinging that it may activate sometimes has deleterious effects of its own, or worse still, makes common cause with the persistent, frustrated libidinal impulse. An example of this mechanism is seen in the person who marries unwisely "on the rebound." If the depletion goes too far, so that it not only attenuates the pathogenic drive but permits the patient to sink into a deep and lasting melancholia, as in the case of the woman I have just described, it must also be considered a miscarriage of defense in the same sense that catatonic negativism is a miscarriage of defense.

If we grant that ego impoverishment can function as an "energetic defense" in the case of loss of love object or narcissistic loss, we have still to discern its defensive function when it appears during the course of neurosis or psychosis. Obviously, it can occur for the same reasons in an ill patient as in a hitherto well-functioning patient. But if these were the only reasons, we should expect the depletion syndrome to occur no more frequently in neurotics and psychotics than in normals. This is clearly not so; I have learned that when a patient is first seen in a melancholic state for which he is treated with an energizer, a definite neurotic or psychotic illness will more often than not be precipitated soon after his apparent "recovery." It must be something in the underlying illness itself which is responsible for the depletion.

At this point, we shall have to return to our account of the general pathogenesis of mental illness. We mentioned that the symptom incorporates elements of gratification, defense, and punishment. I do not propose to take up a discussion of defense (for which the reader may refer to the sources I have already mentioned as well as to Anna Freud's *The Ego and the Mechanisms of Defence*), but I should like to draw attention to the fact that defenses can be divided into three groups. First, there are those defenses that modify the pattern of the instinct, such as regression, reaction formation, undoing, isolating, changing the instinct to its opposite, and turning it against the self. Second, there are defenses that terminate the specific instinctual relation with the object, such as repression, denial, negation, and depersonalization. Finally, there are specific defenses that may be used either to terminate or to reinforce the object relation, namely, identification, projection, and displacement. I mention this classification only to point up the fact that one method of defending against an unwelcome instinctual impulse is to abandon its object. Once the object has been abandoned, there ensues the same energetic problem that we have already discussed in connection with object loss, namely, that the instinct is deprived of all opportunity for gratification, except via withdrawal into narcissism. Those individuals incapable of sufficient narcissistic gratification to discharge pent-up libido now find that by virtue of their defense the instinctual drive has become more powerful than before. Hence, unless discarding the object is accompanied by libido depletion, it solves one problem only to create others. I illustrated this point in the previous chapter with the case of a patient (X. N. Z.) who developed an attack of paranoid schizophrenia whenever episodes of profound aversion to her husband and children were not promptly followed by commensurate ego depletion. Some individuals are able to tolerate this self-imposed object loss by adopting a narcissistic position. In that case, the narcissism must assume the burden of procuring adequate gratification, a burden which is not lightly carried. Individuals whose defense against illness takes this form of intensified narcissism become sensitive about their narcissism, which must be supported not only by the approval of the superego but of love objects and of contemporary society as well. They become arrogant, conceited, and self-righteous. Should the narcissism be offended by the criticism of others, or of the superego, or by failure, illness, or disappointment, it can no longer carry the burden of instinct gratification. At this point, only two courses are possible: the narcissism may be reinforced by a turning away from reality of psychotic proportions, as in psychotic megalomania, or the problem of libido accumulation must be solved by adequate depletion.

In obsessive-compulsive neurosis there is another occasion for depletion. Obsessive patients suffer depletion, as other individuals do, with the loss of a love object or with a serious narcissistic blow. In addition, when the obsessive patient has performed some neurotically impelled act, or achieved a neurotically meaningful success, he may suffer a sudden depletion which automatically evokes anxiety. Under the threat of the impending depletion, he frantically seeks out reassurance from some parental figure that no actual punishment is forthcoming. In analysis it seems that the depletion is a punishment for transgression. In a sense we may say that, here, too, it is object loss that is immediately responsible for the depletion. But in this case the object whose love is lost is the internalized superego precursor. In fact, since subjective guilt is an almost constant component of the depletion syndrome and is generally accompanied by efforts to placate a parental authority, I have speculated that the original childhood experience of depletion was the result of parental rejection. This parental rejection, that is, withdrawal of love, came to be understood as punishment for offending the parent, and remedial measures were undertaken to placate him. Since many of the anti-depletion measures we see are oral, for example, bulimia, it is reasonable to suppose that this sequence of events first occurred during the oral libidinal phase.

To summarize: depletion of the ego's libido supply may be regarded as a defense measure to prevent the emergence of more desperate and primitive efforts to secure gratification after the instinctual object has been lost or abandoned, after the failure of narcissism, or after condemnation by the superego. It follows that when we give a tranquilizer to allay a pathogenic conflict, we are only providing artificially an "energetic defense" which has failed to come about spontaneously. The enervation produced by a tranquilizer may also carry too far and induce either clinging, addictive behavior, serious impairment of ego function, or actual melancholia.

We can take one step further. Let us say that the depletion induced by a chemical tranquilizer provides the defensive depletion that fails to come about spontaneously as a result of object loss, and also that the effect of a chemical energizer is to correct an excessive or fixed depletion. These actions are precisely the ones we strive to achieve by definitive, insight psychotherapy. By making conscious the unconscious, we expect to drain off excessive, dammed-up libido. Secondly, in the transference, the patient finds a mild but constantly available gratification which tends to withstand object loss and object abandonment and, hence, the depletion that these bring about. There are two main differences between the achievement of these effects by drugs on the one hand and by psychotherapy on the other. The first difference is that the effect of the chemical substances is far more powerful and far quicker. Hence they induce therapeutic changes in ego energy in illnesses too severe and emergencies too threatening to be managed by psychotherapy alone. "Only too often," said Freud in the *New Introductory Lectures on Psychoanalysis* (1933), "one seems to see that the therapeutic process is merely lacking in the necessary motive force to enable it to bring about the alteration. Some specific tendency, some particular instinctual component, is too strong in comparison with the counter-forces that we can mobilize against it. This is quite generally so in the case of the psychoses. We understand them in so far as we know quite well where we ought to apply the levers, but they are not able to lift the weight. In this connection we may hope that in the future our knowledge of the action of hormones . . . will provide us with a means of coping successfully with the quantitative factors involved in these diseases; but today we are far from having reached that desirable goal." I believe that we are now in a position to accomplish just this chemical forcing of obstinate maldistribution of energy, about which Freud spoke, by means of pharmaceuticals.

We should note, however, that there is a second difference between the modes of action of the pharmaceutic agents and psychotherapy: that is, the effect of the former persists no longer than the required concentration of the substance in brain fluids does, while the effect of the latter is relatively much more enduring. It is true that once an energetic disequilibrium has been corrected by drugs, months or years may pass before an extreme and serious deviation recurs. It is also true that even the most successful psychoanalysis cannot protect a patient against the conflicts and psychic problems that new experiences and the changes incident to development, maturation, and aging will create. Hence, the difference in the persistence of the therapeutic influence is not simply the difference between temporary and permanent; it is a difference between degrees of permanence. But it is a real difference nevertheless. Drugs correct the abnormality in ego energy content or distribution brought about by the pathogenic process. Psychoanalysis retards the pathogenic process itself. The optimum therapy for those patients who cannot be managed by psychoanalysis alone consists of exploiting the power of chemical agents to restore ego function to a state compatible with participation in the psychoanalytic process, and then attacking directly the pathogenic forces by means of the latter.

I suspect that in "nonneurotic" individuals, the depletion mechanism operates silently to preclude overt neurotic, perhaps even psychotic, symptom formation. The recurrent build-up of ego libido by the pressure of an instinct striving for discharge, followed by conflict, by abandonment of the object (as a sexual object only), and finally mild enervation, may be one source of the periodic mood swings we expect in normal life.

We must now discuss this enervation phenomenon from a third point of view, the theoretic. Our speculations immediately above were only one step removed from clinical observation and could be related directly to data. The arguments that follow will be another step further removed. What is the metapsychologic mechanism of this phenomenon? We know from our discussion of instinct and libido theory that, in conformity with observed facts, the longer an instinctual impulse is prevented from finding discharge, the stronger it becomes. By what mechanism can we now imagine that this libido accumulation gives way to enervation? Again we can do no better than follow Freud. There are two relevant remarks in "On Narcissism" (1914c). In the state of being in love, he says, the sexual object is overvalued while the ego itself is impoverished of libido in favor of the love object. Several pages later he suggests that when libido is repressed, the erotic cathexis is felt as a severe depletion of the ego, because the satisfaction of love is impossible and the libido can be retrieved only when the object is discarded. The recaptured libido is then invested in the ego and the ensuing narcissism serves as a defense against the object loss. In "Mourning and Melancholia," Freud remarks that the ego is impoverished by the work of mourning, and until that is accomplished, libido cannot be withdrawn from the lost object (1917e). Of melancholia he says that the disease "complex" behaves like an open wound, drawing to itself cathectic energies and emptying the ego until the ego is impoverished. These cathectic energies of the ego, also called countercathexes, are energies derived from the troublesome impulse itself and, reflected backward, are used to oppose its entry into the preconscious. From these assertions, we conclude that Freud was aware of the paradox of an enervated ego in the presence of a frustrated, dominant, erotic drive. He attempted to resolve the paradox by ascribing it to a process of "binding," whereby ego energy devoted to the gratification or repression of a dominant drive is withheld from the rest of the ego, which thereby becomes impoverished.

Countercathectic energies contribute heavily to symptom formation, says Nunberg (1955), and therefore their withdrawal from the ego can account for the resolution of neurotic symptoms that follows ego depletion. This sequestering of the energies normally required by the ego for its tonic functions, in order to contain an hypertrophied instinct, contrasts markedly with the normal process whereby the energies of instincts that are subdued in the process of development are contributed to the pool of ego energies as sublimations, reaction formations, and superego identifications. Freud's argument, whether it will ultimately prove correct or not, draws attention to the fact that one of the weakest points in our theory is our ignorance of the nature and extent of communication between the energetic impulse of individual drive and the total energy supply of the ego available for tonic functions.

I was able to use this theory of Freud's successfully on one occasion before I had worked out criteria for estimating libido. A young man who suffered from a studying inhibition was confronted by examinations that were to be crucial for his career. His performance hitherto had offered little grounds for confidence that he would succeed. Analysis disclosed that his mind was filled with erotic, sado-masochistic fantasies, and these were especially active when he tried to study. Reasoning that these fantasies were absorbing too much of the ego's energy supply, I administered an energizing drug in the hope of supporting the libido level. It improved his performance quite satisfactorily.

I must return to emphasize a point that was passed over quickly (see p. 125) in order to avoid disturbing the continuity of the argument. To what extent can narcissism be used as a defense? Let us ask the question the other way: Why should an individual give up narcissism for the less certain, more demanding, more capricious object love? (Freud, 1914c, p. 85.) Apparently narcissism is not able to offer sufficient gratification to erotic instincts since, except for cases of severe illness, no one is content with self-love. The first step from narcissism to object love is the requirement that the narcissism be supported by others. From this point, object love tends to supplant the narcissism as the carrier of the relation to the supporting object. A critical function in the maintenance of narcissism is self-regard, the diminution of which Bibring considered of crucial importance in the development of melancholia (1953). Self-regard, says Freud, is supported by three sources: a residue of infantile omnipotence, fulfillment of the ego ideal, and satisfaction of object love (1914c). When the object has been abandoned, self-regard depends that much more on the approval of the superego and, supporting the latter, the admiration of the community. An individual whose libido supply, narcissism, and self-regard are so dependent upon external admiration is in a vulnerable position. He may be able to maintain this unstable equilibrium for a relatively long time, but it is evident that any infringement upon his self-regard may throw him into melancholia. This starts a vicious circle:

both narcissism and object love are frustrated, ego libido is depleted, and self-regard falls as a result of the enervation. It is for this reason that I stated in the previous chapter that ego libido and self-regard influence each other. A shift in one tends to bring about a similar shift in the other.

If we were to treat a patient with libido depletion with pharmaceutic agents alone, we should have to give him one of the energizing drugs. When we do so, however, we must be alert for a recurrence of the pathogenic conflict and the symptom formation which plunged him into melancholia in the first place.

Theoretically, then, the treatment of mental illness with drugs seems fairly simple and straightforward. In the stage of conflict or of symptom formation, the administration of a tranquilizer can restore the psychic apparatus to its normal equilibrium. When enervation has occurred, it can be undone by the administration of an energizer. Actually this formulation holds only for a few situations occurring at the extremes of the libido range: some cases of mania and paranoia at the upper end, and melancholia and addiction at the lower. During most other mental illnesses, either the energetic deviations are not great and fluctuate up and down easily, or increased libidinal charge of a frustrated drive immediately instigates and temporarily coexists with depletion. Given these circumstances, administration of a tranquilizer would aggravate the depletion, while administration of an energizer would increase the libido potential. Catatonic schizophrenia often presents this kind of problem. We shall discuss specific difficulties in the section immediately following.

By and large, libido depletion is treated by the ego as an oral deprivation and gives rise to oral attempts at recovery. The oral incorporative drives were elucidated in the discussion of addiction. The oral rejection was also mentioned as a form of avoidance of potential love objects. Even compulsives in a temporary state of depletion express their desires and aversions in oral terms. One compulsive patient developed an addiction to vitamins and began to take measures to eat a full diet. Another dreamed that a fishbone was stuck in his throat. (Not all oral fantasies deal with the depletion mechanism or are even functions of energetic changes. Incorporative fantasies of identification or ejective fantasies of projection may as readily be expressions of purely dynamic mechanisms.)

The object-avoiding defenses, such as depersonalization, denial, negation, and repression are treated by the ego as castration. It seems as if the *cutting off* of a segment of the preconscious ego is experienced as though the genital were cut off. The evidence for this statement is that the invoking of such a defense elicits an anxiety response which in dreams and associations is represented as the response to castration. By virtue of this equivalence, the fear of becoming insane, which is the conscious content of such evoked anxiety, becomes, in turn, the fear of castration. This takes us back to the familiar conscious expectation of insanity as the punishment for masturbation, insanity representing the unconscious expectation of castration.

Let me add a comment about the object-abandoning defenses. The biologic paradigm for these is the fight-flight mechanism. If an animal is confronted with an unwelcome intruder, he will either flee or, if the intruder is too close or the first animal is on his home territory, he will fight. While the immediate aim of the fighting is to subdue and kill his adversary, the ultimate aim is to destroy the source of the disturbing visual or auditory stimulus. Eliminating the unpleasant percept is the goal in each case. This can be done variously: by destroying the source, the carrier of the percept (for example, murder); putting a distance between oneself and the percept; arresting the act of perception by a deliberate effort (turning away, or hysterical blindness); destroying one's perceptive organs (blinding oneself); destroying the aroused sexual organs (self-castration or mutilation); or finally, by destroying one's own ego (suicide). It is the avoidance of the percept that constitutes the definitive defense in anxiety hysteria, after the projection and displacement. All of these are sadistic or masochistic acts; they evoke anxiety, they are apt to be followed by depletion, and the depletion has the effect of attenuating the original drive and eliminating the necessity for the defense. This formulation is not entirely consistent with the metapsychologic theory quoted previously (see p. 128), in which the depletion is the consequence of the effort of repression and appears to have no effect on the pathogenic conflict.

It seems to me that since the clinical indications of the conflict disappear with the depletion, the latter may well resolve the pathogenic process. Clinical indications of conflict do not disappear entirely, however, for while the anxiety and the defensive efforts to overcome it are no longer evident, the original repression remains. Perhaps the depletion of the major portion of the ego in favor of the firm containment of the hypertrophied instinct has the effect of fixing the unstable equilibrium and preventing the conflict from involving more of the ego function.

The problem remains unsolved—we cannot decide between the two theories. The former says that depletion occurs because the energies of the ego are all pre-empted by the struggle against the upward striving drives; the latter says that depletion occurs automatically when a powerful libidinal thrust is frustrated and, in effect, attenuates the desire rather than merely counteracting it.

Since the discussion has become rather theoretical and since the interplay of conflicting tendencies is not easy to visualize, I have tried to represent the course of libido changes in pathogenesis in a diagram (Figure 2). I cannot express in the diagram the vicissitudes of the individual impulses and defenses, nor would I wish to pretend that the course of events I have expressed is anything more than a hypothetical paradigm.

The ordinate of the diagram is the libido scale which was described in Chapter III. The arrows to the left of the ordinate indicate that a tranquilizer acts to reduce the libido content of the ego, while an energizer acts to increase it. The abscissa is a time line representing time in the order of magnitude of days, weeks, or months. It is drawn at the mid-point of the scale, that is, at position 5. Thin guide lines are drawn at positions 3½ and 8½, parallel to the abscissa, to indicate the approximate limits of normal variation of libido content.

The course of events is best described in four separate phases, which are indicated by Roman numerals at the bottom of the diagram. In Phase I, the phase of conflict, the pathogenic dynamics commence. An instinctual conflict develops, auxiliary defenses are called into play, symptoms are constructed and the ego reacts to the symptoms by attempting to rationalize them or to repudiate them. Energies are accumulated, discharged, displaced and distributed among individual impulses and defenses, but none escapes from the conflict complex to invade the ego and raise its free libido content. Symptom formation may stabilize the conflict and free libido fluctuations may be easily confined within normal limits. This possibility is indicated on the diagram by the arrow labeled *a*.

On the other hand, symptom formation may be unable to provide sufficient opportunity for discharge, and despite the evolution of one or more symptoms, instinctual energy may accumulate faster

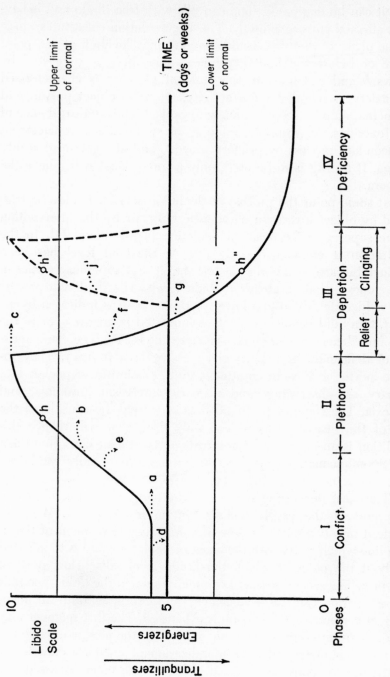

FIGURE 2. SCHEMATIC REPRESENTATION OF VARIATIONS OF EGO LIBIDO DURING THE COURSE OF PATHOGENESIS

than it can be dissipated. The ego fills with free libido and behavior is affected correspondingly. This accumulation constitutes Phase II, the phase of plethora. Libido content may level off at any point above or below the limit of clinical normality, as suggested by arrows *b* and *c*. Clinically this state of plethora is characterized by anxiety, psychomotor overactivity, intensive object pursuit and instinctual activity, by a tendency to project, and by disturbance of ego functions, for example, undoing of sublimations, replacement of secondary process by primary process, and abrogation of reality testing. If a drug is to be used, only a tranquilizer will relieve the plethora.

At some point the process of depletion sets in. It may be triggered by object loss, by a narcissistic blow, or by the intervention of the superego. The onset of depletion begins Phase III. In the illustration it commences only after a maximal level has been reached, but arrows *d* and *e* suggest that it may supervene earlier in pathogenesis, that is, at lower libido levels. The depletion process may reduce the libido to a lower plethora level, as indicated by arrow *f*, to a mild deficiency level, as indicated by arrow *g*, or to the profound deficiency which characterizes Phase IV. The characteristics of deficiency have been given above (see p. 121). They include inertia, a sense of emptiness, guilt, pessimism, hypochondria, primary self-observation and primary narcissism, insomnia, and anorexia. The stage of profound deficiency may be considered the end of the disease process. The only drug that will relieve this condition is an energizer. Electric shock treatment can often do it too. Spontaneous recovery may sometimes occur under conditions which we do not yet know.

The most interesting phase and the one which probably occupies most of the psychiatrist's attention is Phase III. We may divide it into two portions. The first includes the segment of the libido line which starts with the onset of depletion, and is terminated at about the point at which the libido level falls below position 5, 4, or 3. The second segment commences when the libido line falls into a position of definite deficiency and continues until all possibility of corrective mobilization is exhausted. The first segment may be considered to represent simple *relief* from the plethora, while the second is characterized by a mobilization of auxiliary energies in an attempt to counteract the fall of libido. We have discussed this corrective phenomenon before. The activities which result from this corrective mobilization have a *clinging* quality (Chapter III, p. 106); the relation to the object is anaclitic; there is a more or less overt pregenital accent; and aggression plays an important role. It is puzzling and interesting to note that the very same symptoms which were removed by the resolution of the plethora state may be restored by the clinging, anaclitic, pregenital, aggressive mobilization. I have represented the effects of this phenomenon by a dashed line which rises from the abscissa at the beginning of the second segment and falls back at the end.

I have marked a point h on the libido line in Phase II, and a corresponding point h' on the dashed line in Phase III. If h represents the point at which a given symptom, say catalepsy, appears in Phase II, the same symptom may reappear at h' in Phase III. It is for this reason that a symptom which may be resolved by the administration of a tranquilizer in Phase II may reappear while the patient is taking the same medication. I have on many occasions observed the disappearance and reappearance of a symptom when a tranquilizer was drawing a patient down from Phase II to Phase III, and also when an energizer was impelling him upward from Phase III to Phase II.

Given such a symptom then, proper treatment requires that the psychiatrist ascertain the phase of pathogenesis in which the symptom has arisen. The distinction is not easy to make and perhaps sometimes impossible without a therapeutic trial. In general when a patient is in Phase III we see the pregenital accent, the clinging, the anaclitic object relation, and the aggression. In addition there is likely to be more or less overt guilt, a need to appease and expiate, an active interest in religious behavior, oral craving, self-deprecation, and primary self-observation. We are actually dealing here with a state of libido deficiency. However, the threat of progressive depletion elicits anxiety, which in turn evokes this emergency mobilization of pregenital libido and aggressive energies and these create a *virtual* plethora of libido, though not a real one. Strictly speaking, it is a real plethora of some kind of libidinal energy, but it is a kind of libidinal energy which differs from the genital libido of the postpuberal psychic life. First it has the pregenital, anaclitic, clinging, aggressive qualities we have already remarked. Second, its response to tranquilizing and energizing drugs is the reverse of genital libido at certain times, although not at others. I assume that the pregenital libido which prevails during childhood serves as an emergency power supply after it has been superseded by genital libido in the course of development. It is this that is represented by the dashed line of Phase III. The coexistence of a genital libido deficiency with an emergency energy plethora requires that some clinical states be designated by two scale numbers, one belonging to the dashed line, and the other to the solid line. The manifestations of the emergency energy plethora pertain primarily to relations with objects, while the manifestations of genital libido deficiency reside especially in concern with the self, for example, primary self-observation, self-deprecation, and a sense of guilt.

I believe that Phase III neurosis and psychosis constitute the large majority of conditions that the psychiatrist is called upon to treat. I suspect that Phase I and Phase II conditions seldom persist more than a few days, weeks, or months. They either resolve spontaneously or give way to Phase III and Phase IV conditions. Phase I and II conditions may respond relatively easily to treatment. Since the same symptom may occur in Phase II and again in the second segment of Phase III, we are often puzzled by the fact that two patients with apparently the same syndrome, or the same patient on two occasions, will respond quite differently to treatment. During the second and third decades, Phase I and II conditions probably occur much more frequently than they do later in life. I am not sure, however, that they predominate among young neurotics and psychotics. That is to say, I believe that among young people there are many acute conditions which represent Phase I and II but that many or most of those that do not recover soon, pass into Phase III and IV. Hence, given a cross section of young chronic neurotics and psychotics, there may well be a large proportion in Phase III or IV. In the later decades of life, however, I suspect that Phase I conditions quickly give way to Phases III and IV, with little or no excursion into plethora. It follows from these considerations that energizers are much more frequently indicated than tranquilizers, and this is especially true in older patients and in chronic patients. I have indicated the libido state of a typical chronic depletion neurosis by arrow j and its manifestations by arrow j' which comes off the dashed line in Phase III.

The reader who has followed the course of pathogenesis that I have proposed will wonder how spontaneous recovery from Phases III and IV conditions can be imagined. We know that spontaneous recovery does occasionally occur. Some observations I have made may throw a little light on the question. I first saw patient M. H. after an attempt at suicide, in an agitated, angry, but clinging depression, that is in the second section of Phase III. I gave her a daily dose of 300 mg. of Niamid and began to see her daily. I obtained gratifying relief within a week, obviously too soon to ascribe it to the drug. After two weeks I reduced the dose to 200 mg., after another three weeks to 150 mg., and one week later to 100 mg. About two months after I first saw her, she quarreled bitterly with her husband and became depressed once more. I promptly raised the dose to 150 mg. and two days later to 300 mg. daily. Within a week after this last increase she became manicky and delusional. I added 50 mg. of Thorazine and reduced the Niamid to 200 mg. The manic syndrome was terminated within three days, but to my surprise I found that even when I stopped the Thorazine I was unable to undo libido deficiency, despite progressively increasing doses of Niamid up to 500 mg. daily. During this time there was constant conflict with her husband. Under the influence of these large doses of medication, a given quarrel would increase the depression, but the clinging component was relatively weak. Nevertheless, it was quite clear that doses of energizers greater than one that had thrown her into delusional mania a month earlier were no longer able to undo depletion. This is not a unique case. I have observed other instances in which it has become necessary to increase the dose of energizer progressively after shorter or longer periods of time.

I believe that at least two psychologic factors are involved in this increasing resistance to energizing drugs (above and beyond whatever physiologic tolerances might develop). First, the administration of an energizing drug seems to set in action a self-sustaining tendency toward self-cure by finding a new object or new mode of object relation. When no external frustration or internal inhibition defeats the tendency, the patient seems to recover rapidly and to stay well. When the tendency is defeated, however, the *vis medicatrix naturae* fades away and the patient relapses. An increase of dose can then force the patient to approach object relations once more. Second, if again frustration or inhibition opposes the resumption of object relations, the depleting tendency seems to become stronger and to require even more energizer to overcome it. Therefore, the first factor involved in the process of recovery from libido deficiency is a spontaneous reparative tendency set in motion by a relatively small dose of energizer. The second is something that appears to be a pharmaceutic regeneration of libido effected by the drug in opposition to a psychogenic depleting tendency. As the patient rules out all remaining possibilities of resuming satisfying object relations, the psychogenic depleting tendency becomes stronger and stronger and requires more and more drug to overcome it. Since the plethora state is more unstable than the deficiency state, it seems to me that the need for tranquilizers tends to decrease, and the need for energizers tends to increase, during the course of any given illness and, more strikingly, during the course of successive episodes of illness in the same patient.

Since we have evidence from experience with drugs that a spontaneous reparative tendency exists, and that only a relatively weak push suffices to activate this tendency, we may safely suppose that this same tendency is responsible for at least some instances of spontaneous recovery. I should guess that the clinging motivation ultimately finds an object and an opportunity which not only offers immediate anaclitic gratification but also promises ultimate genital gratification. (I mean here, gratification of an impulse appropriate to the genital level of development.) On the strength of this promise the clinging motivation is replaced by a resurgence of genital libido and the depletion tendency is arrested. Wherever this resurgence of genital libido occurs, I believe we can find rebirth fantasies in the patient.

Recovery from libido deficiency does not merely reverse the path by which the deficiency was established. If the clinging mobilization is evoked by the anxiety created by the decline of libido, then arresting that decline, or better still, reversing it, should eliminate the clinging even before sufficient libido has been generated to undo the deficiency. In other words the *virtual* or pregenital libido plethora which is created in the second segment of Phase III by the decline in genital libido is absent in that same segment when the patient is recovering. One can sometimes see a dramatic collapse of the symptom picture from that represented by the dashed line in Phase III to that represented by the solid line—for example, from the clinical state represented by point h' to that represented by point h''. L. N. S. is a twenty-year-old woman whom I first saw in a post-partum agitated catatonic and paranoid schizophrenia. On the basis of the criteria I have mentioned I judged her to be in a state of libido deficiency rather than plethora, that is, in the second segment of Phase III rather than in Phase II. Therefore I immediately administered Niamid (200 to 400 mg. per day). After two weeks the agitation, hallucinations, and delusions suddenly disappeared and were replaced by an inert, limp catatonia. This was the abrupt shift from the dashed line of virtual plethora to the solid line of libido deficiency, from h' to h''. The shift had been brought about by establishing a firm support to the libido level. Within another week, the inert catatonia gave way to a state of great improvement with a recovery of reality testing. Reduction of Niamid and addition of Mellaril for only two days resulted in a prompt relapse to the agitated, hallucinated, and delusional state, which, when the original dose of energizer was restored and the tranquilizer removed, subsided as it had before, but within one week. When now the 400 mg. dose of Niamid was continued through the point of remission, an excited aversive catatonia ensued. In other words, the ego was driven by the medication from Phase III back to the plethora state of Phase II, in this case up to the level of point h. The patient was finally brought to an enduring remission by supporting the libido with a large dose of Niamid and preventing the evolution of the plethora state by means of a small dose of Mellaril.

What does this scheme of pathogenesis tell us about psychoanalytic therapy? I do not have enough data to answer this question concisely and I do not wish to enter here upon an extensive discussion of psychoanalytic technique. There are some interesting implications, though, that I can sketch briefly.

It seems to me that if one could analyze a neurosis in Phase I, one would achieve the greatest success with least effort. The precipitating conflict would be accessible with minimal complication by gross shifts of ego libido charge. The analytic resolution of this conflict would hopefully prevent such shifts. Perhaps this kind of patient is seldom encountered because people seldom seek treatment for a circumscribed symptom, and because they seldom remain in Phase I very long.

When libido plethora (Phase II) has evolved, patients become sufficiently disturbed to apply or to be brought for treatment. There are two difficulties, however. The first is that when the plethora is pronounced, the patient's loss of reality testing and his inability to control himself prevent him from cooperating in the analytic procedure. The second is that the plethora itself initiates a large number and variety of drives, so that the original nucleus of the illness is obscured by a confusing overlay of peripheral and secondary fantasies and activities. In this situation, appropriately small doses of a tranquilizer act to move the ego state toward a normal libido value.

What kind of relation will a patient in Phase II establish with the analyst? First, he may find the analyst an unwelcome intruder, and the need for treatment a blow to his narcissism. Second, he may welcome the analyst as a protector against the anxiety that libido plethora entails. The analyst will be cast in the role of the parent, that is, a true transference will occur. Third, since the libido in Phase II is in the first instance genital libido, the patient may take the analyst as a love object and either offer or demand one or another manifestation of love, or he may defend against this erotic attachment by flight or in some other way characteristic of himself. Not infrequently, when a patient who has clung to the analyst out of depletion anxiety in the second segment of Phase III improves to the point of ascending into Phase II, the clinging transference is terminated and the patient must flee. This occurs whether the improvement comes about as the result of the use of an energizing drug or as a result of psychoanalysis.

The patient in Phase IV has scarcely enough libido for himself and none to spare for the analyst; thus a true transference cannot be established. I doubt that any psychotherapeutic influence can be exerted. Trying to establish a relation with such a patient may be compared with trying to ignite damp, raw logs by dropping sparks upon them.

Again the most important phase to consider is Phase III. To the extent that the patient's relief from plethora is attributed by him to his therapist's care, ties of gratitude will create or strengthen a transference. During this period of relief, however, little of the pathogenic conflict will emerge in treatment. Rebirth fantasies are frequently encountered.

Most of the time spent in treating neurosis with psychoanalysis or psychotherapy will be spent, I believe, dealing with the second segment of Phase III, that is, with clinging, anaclitic object relation. The patient's relation with the therapist will constitute a true transference, at some times positive and at other times negative. He will endow the therapist with the desirable, and then also the undesirable, qualities of the parent whose protective care he requires. The program of treatment resolves itself into two parts. The first deals with resolving the Phase III illness. Just as plethora may induce neurosis or psychosis depending upon the degree of the plethora and the strength of the ego, so the clinging reaction to depletion anxiety may be neurosis or psychosis. In the case of neurosis, the symptom will be derived from the conflict surrounding a pregenital, ana-clitic drive complex. In the case of psychosis, that central conflict will be obscured by a wealth of auxiliary drives, by the aggressions that lead to psychotic breakdown, and by the defenses against the libidinal and aggressive drives. In the presence of psychosis it will probably be necessary to control some of the florid symptoms with medication. But in any case, good analytic-type therapy will have to deal with the conflict surrounding the anaclitic drive. The thera-pist, however, must not deceive himself into thinking that this is the essence of the illness. Often a great deal of analytic work is ex-pended and the genetic and symbolic aspects of the symptom are uncovered, but as the symptoms disappear, an underlying depres-sion comes to light. This is, I suspect, the phenomenon which Freud described in "Analysis Terminable and Interminable" (1937) as a need for illness and suffering. What is happening is that the symptoms of the anaclitic illness may be resolved but the depletion tendency nevertheless persists. When that point has been reached, if not sooner, the therapist must attend to the second part of the treatment. He must devote himself to discovering the obstacles re-tarding spontaneous repletion, and behind them, the genital, Oedi-pal conflict which initiated the depletion in the first place. In a youthful, resilient person, the spontaneous repletion process will probably offer several opportunities for scrutiny as it strives toward spontaneous repair. In older patients, or those ill for a longer period, this recovery tendency fails to appear. Here the administra-tion of an energizing drug will recreate the original conflict and give the therapist a chance to work with it. I assume that ideally it should be possible, after sufficient work on the primary conflict, to withdraw the drug and leave the patient protected against relapse. Actually I have not yet been able to accomplish this but I hope that in several cases now in treatment the withdrawal of energizing medication without relapse into depletion will become possible. It is important, however, to discourage the patient who is receiving this artificial support from taking refuge in narcissistic activities and thereby avoiding the instinctual conflict. As Freud said: "We try to bring this conflict to a head and to develop it in its most acute form in order to increase the instinctual energy available for its solution." Freud was advising abstinence in the transference as a means of bringing the conflict to a head. In the energizing drugs we have a most powerful supplement to abstinence. "Analytic experience has taught us," he continued, "that the better is always the enemy of the good and that in every phase of the patient's restoration we have to combat his inertia, which disposes him to be content with a partial solution of his conflicts."

I have had very little experience treating children, certainly not enough to warrant my drawing any conclusions. From what I have learned of the childhood neuroses of my adult patients, however, and from my inferences from the theoretical constructions I have developed, I would surmise that all childhood illness is depletion illness. The child's libido is entirely pregenital and his object relations are anaclitic. In cases of actual or threatened object loss, this type of libido is increased (until it becomes exhausted) and it creates the symptoms of childhood neurosis and psychosis. If my guess is correct, tranquilizers have little or no place in the treatment of childhood neurosis or psychosis. When medication is indicated, it is probably the energizer which will restore the psychic economy to its equilibrium state.

Before continuing, we should take note of efforts of others to comprehend the effects of the psychopharmaceutic agents on mental illness from the perspective of psychoanalytic psychology. Sarwer-Foner (1957, 1960) observed that the effects of a given drug are not always consistent. He tried to explain these differences as arising from the influences of the drug upon ego defenses, so that variations among individual catalogues of ego defenses would determine differences in response to the drugs. He mentions especially four situations in which tranquilizing drugs exert adverse effects: (1) Male patients struggling to repress feminine impulses may find the repression challenged by the restriction of mobility, the fatigue, and the enervation which the tranquilizing drugs bring about. (2) Patients with hypochondriacal concerns find the physiologic side effects of the tranquilizers an additional threat to their efforts to maintain their somatic integrity. (3) Depressed patients become worse when tranquilizers accentuate psychomotor retardation. (4) Some patients interpret the administration of medication as a sexual assault, and they respond with increased defensiveness. When, on the other hand, the drug helped to control repressed impulses such as aggression, sexual perversion, and feelings of inadequacy, the patient responded well. Sarwer-Foner's observations seem accurate to me, and I believe that the dynamics of unfavorable response to the drugs are properly described by him. It is my impression, though, that the responses of individuals to the drugs can be predicted by referring to the indicators of ego libido, which I believe is the overriding determinant of drug influence. Those of his patients who responded badly to tranquilizers were already suffering a dearth of libido, as indicated by object or narcissistic clinging or by uncomplicated enervation, and they should have been given energizers rather than tranquilizers. In other words, Sarwer-Foner has correctly described the dynamic events in cases of poor response to medication, but he does not see that energetic considerations are prepotent and that in these instances, attention to energetic criteria would have revealed that either the wrong drug, or an excess of the right drug, had been given.

Winkelman (1960) describes the results of his observations of patients in psychotherapy in terms of the effect of the drug on id and ego functions. Tranquilizers, he says, decrease id impulse. They also affect ego function, initially improving it and then impairing it. Reality testing is improved, defenses are strengthened, and the ego achieves some distance from psychic pain. Winkelman's theoretical discussions are *post hoc,* and one misses operational criteria for the administration of drugs. Nor does he discriminate between the actions of tranquilizers and energizers, or between their indications.

Azima and his co-workers (1959, 1961) have also applied a psychoanalytic viewpoint to the understanding of drug actions. Azima is impressed, as others have been, that instinctual drives and energies are the substrate of tranquilizer and energizer action. He makes interesting observations which correspond in most instances to my own. Yet a consistent theory with a predictive method does not emerge from his work. I suspect the reason is that he considers shifts of aggressive energies to be the determining variables, and that he tries to force his data and theories to comply with pre-existing theoretical concepts which do not seem adequate to deal with them. It is my impression, as I have already indicated, that it is the libidinal content of the ego that determines its mode of function. Aggressive drives are elicited by pains and frustrations that arise out of libidinal excess and deficiency.

SPECIFIC AND PRACTICAL
CONSIDERATIONS

Melancholia

This is, perhaps, one of the simplest conditions to treat with pharmaceutic agents, and, from the point of view of the analyst, one of the most important. As I have already explained (see p. 75), I have been using the term *melancholia* to denote conditions of pronounced ego depletion other than the clinging, addictive states. These generally begin with feelings of sadness, melancholy, pessimism, and discouragement. It is important, however, not to assume that every period of affective depression represents melancholia. Depression occurs without ego enervation in the course of any neurosis or psychosis. If drug therapy is to be employed, selection of the drug is determined not by the symptom of depression, or any other symptom, but by the libidinal content of the ego at the time. I have reviewed the several manifestations of melancholia from an energetic point of view, and I have compared depressive states with and without ego depletion in my paper "The Psychic Function of Depression" (Ostow, 1960c).

The pharmaceutic treatment of melancholic depression is important to both the analyst and the therapist because it is one of the most common, troublesome complications likely to ensue during psychoanalytic and psychotherapeutic treatment. Heretofore, such supervening depressions have often necessitated interruption of analysis, hospitalization, and in some cases, electric shock therapy. With the proper application of energizers, there need be no interruption in the analysis at all.

One may use these agents to institute combined analytic or psychotherapeutic treatment and pharmacotherapy. Unfortunately, the increase in ego libido which is effected swells narcissism, and the patient, recovering, comes to believe that he is immune to further attacks. He loses interest in the analysis and is inclined to stop. This is especially true if it is the patient's first melancholic breakdown. In recovery from subsequent attacks, he may retain sufficient memory of his previous relapse to consider insight therapy more important. Cautioning the patient before his recovery about the unwarranted self-confidence that the drug will create may have some small value. If the drug is withdrawn before full recovery takes place, either recovery will continue of its own momentum, or the patient will relapse. In the former case, the renewed narcissism will become a source of resistance; in the latter case, the analysis will begin to take second place to a preoccupation with symptoms and dosages. Continuing drug administration beyond the point of recovery from melancholia is likely to revive the original neurotic or psychotic state upon which it initially supervened. If it is a neurotic state, the drug should be cut back to avoid excessive suffering and extreme neurotic defenses and symptoms. If a psychotic state ensues, the energizing drug should be stopped immediately or, better still, cut to a low dose, and a tranquilizing drug should be given. Retaining a low dose of energizer will tend to "put a floor" under the libido level and prevent a relapse into melancholia. Moderate rather than large doses of tranquilizer are indicated.

If treatment is initiated with a full dose of hydrazine energizer or imipramine, recovery may be expected in three to six weeks. Giving the patient a specific day or week in which he can expect to recover often helps his morale. This is more important when the patient is seen once a week than when he is seen daily. Sometimes symptomatic improvement occurs within a few days. In my opinion, this is likely to be a transference response. Whether and how this is to be interpreted to the patient, especially if it occurs at the beginning of the psychotherapeutic course, is a delicate matter. At any rate, one must be prepared for the resentment and negative transference which will follow shortly when the recovery is not sustained.

After about ten days of energizing medication there is often a resurgence of genital feeling and desire which lasts no more than a day or so. I have speculated that this is the real beginning of the recovery, a first reinforcement of the object libido which is blocked by the disorder. It does not succeed in breaking through the repression; in fact, its chief effect seems to be a reinforcement of the repression and often a perceptible intensification of the depletion.

In some cases, one may follow, in fact even anticipate, the course of recovery by noting the blinking frequency. In many, perhaps most, cases this is not so. The onset of nocturnal sweating is another indication that the drug effect has begun, although clinical improvement may not follow for several weeks.

Some patients will obtain temporary relief with dexedrine,

most conveniently given in capsules containing pellets coated so as to provide sustained action for ten to twelve hours ("spansules"). Since I do not know how to predict which patients will obtain relief from them and which will become more "jittery" or "hopped up," I should advise starting with a 5 mg. capsule and then advancing to a 10 and a 15 if a desirable effect is obtained. Other patients seem to find relief in Librium. Here again, I don't know how to predict which patients will be helped by it. Dosage is tricky, because some patients will become excessively somnolent with small doses and ataxic with moderate doses. Others will obtain the relief before any toxic symptoms appear, but will require relatively large doses. In general, older people seem to tolerate the drug less well. Unfortunately, even when a good response is obtained, it often fades after a week to two, even before the energizing drug can become effective.

Whether a patient should be hospitalized for fear of suicide is a problem which requires astute clinical judgment; it is one about which much has been written and to which I have no special contribution to make. Of course, even in a hospital there is not absolute protection. If one wishes maximum safety all of the time, one will incur unnecessary trouble, distress, expense, and complication of the definitive insight therapy. Some patients will be eager for hospitalization, and in such cases it is often wise to accept their judgment. If a patient should find hospitalization distressing, I am generally not inclined to press it unless there is a clear and present danger of suicide. Where one must choose between hospitalization and daily visits to the therapist, I think in many instances the latter course offers more protection. Inevitably, there are some tragic mistakes. I believe it is unequivocally true, however, that if a melancholic patient is not hospitalized, he is safest seeing his therapist daily and meanwhile following the routine of intensive energizer therapy that I have outlined.

The toxic potentialities of these energizing drugs are considerable. Some of the earlier ones, Marsilid especially, have caused liver diseases and death. The newer ones seem to be less dangerous in this respect. One of the most difficult side effects to overcome is postural hypotension, encountered especially often in older people. Its occurrence impedes treatment seriously, and in older patients it can precipitate coronary attacks or cerebrovascular attacks. Fortunately, there are usually preliminary complaints of dizziness and faintness on arising, which can caution the physician.

I should not like to create the impression that I advocate the use of energizing drugs whenever there is a state of ego depletion. Mild, and sometimes even moderate, states of depletion can be handled with proper analysis or psychotherapy. I would recommend the use of chemical substances only when there is a danger of destructive acting out or of suicide, or when the misery of the depletion and the accompanying inertia block psychologic treatment. I have considered the possibility of using energizing drugs to mobilize an analysis which is static because of a state of mild depletion. Such a patient uses the treatment primarily as a libido support, clinging to the analyst. The pathogenic conflict is withheld, and long periods of time pass without definitive progress. It may be that the judicious use of energizing drugs in this type of situation can have a salutary effect on the treatment.

The course of recovery is not easy to describe. Patients are often discouraged, even when they have been cautioned that they will not recover before four weeks have elapsed, because they expect some sign of improvement earlier. Actually, when improvement sets in, it proceeds fairly rapidly. The patient notices that he feels better when he awakens in the morning. He does not awaken so early, the appetite improves, and there is a renewed interest in sexual activities. Affectionate and social contacts become less difficult and ultimately become desirable. One of the last things to recover is full intellectual capacity. Decision making seems to be a most sensitive indicator of depletion of the ego supplement. The process of recovery is seldom a smooth one. The patient often feels much encouraged by his first relatively good day. If the next day is not as good, he becomes discouraged again. Moreover, in the borderline state which prevails just before recovery, the patient is especially sensitive to dynamic influences. It is useful to know, therefore, that sharp fluctuations in feeling are common during the earliest phases of recovery. The lapse into melancholia often follows just the opposite course. First, there is the feeling of intellectual obtuseness. It is often associated with an intensification of object interest and activities, for example, an increased sexual desire or increased appetite, both of which are manifestations of an attempt to cling. Finally, this too fails and the patient sinks into a state of inert aversion. The lapse into melancholia is often accompanied by irritability, anger, and easily provoked disappointments which threaten the meager residual libido supply.

Mania

In our discussion of the psychologic criteria for the assessment of ego libido, we have spoken of mania as a state of pure libido accumulation. However, the libido plethora is not all there is to mania. From our discussion of the theory of pathogenesis, we must conclude that a neurotic conflict initiated the whole process. If we have the opportunity to see the disease *in statu nascendi,* we will observe that the libido increase accompanies a turning away from the love object. A man may leave his wife, or simply turn away from her sexually. The libido thus spared is then expended in other directions, in narcissistic megalomania, in pursuing other objects which are often selected in such a way as to represent unconsciously the patient himself, and in an intensification of sublimation activities. These substitutes often fail. The megalomania is opposed and limited by the reality principle and finds little support from the outside world. Substitute love objects, chosen in the interest of narcissism, often disappoint. They may leave, or they may reveal themselves as unworthy, or the superego may ultimately succeed in denouncing them as representations of the prohibited Oedipal object. At first, with each successive disappointment, more and more libido is invested in the substitute channels. But the very intensity of these remaining gratifying activities ultimately destroys the possibility of satisfaction, and depletion sets in. Generally, the process of depletion is fairly abrupt. In some instances, however, it comes on over a period of days or weeks or months. In these cases, the patient turns again to the original object in a clinging way, reestablishing as an anaclitic relation the Oedipal attachment which could not survive as a mature, genital relation. He expresses regret for having abandoned her and promises never to do so again. However, as soon as the repletion process starts, he finds, often to his regret, that a strong aversion develops. Such patients behave similarly toward the analyst, clinging when depressed, if they can mobilize enough energy to do so, and turning away when libido is restored.

The pharmaceutic treatment of mania is simply the administration of large doses of powerful tranquilizers. Hospitalization is often necessary. Sedation is required until the tranquilizers have been effective. It is important to remember that the actual tranquilizing effect does not begin to develop before the better part of a week has elapsed, and two or three weeks or more are necessary before the full effect is obtained. If reserpine or phenothiazines of the chlorpromazine (as opposed to the prochlorperazine) series are used, their immediate sedative effect may help to control the patient until the actual libido depletion gets under way. The psychiatrist, however, should not mistake the symptomatic sedative effect for the therapeutic depletion effect.

Some patients lose ego libido relatively easily and, treated with tranquilizers, they tend readily to pass from mania or paranoia into melancholia. Such an outcome can best be avoided by vigilance as improvement proceeds, with specific alertness for early signs of depletion. Patients who have previously suffered depletion syndromes are most likely to overrespond in this way to tranquilizing drugs.

But the energetics of mania may not be quite so simple as we should be inclined to believe. Does our argument apply to the following case? I was recently asked to see, in consultation, a twenty-eight-year-old woman who had been hospitalized after an attempt at suicide by exsanguination. Relatively large doses of tranquilizer had succeeded in reducing her agitation and tendency toward self-destruction, but each time it was proposed that she leave the hospital she relapsed. When I saw her, I observed pressure of speech, flight of ideas, immodest and provocative eroticism, clang association, and joking. I had to agree with the attending psychiatrist that the clinical picture warranted the designation of mania. Yet there were some other features which suggested to me the presence of depletion, namely self-deprecation, frequent self-observation often primary in quality, conscious guilt, occupation with religious ideas, and a tendency to cling. In view of these signs, combined with the fact that she had obtained no significant benefit from tranquilizers, I concluded that we were dealing with the clinical picture of mania arising out of clinging depletion. Accordingly, I advised discontinuing the tranquilizer and replacing it with a full therapeutic dose of energizer. After an initial period of increased agitation lasting several days, the patient (G. H. N.) began to improve and for the first time to approach her usual personality. I had to conclude from this experience that the clinical picture of mania can supervene, not only in response to the intensified motivation of libido plethora, but also when motivation is pathologically intensified by incipient or early depletion. In retrospect, I can recall other manics who showed similar characteristics and who failed to respond to tranquilizers. As in the case of most other psychiatric disease syndromes, the ego's libido content, rather than the clinical diagnosis, must be used as the guide for drug administration.

Schizophrenia, Including Paranoia

While the virtue of tranquilizers was first discerned in their ability to reverse the symptoms of schizophrenia, it is clear by now that not all schizophrenic patients respond to these drugs, that some respond to energizers and not to tranquilizers, and that, in others, only combinations or sequences of drugs produce a therapeutic effect. The difficulties ensue, in my opinion, because we know so little about the energetics of schizophrenia, although we are familiar to some extent with its dynamics. The account which I shall give in this section is certainly not complete and probably not too accurate. Further observations of the effects of the newer pharmaceutic agents on schizophrenics under the psychoanalytic microscope will teach us a good deal about drugs, schizophrenia, and metapsychology.

Since the drugs we are discussing do not act upon disease entities but rather upon the distribution of psychic energies, it is obvious, first, that drugs will be therapeutically effective only when there is a serious disorder of that distribution, and, second, that the indications for selection and dosage must depend upon energetic criteria rather than upon diagnostic or dynamic criteria. Let us try to follow the course of energetic changes in a case of schizophrenia, and from it infer the appropriate pharmacotherapeutic measures.

As in the case of other neuroses and psychoses, the original conflict in paranoia and paranoid schizophrenia lies within the Oedipus complex. The conflict is temporarily allayed by a shift of libido to a homosexual object, originally the parent of the same sex, and subsequently representatives of that parent. The patient does not become a homosexual, the desire is repressed, and so the libido continues to accumulate. The heightened libido is projected onto the homosexual object and creates delusions of persecution by him, and of infidelity by the original heterosexual object. If, on the other hand, the repression of this gathering energy stream is associated with effective impoverishment of the ego, the dynamic process is arrested and a state of depletion appears. When it is resolved, homosexual libido and paranoid symptoms reappear and grow until arrested again by renewed depletion. My evidence for this observation is twofold. First, if an energizer is given to some patients who are initially seen in melancholia, a state of paranoia or paranoid schizophrenia emerges. Second, I have watched these spontaneous, corrective fluctuations in a patient (X. N. Z.) who came into analysis as a paranoid schizophrenic.

Simultaneous administration of a tranquilizer and an energizer is an important maneuver in some schizophrenic and some neurotic conditions. The two drugs do not cancel out each other's effect although their tendencies are opposed. The administration of a moderate dose of energizer and a small dose of tranquilizer does not have merely the effect of a small dose of energizer, and the administration of a small or of a moderate dose of each does have a therapeutic end effect. The chief result of administering the two together is to add stability to the system.

The first patient with whom I had to use this technique was a woman in a moderate to severe melancholic depression. When I gave her Marsilid she improved but simultaneously became paranoid. Removal of the Marsilid and substitution of Thorazine dissipated the paranoia but revived the melancholia. When I gave her both together she recovered again from the melancholia and remained well.

Another patient (R. L. X.) was first seen after a suicidal attempt following a period of alcoholism and then melancholic depression. She did well for a while with Marsilid and Catron but gradually developed a hypochondriacal schizophrenia. Substitution of tranquilizers induced a relapse into melancholia. Only a combination of the two was able to hold her stably in a normal state.

When giving such a combination of drugs, it is advisable to use the smallest effective dose of each. One may think of the energizer as putting a "floor" beneath the libido level, that is, preventing it from sinking beneath a lower limit, and of the tranquilizer as fixing a "ceiling" over it. The administration of the two simultaneously thus defines a channel within which the fluctuations of ego libido are confined. The fluctuations are those we should ordinarily expect from the constant dynamic play of instinctual pressures, superego restrictions, ego controls, and the limitations of reality. Theoretically, we may make this channel as narrow or as broad as we wish. Practically, however, it is difficult to establish, and once it has been fixed, one must be content with maintaining it. If the doses of the two drugs are high enough so that the lower and the upper limits of the channel meet or overlap, we have the conditions for severe psychosis, namely, an overcharged ego nucleus and a depleted ego supplement. The patient becomes helpless and frightened, cowers in a corner, responds with startle to any small stimulus, is constantly hallucinated, and rages, hides, or resists.

If the presenting problem is a libido deficiency, and if the past history, recent performance, and clinical picture suggest that it might be wise to "put a ceiling" over the ego libido, a full dose of energizer might be given to begin with, and then, about a week before its effect is likely to become visible, a small dose of the tranquilizing drug can be added. Conversely, if a tranquilizing drug is called for, but one desires to "put a floor" under the ego libido, one can give a full, though not necessarily large, dose of tranquilizer, and simultaneously begin the administration of a small dose of energizer. Since the latter has a longer latency, it will not become effective until after the tranquilizer has begun to have an effect. When a patient has been stabilized by the simultaneous administration of both drugs and it is desired to terminate medication, both drugs should be reduced *pari passu*. It is important to be especially vigilant in a drug-stabilized situation because important changes can begin quite subtly, and appreciable periods of time may be required to correct them. On the whole, however, once a small dose of any of the drugs has been given long enough to achieve some effect, the response to an increase, let us say a double dose, will be seen after a relatively brief latency, such as one to three or four days. Although I have described this technique here in the discussion of schizophrenia, it will also be useful in the treatment of other conditions.

Let us return to our discussion of paranoia and schizophrenia. If homosexual libido continues to accumulate unrelieved by a spontaneous or induced depletion, it will begin to impair ego function seriously and override reality testing. We know four patterns of fracture of ego function. One is the manic, which we have already discussed. Here there is a retreat from the Oedipal object, followed by volatile flight from substitute to substitute, from opportunity to opportunity, without the organization of any fixed group of instinct derivatives. It is as though the ego's synthetic power were weakened, with a loss of concern for any constancy and an inability to tolerate frustration in any area. Both the manic and the paranoiac show the clinical indicators of extremely high libido supply—namely, exaggerated object love associated with, or alternating with, exaggerated narcissism; megalomania; the use of projection as a technique for both establishing and for defending against object love; a readiness to defend the libidinal position by aggression; tertiary self-observation; delusions of persecution; and serious impairment of ego function. The chief difference between mania and paranoia is that whereas in the former, many different derivatives of the repressed impulse are pursued in random sequence, in the latter, a single complex becomes organized and elaborated. The manic abandons the Oedipal love object, while the paranoiac, even in his shift to homosexuality and narcissism, clings to the object and weaves her into his delusions. In the manic, the synthetic power of the ego is much weakened; in the paranoiac, faced with the libido's explosive effect, the synthetic power becomes more active in tying as many memories and percepts as possible into a single, hypertrophied complex (Nunberg, 1931). While doing so, of course, it neglects one of its most vital functions: the reconciliation of thought with reality. Freud (1914c, p. 86) has pointed out that the involved, pseudological construction of the paranoid complex resembles the construction of obsessional complexes. Primary process masquerades as secondary, magical techniques abound, and in both cases, elaboration of the system consumes narcissistic and, in a sense, autoerotic energies. The paranoiac, like the obsessional, clings to his object, though he changes the nature of the relation. Both fully developed paranoia and fully developed mania, of the plethora type, can be resolved by means of ego depletion.

A third method of fracture is that of catatonia, which Freud (*loc. cit.*) compares to the method of defense in hysteria. In hysteria, the image of the object of the unwelcome impulse is repressed along with the impulse, and the freed libido is reflected back into the ego. However, it attaches only to one specific part of the ego, the image of a particular organ or limb. The subject identifies with the abandoned object by means of this reflected libido. The function of the part of the body thus favored is markedly disturbed; it may be inhibited, distorted, or exaggerated. In the neurotic process, the affected organ stands for the object, the object's genital, and the subject's genital. The hysterical repression of the object is not only a defense but also a sadistic attack on the object, since it eliminates him as a sexual object from the patient's world; it is a castration of the self since the repression and narcissistic reflection of libido onto a nongenital organ deprives the genitals of their function; and it is a kind of castration of the ego since it *cuts off* one part of the ego from the rest. It is not surprising, then, that hysterical dissociation often gives rise to anxiety, to a fear of insanity, and to unconscious fantasies and dreams in which the hysterical repression is represented as a castration. A similar process ensues in catatonia. Here the entire world takes on an erotic tinge because of the tremendous increase in libido strength. The catatonic detaches himself mentally from the entire world, including his own body. What he does is tantamount to destroying the world. He resists recognizing or accepting any influence from the world. Since he attributes his erotic drive to his genitals and other libidinized parts of his body, he may castrate himself or mutilate himself in some other way. Similarly, he may support his mental destruction of the world by actually murdering the current love object. These acts of physical destruction merely intensify the mental rejection of the libidinized world in order to complement the repression of the pathogenic instinct and its derivatives. The psychic state of the tense, negativistic catatonic is probably primary narcissism.

At this point, it is necessary to depart from observed facts and tested theory and turn to theory so far unconfirmed by data. Unfortunately, despite the fact that thousands of schizophrenics have been treated with the newer psychopharmaceutic drugs, there are few data relating specific symptom complexes with response to medication. The recommendations and discussion that follow are based only upon theory and my own meager experience. They have yet to be confirmed. However, I think they represent the best formulations we can make at the moment, and may well serve as a point of departure for further investigation.

Consider again the tense, negativistic catatonic who has cut himself off from the perceptible real world and retreated to primary narcissism under high pressure of libido. We may anticipate that a reduction of the libido pressure will obviate the need for the detachment and relieve the condition.

Before continuing our consideration of catatonia, let us turn to the fourth pattern of ego fracture—paranoid schizophrenia. Like

catatonia, paranoid schizophrenia starts with an abrupt repudiation of the world of reality and a retreat to primary narcissism. However, the paranoid schizophrenia cannot tolerate this dissociation
so well as the catatonic. He begins to yearn for the world that he
has lost. Having repudiated the world, he perceives the world as
having been destroyed. In one patient (X. N. Z., see Chapter VII),
this state was usually preceded by dreams and fantasies of earth-
shattering explosions. Her headaches accompanied libido depletion
and often followed visual phenomena, teichopsia, and the like,
which formed the day residue for her dreams that the world was to
be consumed by fire and explosion. The paranoid schizophrenic
clings with one hand to the world he abandons with the other. As
distinguished from that of the catatonic, his detachment is never
complete. While the world is dead for him as a source of love and
warmth, he is nevertheless usually able to sustain a working contact
via ego functions, such as intellectual and creative activity and
daily household chores. Sometimes such individuals, severely alienated from people in terms of their instinctual life, are yet able to
carry on their daily activities in such a way that friends and neighbors fail to recognize the existence of the illness. Further, almost
as soon as the world is discarded, restitutive measures are initiated.
These form the substance of the delusional systems that are formed
in paranoid schizophrenia. The lost world is now reconstructed,
but only by a synthesis of elements which are projections of the
patient's own psychic life. This process is beautifully illustrated by
the Schreber case (Freud, 1911c).

In fully developed delusional systems one finds projections of
id, ego, and superego, of identifications and introjects, of psychic
processes and psychic forces. The primary self-observation which
prevails during this regression to primary narcissism is expressed
in projections, and its findings are perceived by the subject as if
they were images of the external macrocosm rather than magnified
and externalized visions of the internal microcosm. Just as other
libido plethora syndromes may be terminated by an ego depletion,
this also may. The case of X. N. Z., which was described as an instance of self-correcting ego depletion, conforms to this dynamic
description. If such a syndrome can be resolved by ego depletion,
we may infer that when ego depletion fails to occur spontaneously,
it can be induced by the administration of tranquilizers.

Freud (1914c) suggested that the symptoms of schizophrenia

may be classified with respect to three categories: manifestations of the pre-existing conflict, that is, of the nuclear Oedipal conflict and its consequence, the homosexual conflict; manifestations of the schizophrenic process itself, that is, the abandonment of the world of reality; and manifestations of the restitutional tendency, that is, the delusions we have described, rebirth fantasies, and hallucinations. Under what circumstances do we encounter hallucinations in paranoid schizophrenia? Hallucinations occurred in the Schreber case in the course of an illness that lasted for several years. However, they did not occur in the relatively short-lived case of X. N. Z. until *after* the administration of the tranquilizer that alleviated her condition. We may revert here to our discussion of hallucinations, in which we concluded that they were apt to appear during a partial depletion of the ego when primarily the ego supplement is affected, while the ego nucleus remains relatively intensely energized. Just as hallucinations may be induced in a case of paranoid schizophrenia by a tranquilizer, they may similarly be induced by spontaneous ego depletion and occur during the period of disequilibrium; in each case, the degree of depletion of the ego supplement exceeds the degree of depletion of the ego nucleus.

Let us return now to our consideration of catatonia. A full ego depletion, spontaneous or induced by tranquilizers, can resolve a tense, negativistic catatonia. In catatonia, however, as in hysteria, an incipient ego depletion originating in the ego supplement which is psychically completely detached from its nucleus only serves to reinforce the split. The process of depletion does not readily extend to the ego nucleus. There ensues a picture of disequilibrium with delusions and hallucinations. While these hallucinations may deal with attempts to restore the lost world by parthogenetic, rebirth fantasies (Nunberg, 1920) before depletion has gone too far, more extensive depletion is accompanied by delusions and hallucinations expressing the need for oral sustenance (or a repudiation of these, for example, the delusion of being poisoned) as occurred in the case of M. T. In this state, the dissociation is generally not fixed or complete, and by virtue of the residual libido in the ego nucleus, the patient clings, through the partially dissociated and partially enervated ego supplement, to possible love objects. This he does by any of the usual techniques of clinging, by speech, by symbolic incorporation, by offering himself as a sexual object, even by aggressive attacks. When depletion continues beyond this point, the result may depend upon the dynamic forces operative at the moment. If the immediate cause of the detachment has disappeared, further depletion may bring the libido content of the ego nucleus into equilibrium once more with the ego supplement at a level not too far from normal, and the patient will seem to have recovered. If, on the other hand, the conflict which precipitated the detachment continues unabated, as it did in the case of M. T. (that is, renewed fury with her husband for interfering in her relation with the analyst), further depletion fails to heal the split, and instead of cure there ensues an apathetic catatonia, resembling in many ways profound melancholia. If an energizer alone is given at this point, the patient loses the pain of the depletion and becomes more content, although still completely detached from reality. The picture, in the case of M. T., was that of a silly, grinning hebephrenic, but with warm skin and more vigorous postural tone. Just a little more energizer in this case induced a tense, negativistic catalepsy.

What may we infer regarding therapy? Clearly, the diagnosis of catatonia is not sufficient to determine the selection of a drug. The tense, negativistic catatonic is likely to respond to tranquilizers. The apathetic catatonic will only become worse with the same treatment (Freyhan, 1960, p. 54). The latter will respond to energizers (Bucci and Saunders, 1960). He will either revert to a tense, negativistic catalepsy if the energizer is given alone and if the conflict causing the split is still active, or he may emerge into a relatively normal state if the pathogenic conflict has subsided or if proper doses of tranquilizer are added at the proper time. Given a patient who has sustained a split but also a partial enervation, drug treatment becomes a delicate matter. More tranquilizer may lead to an apathetic catatonia; more energizer will intensify the detachment. In such instances I would recommend a small dose of each.

In practice, the balancing of tranquilizer versus energizer in the treatment of catatonia is a most difficult and delicate technique. The re-innervation of the depleted ego of the catatonic more often leads into hebephrenia than into normality. Also, the administration of a tranquilizer to the excited catatonic will reduce his ego libido content to a normal value, but it will then proceed to reinforce the ego split by pathologic depletion of the ego supplement. Hence one often reaches a point from which either further depletion or further energizing reinforces the ego split. The problems are compounded by three other circumstances. First, there is a lag between the change in level of medication and the ultimate psychic effect of the change, so that manipulation is clumsy. Second, the pattern of ego dysfunction is similar, whether the energy plethora of the ego nucleus is the result of primary libido plethora or of the clinging caused by incipient depletion, and whether the disturbance of function of the ego supplement is due to the detachment effected by excessive energy filling the ego nucleus or to excessive depletion of the ego supplement. Finally, the fact that such patients are often violent and suicidal makes it difficult for the psychiatrist to be satisfied with the trial administration of the balanced small doeses that are needed. They should be seen daily and the medication adjusted at frequent intervals (Gosline, Bluestone, and Saunders, 1960). Because of these difficulties, I believe that psychotherapy can be more effective than drug therapy when the ego split is not complete. The patient may be ready for a relation with a hitherto uninvolved love object. Such a relation may permit a gradual re-innervation of the ego supplement and, at the same time, on behalf of the therapist, the split may begin to heal. If the patient continues under pressure from the family and reality, this psychotherapeutic cure will be seriously compromised, and here the administration of small doses of both kinds of drug is likely to have a stabilizing effect.

In paranoia and paranoid schizophrenia, correction of the energetic disequilibrium generally restores full contact with reality and full reality testing. This is less frequently true in catatonia. It has been my experience that the catatonic patient may remain detached even when optimal energetic balance has been restored. In one such patient (D. N. O.), the administration of half a gram of amytal a day temporarily increased contact with external objects, but the improvement lasted only a few days, and withdrawal of the amytal accentuated the detachment. Two electric shocks, however, were sufficient to undo the detachment and bring the patient back to full prepsychotic function. That medication was basically responsible for her recovery is indicated by the fact that in a previous episode of illness, as well as in this one, long series of electric shocks had failed to achieve an enduring remission. Only after the energy balance had been re-established was the ECT more than temporarily effective. One wonders how to describe just what the ECT effected in this case. Like the amytal, it seems to have decreased the sensitivity of the ego to the impact of love objects.

Bleuler (1950) drew attention to a condition which he called *schizophrenic melancholia.* This condition resembles melancholia in every way, except that the same patient at other times shows schizophrenia. The process of depletion, which I have described as a corrective tendency in the different varieties and phases of schizophrenia, will if carried too far necessarily induce the syndrome of melancholia. This must be essentially the same, no matter what the starting point. When we see such a condition supervene in schizophrenia, or when treatment of melancholia with an energizer elicits a form of schizophrenia, we may make the diagnosis of schizophrenic melancholia.

There are forms of schizophrenia other than inert catatonia and schizophrenic melancholia which occur in states of depletion. As we have stated, when the entire ego, nucleus and supplement, and the several component structures of each, lose energy concurrently, a state of simple melancholia ensues. However, the loss does not always affect the object-oriented ego nucleus and the reality-testing ego supplement to the same extent. The tendency to cling, which some patients with incipient depletion exhibit, is one factor making for a disparity in energy supply. Other factors may reside in constitutional differences in ego strength and in constitutional points of minimal resistance. We have already described (Chapter III) the occurrence of confused, perplexed states often with hallucinations, when the ego nucleus is relatively more strongly innervated than the ego supplement. From the occurrence of hallucinations alone, then, one cannot determine whether the entire ego system suffers from libido plethora or libido deficit.

A nineteen-year-old girl (L. N. S.) was first seen a few days after electric shock treatment had relieved her of the symptom as of post-partum psychosis. She told me that during her illness she had vowed that if she recovered and was released from the hospital, she would become more observant of religious obligations. Five days later she began to show signs of a relapse, chiefly depression, weakness, erotomania, and clinging. For a few days there were expressions of guilt about erotic wishes directed toward her brothers and toward strange men. Soon, however, she began to preach observance of religious laws to others. She accused everyone of lying and claimed that she alone knew what God wanted. He communicated his wishes to her by feelings. Her explanation of God's commandments was disorganized. This was plainly a delusion, the effect of which was to "identify" with her disapproving superego and to project her sinful ego out upon others. While she denounced everyone vigorously, she clung to them with equal vigor. She even found a place for her erotomania in this pseudoreligious system. She was God's wife and she would have sexual intercourse with him. One might say that the image which she called God was the projected superego. But if the superego was projected, it did not remain distant from the ego, for she claimed that she spoke in God's name and knew all that he knew. In effect, only the ego was projected. The function of self-observation here was usurped by the superego, as it is in melancholia. Within a few days, while the patient was receiving Niamid, the schizophrenic picture resolved and gave way to a state which resembled inert catatonia and melancholia, in which she expressed strong feelings of guilt for her erotomania.

The onset of depletion brought about a return to religion in a clinging fashion in the preceding episode of illness, which had been arrested by electric shock. As she became more desperate while ego function deteriorated, the clinging to God, now a personified superego, proceeded to an "identification" with him. Perhaps the rejection of the ego and the "identification" with the superego, that is, the transfer of the function of self-observation to the superego which we regularly see in melancholia, may be regarded as a regressive clinging to the introjected image of the parent.

It seems evident that the criteria given in the scale of ego libido values are inadequate to deal with these phenomena resulting from an unevenly fractured ego, as opposed to a uniform ego depletion or plethora. In the former instance, the clinical consequences of disequilibrium in the energy supply of the several components of the ego overshadow the manifestations of the deviation of the total ego libido supply from normal. What criteria can we use? Sometimes, if we are fortunate enough to have observed the onset of the illness, we may be able to infer from the initial manifestations the direction of the deviation. When the patient is catatonic, the plethora state is associated with muscular hypertonicity, while the depletion state is associated with hypotonicity. When the patient is not a tense catatonic, isolation from objects suggests depletion, while object pursuit suggests plethora. Object relation that has a clinging quality is likely to indicate a threatening or incipient depletion state. Similarly, the expression of oral wishes is more likely than not to be associated with a clinging defense against depletion.

The conscious expression of a feeling of guilt is also a generally reliable indicator of depletion. Often the feeling of guilt is associated with, or represented by, a newly found or accentuated religious interest. Bulimia is a fairly reliable indicator of depletion. Nocturnal awakening followed by eating has a similar significance. One may also use the occurrence of nocturnal sweating as a criterion. All of these are relative rather than absolute criteria. The mode of evolution of the illness is perhaps the most trustworthy of all these clues. If all else fails and we can make no certain evaluation of ego libido state from signs and symptoms, we may have to resort to a therapeutic test. This should be a last resort, for it not only wastes time, but the administration of the wrong drug may drive the patient to acts of severe aggression against himself or others.

Perhaps a word should be said about the so-called borderline patient. The term is generally applied to individuals who show no signs of gross psychosis but who avoid affectively significant object relations. This detachment usually brings with it a commensurate degree of depletion, so that the patient remains able to function in a limited way, but the resultant degree of motivation is rather small. If the depletion is undone by the administration of an energizer, not all of these people will lapse into clinical schizophrenia. Some may exhibit other neurotic or psychotic plethora syndromes. The term is not a felicitous one. The degree of detachment and of depletion, and the nature of the plethora syndrome which the depletion precludes, tell us more about the clinical state. At any rate, the combination of detachment and depletion makes such patients cling to the analyst but resist analysis. The administration of an energizer alone will generally only increase the defensiveness and resistance, while the administration of a tranquilizer will accentuate the depletion. One hesitates to initiate the difficult and complicated balancing procedure in a patient who is functioning reasonably well, but if treatment cannot proceed without it, it may be worth trying.

Delirium

Our considerations of delirium (Chapter III) have led us to the conclusion that this condition supervenes when the ego supplement becomes too weak to contain the energies of the ego. Weakness of the ego supplement may come about as a result of partial depletion of the ego, spontaneous or induced by tranquilizers; intoxication by drugs—chronic intoxication in the case of sedative

drugs and narcotics and acute intoxication in the case of hallucinogens; sensory isolation; fever; metabolic disorders; and to the extent
that the dream may be considered a form of delirium, sleep. While
the acute management of delirium requires the use of sedation,
tranquilizers can be effective in reducing the tendency to delirium
by decreasing the libido charge of the ego nucleus. The effect of
tranquilizers requires at least several days to become manifest.
However, if those tranquilizers with immediate sedative action are
used parenterally, speedy symptomatic control may soon be supplemented by definitive libido decrease. When hallucinations are induced merely by partial ego depletion, we no longer speak of delirium, but of schizophrenia or hysteria, and the treatment is different. The specific differences in clinical syndrome are determined
by the pattern of fracture of the ego, which in turn varies with the
immediate source of ego weakness: depletion, intoxication (here
the specific intoxicant is important), or sensory isolation.

Diffuse Encephalopathy

In conditions of chronic organic brain disease, energy disequilibrium is seldom a crucial determinant of clinical manifestations.
Under certain circumstances, however, significant energy shifts are
observed. As a result of impairment of ego functions, finer dynamic
defenses are lost, and accumulations of libido begin to develop
which are handled by more primitive defenses, such as gross projections. The need for intimate physical care has a sexually stimulating effect. Depletion may develop in defense against impulses
aroused in these ways, or as a result of insight into the disability
and prognosis. If such energy deviations are encountered, they can
be treated successfully by the appropriate drug. It must be kept in
mind, though, that patients with organic brain disease cannot easily handle extremes of libido supply, high or low. Hence dosages
must be kept relatively small. The psychotherapist and the psychoanalyst, of course, will seldom be called upon to treat these conditions.

Obsessive-Compulsive Neurosis

The treatment of the neuroses is the province of the psychoanalyst and psychotherapist. Even if definitive insight treatment
were not desired or not available, the tranquilizing and energizing
drugs have not been found generally effective in the treatment of

neuroses. Some of the newer sedatives, especially meprobamate, seem to be good anti-anxiety agents, but aside from providing this relief and, of course, deterring more desperate anti-anxiety measures, they resolve nothing. Drugs play a very small role in the proper management of the neuroses. They are indicated when a defensive depletion has advanced too far and created a melancholia which threatens the patient's life, drives him to destructive acting out, or arrests the analysis. They may be useful in those cases where the acuity of the conflict has been dulled by a mild to moderate depletion so that the patient carries on in an unenthusiastic, mildly enervated way, taking little interest in life but clinging tenaciously to the analyst for support. Such patients, because their pathogenic conflicts are not active, do not bring these conflicts to the treatment, and no definitive response can be obtained. I believe that the judicious use of energizers might activate the conflict and the therapy. I have no personal experience with such use of the drugs, but I have seen the effect I describe in situations where I have had to use energizers to treat melancholia which has supervened in analysis. When administration of the drug has continued past the point of recovery from the melancholia, I have found the pathogenic conflict activated, and then its dynamic defenses. Even though pharmaceutic agents cannot in general be recommended in the treatment of neurosis, it is of theoretical interest to examine the energetic changes which occur.

The obsessive-compulsive neurotic tends to avoid making clean breaks. He responds to dynamic pressures and tensions by modifying, reversing, and displacing his impulses. Hence he does not completely resolve his Oedipus complex. In a way, he clings to the idea of a sensual relation with mother in defiance of father. Another characteristic defense of the compulsive is regression to anality. He shifts the content of the struggle from the genital and phallic plane, in which superego punishment is castration, to the anal plane, in which superego punishment is loss of love and the inflicting of pain, libidinized as masochistic beating fantasies. Given a situation in which the pathogenic conflict is activated, the patient attempts to secure gratification by means of displacement, regression, and a return of the repressed through the defenses. Since he is operating at a high libido level, there is an absence of guilt feeling. The superego is projected upon the outside world, and punishment is not perceived as such. It appears to be no more than an accidental misfortune, a caprice of fate, or the revenge of the injured person. If an actual injury occurs in relation to the symbolic transgression, it is seen as a penalty for poor judgment or for impulsiveness, but it is not understood as retribution for Oedipal crime. But even if no injury occurs, trivial events are taken as ominous portents of suffering. The punishment for anal and sadistic defiance of the superego is often condensed with the fantasies of masochistic sexual assault by the very parent who is defied. The modulations, reflections, and displacements of the instinctual impulse create ambivalences. Hence the parent who is defied with venom is invited to retaliate with a cruel sexual attack. The characteristic behavior of the compulsive at this time consists of repeated anal-erotic sallies which, in analysis, can usually be traced back to specific acts of defiance of the parents. The anticipation of retribution causes recurrent states of anxiety. Characteristically, these lead to attempts to placate the authorities, and these very efforts, on reconsideration, turn out to be improper acts which must be punished. A vicious circle ensues with acts of greater and greater desperation separated by accesses of greater and greater anxiety. Because of the compulsive's proclivity to invert and reflect impulses, narcissistic retreat to masturbation is a ready and easy defense when the anxiety becomes intolerable. The anxiety may build up to a surprising degree, however, because it is not merely punishment but masochistic gratification. Even in the narcissistic retreat, old masturbation conflicts are revived which lead again to the same vicious circles of gratification—anxiety—undoing, which is itself further gratification—anxiety—and so on.

One might think that the whole problem could be resolved by administering a drug to reduce the urgency of the drive, a tranquilizer. Such a step is seldom necessary at this stage, for a reason which we shall take up in a moment. But first, let us ask what would happen if the vicious circle would continue and libido were permitted to accumulate? It is my impression that such a patient might go on to paranoia, or possibly to paranoid schizophrenia. In both paranoia and obsessive-compulsive neurosis, there is regression to anal, sadistic tendencies. In both, there is a tendency to complex formation, to ambivalence, to ritual practices, and to retention of the object. Paranoid patients generally show a compulsive character structure, and compulsive patients at times contemplate paranoid fantasies. Should this psychotic deterioration supervene, the administration of a tranquilizer is likely to be required. Most often, however, ego depletion occurs spontaneously and prevents psychotic breakdown. What triggers it? First, the anxiety generated in the vicious circles of object or narcissistic relations may become overwhelming and so force an abandonment of the object or of the narcissistic gratification. Second, the superego can directly effect the withdrawal of libido from the ego and leave it depleted. This reproduces the experience of the child who feels that his parent has withdrawn his love because of bad behavior.

Here is an interesting paradox. The withdrawal of libido from the ego terminates the pathogenic efforts at gratification. The depletion, itself, however, is a danger. When it begins, the patient feels threatened and responds with vigorous efforts to cling, to protect himself. Here again the clinging may create an anaclitic object relation in which the object is tormented and is forced to provide the requisite love. Or, the depletion may create a narcissistic effort to isolate oneself and conserve one's resources. The same anality and sadism which characterized the object-directed efforts at the upper end of the libido scale appear now in the clinging. In addition, an oral element appears. The patient becomes concerned about the wholesomeness of his diet. His fantasies and dreams express needs to be fed and fears of being poisoned. He requires a great deal of sleep. Clearly, the symptoms at the upper and lower levels in both object pursuit and clinging are constructed in a similar fashion. Ambivalence, complex formation, ritual, compulsions and obsessions, sadism and masochism, appear in both. For this reason, the diagnosis of obsessive-compulsive neurosis extends to the two opposed conditions. The chief clinical distinctions are: first, in the clinging phase, there is greater orality than in the object-pursuit phase; second, there is more conscious guilt and primary self-observation in the former than the latter. Similarly, the other indicators that we have studied will contribute to the distinction. Obviously, if the obsessive-compulsive in the impending or actual depletion phase were to be treated with drugs, an energizer would be indicated. Since some compulsives seem to "get stuck" in this phase, an energizer might be used to mobilize such an immobile, self-restraining, inactive person who utilizes therapy for anaclitic support only, and who cannot rise to a more highly energized level. Many compulsives, however, after a period in this defensive, self-replenishing condition, show a regeneration of libido, and a swing back to active conflict in object pursuit. We see now why drug therapy is seldom indicated in obsessive-compulsive neurosis. The corrections of libido deviation generally occur spontaneously and do not have to be induced by medication.

Just as failure to correct an excess of libido may lead to a psychosis of the paranoid type, failure to correct libido depletion may lead to melancholia. In my experience, shorter or longer periods of libido depletion sufficiently marked to warrant the term *melancholia* have been precipitated by: (1) impotence (since impotence led to a loss of self-esteem and an inability to sustain the genital mask for the anal-erotic activities); (2) conscious abandonment of the love object (after a year of courtship during which the girl refused to consent to marriage); (3) superego protest (in the same case, when the girl agreed to marry); (4) threatened loss of love (when the patient's wife became pregnant, and he associated the impending birth of the child with the unwelcome birth of his younger brother). With compulsives, even these depletion excesses tend to repair themselves spontaneously. Therefore, energizing medication should be withheld for a few days or weeks, depending upon the severity and duration of the depletion syndrome.

If any use were to be made of psychopharmaceutic medication in obsessive-compulsive neurosis other than their use for the correction of excessive swings up or down, the only possibility I can see is the simultaneous administration of small doses of energizer and tranquilizer in the hope of stabilizing the ego with respect to its libido content. I cannot predict how well such a scheme would work. I doubt that it would be very much more economical than analysis, because the patient would have to be seen quite frequently to adjust medication to altered libido pressures, and treatment would have to be continued indefinitely, since only insight therapy can arrest the pathogenic process.

Hysteria

While it is true that psychiatrists today seldom encounter the grand hysteria of the nineteenth century, hysteria is nevertheless an important disorder. Hysterical symptoms are not infrequently encountered in most patients in analysis. One sees, not gross paralyses, but mild disorders of function, tingling, bizarre sensations, visual scotomas or illusions, amnesia, denials, genital anesthesia, faints, and even fugues. Much of the discussion of hysteria has been anticipated in other connections.

The pathogenic Oedipal conflict, when it is aroused in the adult life of the hysteric, is resolved by a repetition of the repression. The individual who represents the desired parent loses his or her sexual charm and the patient loses genital sensation and sexual desire, except under special circumstances, as, for example, with a degraded object. The idealized parent or parent representative is a castrated being—one with no genital organ or sexual desire. The libido withdrawn from the object is now *reinvested* in a portion of the subject's own body image, an organ or organ system. Hence the object loss is compensated by an increased narcissism, and erotic pleasure is obtained, not from the genitals, but from a somatic substitute. The situation is comparable to catatonia in which the same two steps occur. First, libido is withdrawn from the entire world, and second, it is reinvested in a primary narcissism and in excessive innervation of the musculature of the entire body. The difference between the two disorders lies in the fact that in the psychosis, the entire world of reality is repudiated, reality testing is abrogated, and even the unconscious images of objects are rejected, while in the neurosis, only the impulse and the object are repressed, reality testing is suspended only with respect to the symptom, and the rejected objects continue to be cathected in the unconscious, finding representation in the affected body organ.

As in the case of catatonia, the split ego is especially vulnerable to depletion. However, in contradistinction to the situation in obsessive-compulsive neurosis, but similar to the situation in catatonia, incipient depletion of the ego supplement in hysteria only reinforces the split. In fact, the split and the ego depletion reinforce each other in a vicious circle, and hysterics who are ordinarily content with their neurosis, manifesting little subjective distress, tend relatively easily to lapse into an ego-depletion depression. The woman who, upon emerging from a melancholia, exhibited hysterical fury in attacks on her husband (see p. 123) illustrates this point. Before a full depletion syndrome develops, however, the clinging, addictive phase appears. In it, the energies of the death instincts, which cut off the love object from perception in the first place are now brought to bear on the same object in an attempt to wrest from him the requisite oral supplies. Fantasies of oral sadistic incorporation of the penis or breasts are common. Self-destructive addictions appear. Sometimes the genital impulses are rescued from repression and reappear as sado-masochistic performances. Dramatic, suicidal efforts meant to hold the love object are not uncommon.

Here again, it is evident that sadistic and incorporative identification which is a disengagement technique at the upper, object-pursuing libido level, also constitutes a clinging technique at the lower libido level. It seems evident that drug therapy is not likely to do any better than the spontaneous, corrective libido fluctuations which normally hold the disease process within limits. When depletion fails to hold the libido in check at the upper end so that catatonia ensues, or when it goes too far at the lower end so that melancholia develops, the appropriate drugs can swing the mechanism into normal range once more. As in the case of the other neuroses, psychoanalysis is the treatment of choice, or, failing that, psychotherapy. The question whether a patient should be stabilized by combined energizer and tranquilizer medication can only be answered as it was for obsessive-compulsive neurosis.

Anxiety Hysteria

Just as paranoid schizophrenia may be viewed as a compromise between the dissociative tendency of catatonia and the object retention of paranoia, so anxiety hysteria can be viewed as a compromise between the dissociative tendency of hysteria and the object retention of obsessive-compulsive neurosis. The difference between the psychotic series and the neurotic series is essentially a difference of scope. The entire world of reality, including the patient's own body, is involved in the psychotic series, while only the particular object, the particular sexual contact organs, and the particular impulse are concerned in the neurosis. Reality testing, which is abrogated completely or almost completely in the psychotic series, fails only with respect to the specific object, contact apparatus, and impulse in the neurotic series.

Confronted with a revived Oedipal conflict, the patient with anxiety hysteria takes the same first step that the hysteric does; namely, he represses the object, apparatus, and impulse. The object has no sensual meaning for him, his genital organs are not aroused by the object, and he is aware of no physical desire for that object. The second act of the hysteric defense, it will be recalled, is a reinvestment of the same libido in the images of organs, organ systems, or limbs. The corresponding process in the case of anxiety hysteria is a reinvestment of the libido in the images of the object's and of the subject's body which are included in the microcosm of images of the ego supplement. One immediate consequence of this act is that the process of cathecting and repressing, turning attention to and away, become important psychic events. By means of them, objects can be magically detached and retrieved. In fact, the anxiety they create and the pleasure they give rise to in these entirely narcissistic acts provide a sublimated substitute for masturbation, and lead to a libidinization of the brain and head. In contrast to the hysteric, however, the patient with anxiety hysteria is not content with this narcissistic reinvestment and, like the paranoid schizophrenic, he rebuilds the object relations he has lost, not by resuming the original relations, but by projecting his intrapsychic images upon the natural world of animals, hills, roads, bridges, rivers, caves, open and closed places, high and low places, fire and water, and so on. To a certain extent, we all respond to sunlight and warmth and grandeur and beauty, probably on the basis of archaic releasing mechanisms with which we are constitutionally endowed. This pre-existing responsiveness to nature forms a convenient framework upon which the projections of the anxiety hysteric converge.

But the anxiety which effected the termination of the original Oedipal object relation and its current replacement now appears in response to the renewed pleasure, via the projection. Therefore, when the patient encounters such natural objects or configurations, anxiety appears once more. This time the detachment from the anxiety-arousing object takes the form of actual physical escape or aversion. Neither the object nor the genitals of the object are the triggers for anxiety; they have been repressed. The carriers of the projected images of the object and genitals, typically, the topographic features of the natural world, are now the triggers for anxiety. Usually, in analysis, some association from personal history can be recaptured in which the origin of the sexualization of the specific anxiety-arousing natural configuration is revealed. For example, a woman (K. N. X.) developed anxiety in subways. She recalled in analysis that before her phobic symptoms had started, she used to enjoy sensual, genital sensations as a result of the rocking and jolting of subway cars, while at the same time inspecting the faces of her fellow passengers in search of a suitably attractive man. Her father used to rock her and dance with her as an infant. Configurations which arouse anxiety in phobias do so because they promise, symbolically, sexual pleasure. Following the establishment of specific phobias, the conflict between object pursuit and avoidance continues to widen the spectrum of attractive targets for projection which invariably become releasers of anxiety.

It is usually not necessary to give a tranquilizer to terminate this widening circle of attractive and frightening objects. The frustrating pattern will generally result in depression with depletion. The symbolic object pursuit sooner or later fails to prevent the depletion which the withdrawal from the actual love object induces. Depletion may also ensue as a result of impaired narcissism due to loss of self-esteem which, in turn, results from the increasing restriction of the patient's activities. As we have seen with the two previous neurotic conditions, when incipient depletion evokes a clinging response, paradoxically, the very same techniques that were used in the original object pursuit are called into play again. Only this time there is often an oral orientation. Whereas physical and literal approach to objects generated anxiety at the upper end, physical separation now generates anxiety at the lower end; this is why locomotion and traveling are so prominent in phobias. The fearful animal that represents the entrapping genital of the tempting parent or the punitive genital of the offended parent at the upper end, becomes a projection of the hungry, devouring self at the lower end. For this reason, it appears that the treatment of phobia with a tranquilizer fails to cure, and it may even induce melancholia. Actually, drug therapy is not indicated in anxiety hysteria except in the case of a melancholic decline. The question of balanced doses of tranquilizer and energizer for the purpose of stabilizing the libido level comes up for discussion again. The technique might be attempted where psychotherapeutic assistance is not available, but the definitive treatment is psychoanalysis.

Addiction

Although usually a neurotic rather than a psychotic problem, addiction has always been a difficult challenge to analysis. In the first place, whatever misery the addiction brings the addict, he dreads losing the solace it affords at times of great anguish. In the second place, we must consider why it is that one individual clings through an object relation, while another person who avoids object relations takes the source of strength into his own hands, and narcissistically provides himself pleasure. It is likely that this narcissistic form of clinging is a defense against the intense, desperate, anaclitic object relation that the need to cling generates directly. Clinging for support of libido level probably represents a return to a desire for oral gratification from the mother. In men, this turn of events impels them back into the Oedipal situation which was their point of departure. Again they must escape by shifting to a homosexual position, which is no more acceptable in the clinging relation than in direct object pursuit. In women, oral clinging to the mother reconstructs the homosexual danger from which they escaped by repression, and the alternative is even more threatening, the Oedipal conflict. The way out of this trap is narcissistic self-support via the medium of symbolic innervators such as food, or via actual anesthetics.

In three patients with severe ego depletion syndromes, I have encountered dreams and fantasies of urinating into the bath or into one's own body. These have represented, I believe, attempts at self-nourishment and parthogenetic self-impregnation resembling the drinking of urine by people isolated without drinking water. The patient identifies with the nourishing mother. The fact that these phenomena are usually associated with voluptuous sensations betrays the extent of the regression which permits their appearance. The homosexual, social gratification that accompanies drinking with others is a return of the repressed. Clinging individuals who can accept love from supporting love objects will welcome a relation with the therapist and quickly establish a firm and positive transference which will last, unless the libido level sinks lower despite the supporting anaclitic relation. One important exception is the case in which the prospective patient feels that his love object is trying to discard him by relegating him to the psychiatrist. The psychiatrist then comes to represent the threat of losing rather than gaining an object. The patient who has turned to narcissistic self-support through narcotics will be as reluctant to establish an erotic clinging relation with the therapist as he was with anyone else. A third important source of difficulty in treating addicts is that so long as the patient continues with his addiction, the treatment can be concerned only with its consequences and not with its cause. The patient is seldom able to tolerate abstinence in the interest of facilitating analytic exploration long enough to permit analytic resolution of the problem.

The administration of energizing drugs makes it possible to bring these people into treatment and to hold them. The energizers increase ego libido and eliminate the need to cling. Why, it may be asked, is it then necessary to complicate matters with analysis or psychotherapy? Obviously, because this symptomatic relief has resolved none of the problems which gave rise to the addiction in the first place, and which are certain to recreate it when medication is withdrawn. Moreover, long-term management of the condition requires an agile adjustment of dosage in order to avoid the Scylla of precipitating the object-seeking neuroses of the upper level and the Charybdis of permitting the clinging of the lower level to reappear. If there is no other solution possible, drug therapy alone may be tried. It is ironic, however, that proper regulation of dosage requires frequent visits in which the psychiatrist cannot avoid an interest in, concern with, and remarks about, the dynamics of the problem—he becomes involved in psychotherapy, willy-nilly.

Clearly, for facilitating—in fact, for making possible psychotherapy and psychoanalysis—the energizing drugs are invaluable. By reducing the need to cling, medication renders the transference less intense and less threatening. In a sense, it is paradoxical that an energizer, in this case, should reduce the intensity of an instinctual drive. It immediately removes the secondary personal and social complications of the addiction. Finally, the artificial energizing of the libido forces a confrontation of the precipitating conflict. Moreover, the psychiatrist, by regulating the dose, can determine just how intense the conflict will be, and he can use this power to maintain a pressure neither too high nor too low for therapy.

I cannot claim that all addiction is a defense against depletion. In fact, a patient who had been given meprobamate to relieve anxiety in a state of mild depletion refuse to give it up when his anxiety persisted as he entered a state of mild plethora. Here the anxiety which demanded sedation was a response to the threat of object loss by hysterical detachment. It is difficult to say how often addiction is created by plethora anxiety as opposed to depletion anxiety. In the former instance, however, it is probably necessary that the ingested agent have an ego-anesthetizing effect, for example, alcohol and the sedative and narcotic drugs. In the latter case, oral needs must become paramount, so that the patient may become addicted to food.

Smoking must also be considered an oral addiction. In the definitive depletion of melancholia, the smoker develops a distaste for smoking, just as the eater stops eating and the drinker cannot drink. The inhaled smoke probably has little or no significant ego-anesthetizing effect. In the clinging phase of incipient depletion, smoking probably provides the craved oral gratification. In a state of plethora, smoking helps to attenuate the object relation by diverting part of the libido to narcissistic, somatic gratification.

Post-Partum Psychosis

This subject is included primarily to point up a gap. I can make no statement about the energetics of this condition, although I have little doubt that energetics play a principal role in determining the onset and content. Nor is there, as far as I know, any way of determining to what extent the concurrent energetic changes are the result of the psychic experience of parturition and motherhood, and to what extent they are caused by sharp changes in endocrine and steroid equilibrium.

I have, in recent years, treated two cases of post-partum psychosis. The first, Q. S. T., was a patient who had been in remission from paranoid schizophrenia for ten years with the aid first of analysis then of once-a-week therapy. Within a few days after the birth of her daughter, she showed classical signs of post-partum psychosis: fears of injuring the infant and of starving her, inability to function, confusion, agitation, pessimism, despair, and a fear of losing her mind. The energetic picture was that of a depletion melancholia, and the death wish toward the infant seemed to arise from the mother's resentment at being burdened by a demand which she could not fulfill. Librium brought pronounced subjective relief within a few hours, but this was accompanied by delusions and hallucinations, and the relief itself diminished after two or three weeks when some toxic confusion became evident. Even with her distress thus eased, during a session on the couch the underlying depletion syndrome was unmistakable. Niamid was prescribed at the same time, starting with low doses, and after six weeks there was clear evidence of repletion. Unfortunately, the patient began to suffer dizzy spells, due probably to postural hypotension, and finally she had a series of six convulsive seizures. All medication was stopped immediately. When I saw her ten days later, she had a distinct plethora schizophrenia with hypochondriacal symptoms. Moderately large doses of Trilafon were begun and in a week a clinging syndrome became evident. For over a month, regulation of dosage was difficult because sufficient drug to reduce the hypochondriacal delusions and detachment phenomena also induced mild depletion. As depletion became more prominent, the medication was gradually reduced, and she recovered to her usual condition.

Through all these states there was constant hostility to the infant, the conscious manifestations of which horrified the patient. When there was no depletion, there was a sense of detachment from the child. During the initial melancholia, the patient had the fantasy that she was the baby. Here was an identification which permitted the patient to isolate herself from her child. From all the dynamic data that was accumulated in this case, I reached the following conclusion. Despite this woman's recovery from paranoid schizophrenia, she retained an intense, narcissistic cathexis of her body, which, even during remission, led to hypochondriacal worries. The pregnancy produced, of course, an intensification of the narcissism. At first it made her happy, but toward the end of her pregnancy she became concerned about the changes in her body and she began to resent the foetus. After parturition, which in itself created anxiety by gratifying her pregenital needs for anal exhibition, the narcissistic cathexis of the body automatically became a homosexual object relation—that is, the part of herself which she loved so intensely became another person. The consequent anxiety was especially great because the object relation that evolved from the narcissism was powerfully reinforced by the mother's normal, instinctual attention to the infant. This intensified homosexual anxiety led to repression, detachment, and then depletion. It was the state of depletion modified by the attempt to detach herself from the infant, by destroying both if necessary, that presented as the post-partum psychosis. Repletion by means of the energizer, and possibly also by the seizures, accentuated the dynamic defenses of detachment, depersonalization, and narcissistic cathexis of the body. These created anxiety and left the patient yearning for her lost love for the baby. In summary, parturition undid a narcissistic defense against object love; this necessitated a renewed repression and detachment which led, in turn, to a depletion syndrome.

This dynamic and energetic picture may not be typical for post-partum psychosis. One woman (K. N. X.) currently in analysis with conversion and anxiety hysteria had suffered a post-partum depression eight years previously. She was seen in a more recent moderate melancholia. At present, she readily yields narcissistic libido to a homosexual object relation with her little daughters, but promptly develops anxiety and withdraws once more. She is prone to become depleted after withdrawing. I can imagine that the dynamic and energetic processes in this patient's post-partum psychosis resembled those in the previous case, but there is no proof.

The second post-partum patient, L. N. S., was mentioned above in the discussion of depleted forms of schizophrenia. She was in temporary remission from illness after seven electric shock treatments when first seen, and although no longer psychotic, she complained of a sense of estrangement from home, husband, and baby. Within a few days this detachment was lost, and simultaneously a psychotic depletion syndrome set in. There were somatic conversions, paranoid delusions, many with religious content, and auditory hallucinations. Later there was inert catatonia. Large doses of Niamid (400 mg. daily) were required to undo the depletion. Without the addition of a tranquilizer, she quickly passed into a hebephrenic, and then into a tense catatonic, syndrome. After two months, a balance was established. However, I have not yet had the opportunity to reconstruct the pathodynamics of the illness. Energetically, it seems that her illness consists of a powerful libido depletion complicated by clinging and ego dissociation. The depletion itself was a corrective reaction to a schizophrenic plethora induced by the parturition. However, I have established that the pathogenic process actually began with her betrothal and was accentuated by the pregnancy.

Energetic studies of post-partum psychosis are needed. The study of energetics can take place via the psychologic criteria, such as those I have presented, and also by observing responses to the psychopharmaceutic drugs. Ultimately we shall have to distinguish between endocrine and psychic determinants of this illness.

Character Neurosis

Two general groups of patients are considered cases of character neurosis. First, there are those patients whose sublimations, reaction formations, and ego and superego identifications remain highly libidinized. The individual, in his social, vocational, and family relations then behaves in a way which is not well coordinated with reality requirements and expectations. Repetition compulsions and impulse gratifications break through. Conflict does not issue in flagrant symptoms, but gratification and punishment are unconsciously interwoven in the conduct of daily affairs. As a consequence, the individual is unsuccessful in one or more areas of life. It not infrequently happens that such a person achieves unusual success in one circumscribed area, but punishes himself by arranging for misery in other areas. While these individuals are often highly motivated, they find paths for discharge which prevent excessive libido accumulation. The only satisfactory treatment for such cases is psychoanalysis, or, in its absence, insight psychotherapy as intense as possible. Drugs, I believe, have nothing to offer such patients. If tranquilizers are given, they can retard the acting out of unconscious fantasies, but only at the cost of retarding the patient's psychic life as a whole.

A second group of patients to whom the term character neurosis is assigned consists of individuals who have achieved some rest from neurotic conflict by a mild, general depletion. They trudge along with little verve and sparkle, forgoing opportunities for pleasure in order to avoid the possibility of incurring pain. Such patients may take readily to analysis and form a strong clinging, positive transference, but they will progress little or not at all once they have overcome their initial, mild anxieties. In this group, the administration of small doses of energizer, over a relatively long period, may force the emergence of some object libido and thus reactivate the old conflicts from which the depletion offered surcease.

Homosexuality and Perversion

I have little experience with energetic changes in this area. I cannot guess whether these behavior deviations are driven by excessive object libido or by a clinging, anaclitic drive—or possibly now by one, now by the other, as occurs with many neurotic symptoms.

Several months ago I began to treat a young woman (X. C. T.) who had been hospitalized for a year following an attempt at suicide. This event followed a long period of masochistic, degrading promiscuity. She came to me in a state of depletion due, at least partially, to relatively large doses of tranquilizer which she had been given during her hospitalization. The tranquilizer was discontinued and replaced with Niamid. Within ten days there was a revival of her promiscuity wishes and fantasies, concomitant with a rise in libido level from 3 to 5, 6, and 7. An oral orientation betrayed a continuing downward pull. When, four weeks later, the libido level had risen to a reliable 7 and 8, the promiscuity fantasies disappeared and gave way to direct Oedipal material. I have not yet seen a recurrence of the promiscuity material at high libido levels.

Dr. Sidney Furst has told me of a sixteen-year-old girl who was brought to him for help in breaking away from a homosexual companion. The separation was accompanied by depression and work paralysis. Dr. Furst gave Niamid to cancel the clinging tendency which, undisturbed, might have driven the patient back to homosexuality. The maneuver was successful, and he has been able to proceed with the analysis.

Dr. Louis Linn has reported effective termination of a sado-masochistic perversion in an obsessive-compulsive by the use of a psychic energizer.

Psychosomatic Illness

I have few data concerning energetic changes in psychosomatic illness and its response to the energy-regulating drugs. I suspect that energetics will make a significant contribution to the understanding and treatment of these conditions.

In the case of one patient with ulcerative colitis (Z. F. O.), I administered a monoamine oxidase energizer (Parnate) because psychologic criteria indicated moderately severe depletion (libido scale values of 2 and 3). As the libido level rose, the physical condition improved *pari passu*. For more than a year now, Parnate, together with analysis, has been able to provide almost complete control of the colitis, an effect which medical treatment, including the use of steroids, had been unable to achieve previously. Without the energizer, analysis would probably not have had sufficient time to effect relief. Without analysis, but with the drug, the patient would have had a much rougher time than she has had, since her depression and depletion resulted from impairment of object relations. The only hope of withdrawing medication lies in a successful analysis.

GENERAL TECHNICAL CONSIDERATIONS

Pharmacologic

(1) Drugs should not be used in psychoanalysis or psychotherapy unless they are essential to protect the patient or to protect the treatment. If treatment can be successfully conducted without drugs, none should be given.

(2) When drugs are given, the smallest effective dose should be prescribed, but the dose must be sufficient to be effective. More than minimal doses are likely to create undesirable psychic effects, physiologic side effects, and toxic complications.

(3) The tranquilizing drugs have a latency of days to weeks; the energizing drugs have a latency ranging from weeks to months. Even though the first effects of a tranquilizer may be observed within days, the full reconstitution of the shattered ego in a patient severely ill for a long time may require months. This reconstitution is spontaneous, not driven by the medication. It can be facilitated greatly by psychotherapeutic insight. Any effects seen too soon are likely to be transference effects.

(4) It is important to distinguish between the sedative and the tranquilizing effects of the chlorpromazine series of phenothiazine tranquilizers. When a member of the chlorpromazine series is employed, the sedative action may obscure signs of incipient overdosage, such as restlessness, difficulty in thinking, and inner distress. On the other hand, in dealing with excited patients such as manics, the sedative effects of the chlorpromazine group may be exploited to quiet the patient until the tranquilizing effect takes hold. One is tempted to use the same drugs for the treatment of agitated, delirious patients, but some of these may turn out to be sensitive to tranquilizers, and under cover of the sedation, it becomes relatively easy to give too much.

(5) When administering the tranquilizers, it is important to be alert for evidences of basal ganglia dysfunction which appear as side effects. While akathisia and Parkinsonian syndrome are distressing, the dystonias are frightening. It is best when giving more than a small dose of the prochlorperazine series to prescribe an accompanying prophylactic dose of one of the anti-Parkinson drugs. This is given either once or twice a day, depending upon the dose

of tranquilizer. Since some of the anti-Parkinson drugs may have a slight sedative action, it is advantageous to order them taken at night. If a patient who has not been given a prophylactic dose of an anti-Parkinson drug develops an acute dystonia, the latter can be resolved within a matter of minutes by parenteral administration of one of these drugs, or of a barbiturate or caffeine. Conversely, it should be remembered that a patient taking a tranquilizing drug is more sensitive than usual to other drugs, especially to sedatives and physiological depressants. An individual who is on a moderate dose of a tranquilizer is liable to get as drunk with one drink as he would ordinarily with two. In the case of a patient who does not take medication reliably, such as, a catatonic, it is disadvantageous to give a piperazine phenothiazine, for the anti-Parkinson drug may be omitted and a distressing dystonia ensue.

(6) Autonomic effects such as dryness of the mouth, blurring of vision due to poor accommodation, or stuffiness of the nose may accompany the use of any of these drugs. Hypotension occurs with some of the tranquilizers, especially reserpine.

(7) The energizing drugs have only a single important side effect, postural hypotension. When it occurs, the dose must be reduced, or, if it cannot be reduced without endangering the patient, compensatory measures must be instituted. A tight girdle and supportive elastic stockings are the simplest devices to recommend. Liberally salting the diet and, if necessary, adding salt tablets tends to combat hypotension. Unfortunately, the addition of salt seems to weaken the energizing effect of the drug. If nothing else will do, one may add small amounts of an amphetamine. This must be done most cautiously, since the action of the amphetamine will be exaggerated by the energizer, and a hypertensive rebound may be produced. Severe headache and possible seizures may ensue. I have found that the contents of a Dexedrine spansule may be used in very small doses. A few granules may be given on the first morning, more on the second, still more on the third, and so on, until the patient obtains the desired relief from hypotension. The use of spansule granules tends to produce a smooth effect lasting ten to twelve hours. One morning dose a day may suffice.

Some of the drugs may be less apt to provoke hypotension than others. Other side effects, such as sphincter disturbance, are handled more easily. Like the tranquilizers, the energizers potentiate the action of many other agents, and so dosage, especially of other drugs acting upon the central nervous system, must be kept relatively low.

(8) When energizers and tranquilizing drugs are given together, their respective effects are intensified. This is especially true of toxic effects. Thus, a phenothiazine is more likely to precipitate a dystonia when it is given simultaneously with an energizer than when it is given alone.

(9) The side effects of the drugs may be serious and interfere with the free regulation of dosage. It has been my experience that when a drug is helping a patient, he uncomplainingly tolerates the side effects. Serious complaint about the side effects may indicate that the drug has been improperly selected or that its dosage is too great. Insomnia is often a troublesome side effect resulting from the administration of either tranquilizers or energizers. In the case of the energizers, it is disagreeable but not serious. So long as they feel well upon arising, patients who are taking energizers mention insomnia, but they seldom complain about it. When they do, there is no harm in giving adequate sedation. A tablet or two of meprobamate, together with a sustained action capsule of the same drug, is effective in such instances. Other sedatives may be used as well. The dose required will be smaller in the presence of the energizer than would ordinarily be needed. In general, I try to avoid giving sedatives, and unless there is real distress from the insomnia, I offer none. When it is a tranquilizer that is causing the insomnia, the complaint should be taken more seriously, for I believe it indicates energy disequilibrium due to excessively rapid depletion. It is well in such cases to consider reducing the dose lest the depletion get out of hand. This valuable indicator of excess medication is obscured if sedative tranquilizers are given at bed time. Therefore, when regulation of dose is delicate, nonsedative tranquilizers are to be preferred.

(10) Since the effect of the drug in lowering or raising the ego libido level requires days or weeks to become established, it is evident that it is not important that the dosage be distributed evenly during the twenty-four hours. Administration of the proper dose even once a day may be adequate, and if the drug is given twice a day, the distribution is certainly more than adequate. Only when drugs with sedative action are prescribed is it important to take into account what time of the day they are taken. It may some-

times be helpful to give a nonsedative tranquilizer in the morning and a sedative one at bed time.

(11) The dose of either tranquilizer or energizer required to bring about a shift in ego libido is considerably greater than the dose required to prevent a reverse shift. For example, a dose of 300 mg. of Thorazine daily may be necessary to return a paranoid schizophrenic to normal, but a dose of 50 mg. daily, or only 25 mg., may be adequate to prevent a relapse, once he has achieved this state. The same applies to the energizing drugs. In this connection, Deaner, which is not powerful enough in practical doses to resolve a melancholia, may serve nicely to "put a floor" under the libido level and so prevent a relapse in circumstances that would ordinarily induce one.

(12) When the dose of a drug is reduced in response to a patient's improvement, it is wise to reduce in approximately equal percentage changes. Thus, from a dose of 8 mg., one could decrease in the following sequence: 6, 4, 3, 2, 1, ½; or from a dose of 400 mg.: 300, 200, 150, 100, 75, 50, 25. When a balanced dose of energizer and tranquilizer are given, the two drugs should be reduced *pari passu*.

(13) Earlier (see p. 145), in discussing the treatment of melancholia, I mentioned the use of amphetamine derivatives or Librium to give some symptomatic relief until the energizer has taken effect. Meprobamate may also be helpful.

(14) While only the tranquilizers and energizers can produce significant changes in energetic equilibrium, certain of the drugs that affect the ego directly can help to bring relief to a patient who is suffering. Ordinarily in analysis we try to avoid taking such steps to make the patient comfortable lest we cut off the flow of material. A comfortable patient has little motivation to produce analytic material. If the patient is too distraught, however, no analysis can be accomplished, and at times it may be wise to afford him some relief. Also, during periods when the patient is not seen, for example, during vacations, there is no harm in offering chemical help if suffering is otherwise too great. For this purpose, the agents acting directly on the ego have some advantages. By and large they are less toxic. Since their effects are relatively prompt, and terminate within a few hours, the regulation of dosage is easier. One of the amphetamines may be helpful for very mild depression, and I

have found meprobamate to be a useful agent in managing anxiety. With these drugs, of course, timing of doses is important, and it may be wise to use capsules containing coated granules which offer a sustained action, or pills which have repeat actions.

(15) Drugs which act directly upon ego function without influencing ego libido may produce some effects which resemble the effects of tranquilizers or energizers. This they do by acting upon the perceptual apparatus. When perceptual sensitivity or affective response to perception is dulled, the clinical result may resemble that produced by a tranquilizer. Conversely, when perception is made more acute, the effect of an energizer may be simulated. Therefore, these drugs may be employed to produc temporary effects, but there are severe handicaps to such use. First, the same drug which in low doses produces the one effect, will in larger doses produce the other. For example, barbiturates will at first reduce perceptual sensitivity so that they can be used to dissolve catatonia; but with continued administration they may increase sensitivity to perception to the point of producing hallucinations and delirium. Hallucinogenic agents, on the other hand, will sharpen perception initially, but if continued they cause perceptual dulling and sedation. Second, whatever effect is achieved by building up a level in body fluids will be reversed when the drug is withdrawn. I have found, for example, that when a barbiturate is employed to reduce the catatonic's aversion to the world of external percepts, the beneficial effects endure only so long as the dose is increasing. When the dose is held steady over a period of several days or weeks, the salutary effect disappears. When the drug is withdrawn, the patient is made more sensitive to percepts, and the clinical condition worsens. Third, most of these drugs achieve their effect by impairing one element of ego function or another. Our task in the treatment of psychosis or neurosis is to strengthen, not weaken, ego function. Hence best results will be obtained by relying principally upon tranquilizers and energizers, and restricting the use of ego-toxic agents as much as possible.

One should remember that the anti-Parkinson drugs in current use have an ego-toxic effect. This is exaggerated by the concurrent use of energizing drugs. Hence when given in the presence of an energizer, they may tend to create a false impression of libido plethora by sensitizing perception. They may even cause a full delirium in this combination, despite the fact that they are prescribed in therapeutic rather than toxic doses.

(16) If the patient is to take a complex set of drugs, it is useful to provide him with a written schedule. In some instances, for example, one may be giving a nonsedative tranquilizer in the morning, a sedative tranquilizer at bedtime with an anti-Parkinson agent, and possibly an energizer, with one or more doses of a sedative. Or, again, the major medication may be an energizer, with an amphetamine in the morning and a sedative at night. A written schedule prevents confusion. Pharmacies occasionally err, and it is wise either to inspect the drugs or to check on color and size of the pills.

(17) There is one particular error in drug therapy which I have found to be especially common and unfortunate. Given a patient who is agitated or overactive, the psychiatrist is likely to assume that he requires a tranquilizer to overcome his excitement. If a tranquilizer is then given, the patient will probably quiet down, but in half of such cases or more, the improvement in level of activity is liable to be followed by clear-cut depletion, often with depression. The error has arisen from the fact that threatening or incipient depletion can lead to overactivity and psychosis just as surely as libido plethora does. It is not the level of activity which can be used as a guide, but only the criteria which have been enumerated in the previous chapter and in this one. Sometimes the criteria will indicate that an energizer is required, and its administration will make the patient more agitated than before. This period of increased agitation must be traversed boldly. If the calculations have been correct, the pathologic activity will subside when the energizer has taken firm hold. It may be replaced by a state of quiet depletion which, after a few days or weeks, will itself give way to energetic normality. Of course, the latter state may follow termination of the excitement directly.

I do not approve of prescribing a combination of tranquilizer and energizer upon the initiation of treatment, because one cannot know in advance whether a combination is required, and if it is, what constitutes the proper ratio. Moreover, if undesirable consequences ensue, one cannot know which of the two drugs is at fault. I recommend that an effort be made to achieve control by administering that drug which the libido state requires. If a stable position cannot be maintained by the use of one drug alone, then one should give a slight excess of the first drug and counter it with as small a dose of an opposing drug as possible.

Whenever new drugs are introduced by pharmaceutical laboratories, it is important to determine from the literature, if possible, whether they are tranquilizers or energizers, on the one hand, or whether they affect ego function directly, on the other. I cannot predict whether drugs of an entirely different variety may be discovered, but I believe that all currently available psychically-active drugs fall into these two categories.

Psychologic

No drug should be given in the course of psychoanalysis or psychotherapy which is of the uncovering, insight-giving type, unless the treatment cannot proceed without it, or unless there is a serious threat to the patient which medication can alleviate. No drug can substitute for good psychotherapeutic technique, and drugs should not be invoked simply to overcome resistances which should properly be handled by interpretation. The correct administration and regulation of pharmaceutic agents is often simple, but just as often turns out to be complex and difficult. Moreover, it always complicates the treatment. If medication is used in situations which do not call for it, no success will be forthcoming, and the treatment may be adversely affected. On the other hand, when there is an acute need, and the right drug is given at the right time, its effect on both the patient and the therapy is striking.

Pharmaceutic treatment may begin with the beginning of therapy, or it may have to be instituted in the course of an already established therapy. Let us consider the first possibility. In all cases it is important to see the patient as frequently as possible. The more known of the patient's psychic state, the more precise will be the drug regulation. If the patient is psychotic, the first phase of the psychotherapy consists, essentially, of permitting a positive transference to develop and, at the same time, assisting the patient to re-establish reality testing. If the illness is at a stage in which the dominant attitude is clinging due to impending ego depletion, this tendency is itself sufficient to form the basis for a strong transference. The chief exception to this, as I have mentioned, is the situation in which referral to a psychiatrist is regarded by the patient, and often correctly so, as an effort on the part of the love object to disengage himself. A second kind of exception is that which arises when acceptance of psychiatric help becomes a blow to self-regard. This, in turn, tends to attenuate ego libido even further. In any case, the relief from the psychotic distress which the drugs do bring about forms the basis for a powerful, positive, anaclitic transference—a magical relation which gives the therapist a solid position from which to initiate actual analytic work. The process of resuming reality testing is one of the first wholesome activities one observes. The therapist can do no better than to support this activity. As always, tact and respect are required. Nothing is gained by forcing a confrontation which the patient is not ready to accept. It threatens his defenses and makes an enemy of the therapist. On the other hand, a sensitive therapist detects when and where the patient's own doubts are developing, and he can be of assistance by supporting these doubts and providing the answers which the patient is almost ready to find himself. Ultimately, the patient comes to suspect how seriously ill he has been, and may even suspect the diagnosis. Only good can come from confirming the patient's suspicions when he is ready. A frank acknowledgment of the extent and nature of the psychiatric illness is necessary as a sound basis for subsequent analytic work. This can begin only after reality testing prevails once more.

With mildly or moderately melancholic patients, after some initial transference work, the therapy often bogs down into sessions of complaints about misery and expressions of pessimism. In such cases, while waiting for the pharmacologic effect to appear, there is no reason why the therapist should withhold gentle expressions of concern which could be supportive to the patient. It is important, of course, not to go so far as to compromise the subsequent transference and the policy of nonintervention required for sound analytic work. When a tranquilizing drug is given, for example, in schizophrenia, its depleting effect, though welcome, tends to make the patient more dependent upon the psychiatrist; hence the tendency to wish to continue treatment even after recovery from the psychosis—obviously, a desirable state of affairs. When, on the other hand, an energizer is given, the recovery from a depletion state issues in a gratifying narcissism characterized by feelings of wellbeing, invulnerability, and self-sufficiency. Continued psychiatric treatment is regarded as a limitation of self-esteem and the patient is inclined to discontinue treatment. If further increase in libido tends to re-establish an object relation with the therapist of the kind which has hitherto been repressed, the transference assumes an even more threatening character and the patient will tend to terminate. Aside from offering appropriate interpretations, I generally make no effort to deter him. After a second such attack, the patient becomes more realistic and less likely to flee. The renewed object libido, in some cases, may contribute to a transference and counteract the impingement of the therapy upon narcissism. It should be remembered, however, that this tendency to leave treatment after recovery from melancholia applies not only when recovery has been accomplished by medication but also when the same recovery has been achieved by long, arduous analytic work.

Addicted patients, of course, readily substitute a pill for an intoxicant, and may obtain considerable relief even before the pharmacologic effect can take hold. Addicts seldom come into treatment unless they have encountered some difficulty from which psychiatric treatment promises to rescue them. This expectation alone is often sufficient to overcome, for a brief but adequate period, the threat implicit in a clinging transference. Once recovery has occurred, the patient has no difficulty in giving up the medication, for the clinging state no longer exists, and narcissistic self-confidence often replaces it. Whether or not such a patient will remain in therapy after he has overcome his addiction depends upon a number of dynamic factors, such as those discussed above. When a patient observes that a withdrawal of medication is followed by a resumption of distress, he is less likely to terminate treatment.

Occasionally, a psychosis may supervene upon a psychoanalysis or erupt in the course of ongoing psychotherapy: such a breakdown is more often a melancholia, or at least a depletion state, than a plethora state. Less frequently, an addiction will appear. Or a real crisis may develop to which the patient is unequal, for example, a crucial examination, or a business project which cannot be deferred. A threatening suicidal urge is always an emergency. In such cases, the therapist may consider administering one of the psychopharmaceutic agents. It has been my procedure on such occasions to mention to the patient, at an appropriate point, that I have been thinking of offering him emergency pharmacologic assistance. This statement generally raises some questions, both positively expectant and negatively apprehensive. These I have answered in two ways: first, by discussing the reality situation, and second, by interpreting the unconscious fantasies which give rise to the questions. Unless the emergency requires instant action, I generally wait several days to examine, in symptom, transference, action, and dream, the unconscious significance of this step. Only after this preliminary work has been done do I administer the drug. I try to tell the patient that I expect it to give him relief, and I indicate in a general way the area in which the relief will be appreciated. I make an effort to avoid listing specific effects so as not to prejudice the value of the behavioral indicators. While I convey to him the idea that there will probably be some latency, I do not specify the period of time I have in mind, for time gaps and latencies are often helpful clues in distinguishing pharmacologic from psychologic effects. Though I indicate that these are powerful and occasionally toxic substances, I prefer not to specify the toxic or side effects that concern me. When a toxic or side effect does appear, I promptly identify it as such for the patient and make whatever adjustment is indicated. Whenever possible, I try also to work out the psychologic meaning of this phenomenon and relate it to the analytic work in progress.

I have scrupulously avoided becoming involved in any kind of physical examination or manipulation aside from looking at my patient while talking to him. When toxic effects appear that require medical control, I refer the patient promptly to competent medical consultants. However, I retain control of the administration of the drug. No physician other than the treating psychiatrist can select drugs or regulate doses in the treatment of mental illness.

After some experience, patients begin to recognize and anticipate the effects of these drugs. When they have learned enough about their illness, it becomes possible to share with them the rationale of the selection of drugs and adjuvants and their dosages. In certain instances where ego stimulants and intoxicants are used, I have found it convenient to let the patient use medication *ad libitum,* provided that its use is reported, remains within reasonable limits, and is not designed to interfere with the therapeutic sessions. The intelligent patient who requires these drugs can regulate the dose more fluidly than the physician, and the treatment does not become too preoccupied with drugs, effects, and doses.

The chief transference fantasies stimulated are, of course, those of oral gratification. This is especially relevant in the case of depleted patients whose current fantasies are oral to start with. Feeding fantasies become poisoning fantasies when the feeding becomes a source of distress. This may happen when the gratification poses an instinctual threat and provokes anxiety. For example, when a male therapist gives a pill to a male alcoholic, the homosexual, fellatio fantasies and gratification that follow may create sufficient anxiety to render the transference threatening. The feeding also becomes a source of distress when the drug has an unpleasant pharmacologic effect, for example, when it is the wrong drug, or the dose is too great, or the side effects are too upsetting. As I have previously mentioned, patients are generally willing to tolerate distressing side effects when the primary action of the drug is relieving. Excessive complaint about side effects is often a clue that the drug has been improperly selected.

Another fantasy commonly stimulated in the transference by the administration of medication is an impregnation fantasy. Recovery from a severe medical or surgical illness is often accompanied by fantasies of rebirth. These also appear fairly consistently in recovery from psychosis or severe neurotic disability, and it may very well be that the rebirth fantasy is an essential, operative, psychic process by means of which the recovery actually takes place. In the case of schizophrenic dissociation from the real world, retrieving it is experienced as rebirth. Similarly, in the case of ego depletion, the process of repletion is experienced as rebirth. If these processes are initiated or driven by a substance which is taken into the body, a fantasy of impregnation appears. While reality favors oral impregnation fantasies, more specifically, fellatio, the preferences of the individual may cast them into other forms, such as anal impregnation, oral impregnation via mother's breast, coprophagia, and so on.

The hypochondriacal patient may assign to the drugs the responsibility for the imminent physical collapse he fears. This will occur before the drug has had an opportunity to alleviate the patient's distress, or if medication is given over too long a period, or if the wrong substance or an excess of the right substance is given, or if the side effects of a drug appear before its therapeutic effect.

Where self-esteem is crucial, continuing medication or having to resume it interferes with the patient's need to reassure himself against illness, and so he may resist such continuation or resumption. This same consideration operates to discourage a patient from underestimating psychotherapy vis-à-vis drug therapy. The patient who does disparage the value of psychotherapy or analysis following success with medication is giving voice to a resistance which must be analyzed. I have found this an infrequent occurrence, and one easily handled by analytic work.

It is my opinion that good psychopharmaceutic therapy cannot possibly be carried out except by determining drug and dose with the aid of indicators of ego libido. This is true in psychoanalysis, psychotherapy, and even in drug therapy alone. The closer the observation and the better the understanding of the dynamics, the better the drug therapy. Under optimal circumstances, the best treatment we can offer to the patient who needs it, is psychoanalysis assisted by drug therapy. Following such physical indicators as blink frequency, nocturnal sweating, and trunk edema may have value in some cases. I recommend keeping consistent and accurate records, though I would not compromise the analytic work by diverting too much effort to record keeping.

If the indicators of ego libido content are followed, one will be able to determine when medication is to be reduced and eliminated. When it is clear that the desired correction of libido level is about to become an overcorrection, medication must be reduced. I have indicated the need to diminish dosage in approximately consistent proportional steps. The interval between successive decreases should be relatively long, if possible. In the case of tranquilizers, five or ten days may elapse before a second decrease is added to a first; in the case of an energizer, ten days to two weeks. When the situation is not urgent, it is well to let the patient continue with a minimum dose for a relatively long period of time, a month or more, before stopping medication entirely. In this way, the therapist will obtain some idea of the patient's volatility while he is still somewhat protected.

It is not easy to steer a moderate course between courageously attempting to handle renewed deviations of libido with psychotherapeutic techniques alone, and offering medication to prevent excessive deviation, knowing that some latency will delay the desired effect.

Finally, I have noticed an occasional tendency on my part to be diverted from full concern with the analytic material by my interest in the energetics. This may be ascribed partly to my special interest in working out these problems, but partly also to the fact that energetic problems are easier to solve than dynamic problems. I must caution against permitting this to happen. While I believe that energetic studies are of great importance in all psychoanalytic and psychotherapeutic treatment, with or without the use of drugs, they are no more important than dynamic studies. The bedrock of all psychoanalytic and psychotherapeutic technique is the understanding of the patient. Nothing must be permitted to interfere with obtaining this understanding.

CHAPTER V

Illustrative Case:

Conversion and

Anxiety Hysteria,

with Melancholia

To ILLUSTRATE the use of principles of energetics in comprehending the clinical course of an illness, I have prepared two case reports of patients whom I have analyzed over the past several years, one a classical neurotic and the other a schizophrenic. For understanding the pathogenic process itself, I have substituted nothing for Freudian genetics and dynamics; the introduction of the study of energetic perturbations lends a supplementary dimension to the elucidation of the psychic events which constitute the psychoanalysis, or—from another viewpoint—the course of the illness. The interaction between dynamic and energetic factors I have indicated and interpreted, insofar as these factors have been understood. In each of these cases, I have employed pharmaceutic agents to produce the minimal psychic stabilization required for the patient's induction into psychoanalysis and participation in the therapeutic process. Energetic considerations provide the necessary rationale for such pharmacologic treatment. Finally, in wholly practical terms, these cases demonstrate the day by day management of drug administration and the constant precise monitoring of its effects through the use of psychologic criteria and indicators of ego libido content. These events are concisely recorded in the graphic figure accompanying each case report.

The case reports suffer from two specific defects. Full understanding of the pathologic manifestations is limited by the fact that neither analysis has been completed; the patient is still in treatment. Then again, all psychoanalytic case reports suffer from their inadequacy—due to realistic restrictions of time and space—in conveying in all its fullness the rich complexity of a case study. Finally, I must add that these reports have obviously been weighted to emphasize energetics. It would be gratuitous to reiterate that in practice the interest in energetics supplements, but never outweighs, the traditional analytic work with dynamics and genetics.

The initial report concerns the less profound illness: a case of conversion and anxiety hysteria, with episodes of melancholia. The text summarizes the progress of treatment, session by session, for fifteen months, commencing with the very first interview. Illustrations and confirmations will be found of some of the mechanisms of symptom formation which have already been discussed theoretically. This case study is particularly interesting for the number and variety of somatic symptoms presented, which serve as useful indicators of the clinical course of the illness. The numerous, perhaps unwieldy, group of variables ranged along the ordinate of the graphic figure is composed largely of these symptoms, whose vicissitudes may be read against general psychologic and energetic criteria.

HISTORY

A thirty-nine-year-old married woman consulting me one Friday morning, complaining of early waking with retching and vomiting and feelings of depression. She had been quite well until about a week previously when the subjective depression appeared. On the Tuesday before seeing me, she had suddenly become anxious while in a restaurant with her husband and had had to leave abruptly. This woman, K. N. X., had been in analysis with a colleague for longer or shorter periods of time on several occasions in the past, starting at the age of twenty-four. The chief symptoms had been phobic anxieties and depression. At the initial interview, I had the impression that I was dealing with a mild depressive state in a phobic woman. The libido state seemed best represented as 3 on the scale I was using, signifying moderate but pathologic depletion. We agreed to undertake psychoanalysis.

At eight o'clock the following morning, Saturday, she called and told me that all the previous night she had been unable to sleep and lay awake preoccupied with thoughts of suicide. She had been vomiting since 5 A.M. and suffered from diarrhea. She requested me to visit her at home, which I did. When I saw her, she asked to be taken to a hospital. "I don't want the responsibility," she said. "When the children talk to me, I retch. I want to be taken care of." The degree of unhappiness, the suicidal preoccupation, the inability to perform at all, the discouragement, insomnia, nausea, anorexia, and inability to tolerate husband and children, together with some complaints of difficulty in thinking and psychomotor retardation all combined to form a picture of a moderate depression of the melancholic type. I admitted the patient to a hospital and began the administration of Catron, 12.5 mg. daily.

The patient was the last of three children. During her childhood, she had witnessed considerable discord between her parents, who at one time before her birth had been separated for several years. She would often vomit before going to school in her early years. Menarche occurred at twelve to the accompaniment of much physical distress and mental anguish. She has suffered with each menstrual period since. During her fourteenth and fifteenth years there were frequent episodes of depression with feelings of unreality and with vomiting. Ten years later, after having been disappointed by a married man whom she loved, the patient became "nervous," that is, she trembled in company, especially on dates and while dancing, and she became phobic with respect to traveling. Subway riding was especially difficult for her. She began psychoanalysis and continued for two years. At one point during the analysis, she was unable to work and was troubled by thoughts of suicide. Her father's refusal to contribute to the financial support of her analysis after her own funds had run out disappointed and angered her.

Evidently she improved considerably, for at the age of twenty-eight, she married a responsible and successful young businessman, albeit with many misgivings and much anxiety. Their sexual relations were bad from the beginning, since she was frigid and he, either impotent or premature. His performance improved after several years of analysis which terminated about half a year after

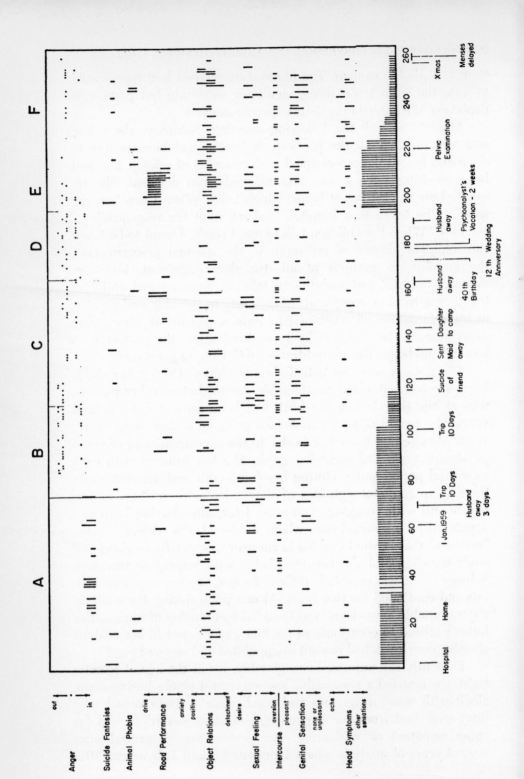

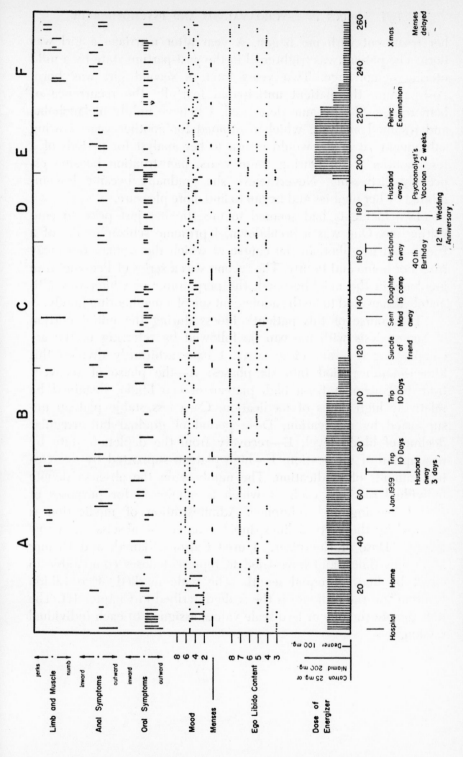

FIGURE 3. VARIATIONS OF DRUG DOSAGE, EGO LIBIDO CONTENT, SYMPTOMS, AND OTHER EVENTS DURING THE YEAR AND A HALF OF PSYCHOANALYSIS IN THE CASE OF K. N. X.

her treatment with me began. A year after marriage a girl was born. The patient was frightened in the post-partum state by a mild uterine hemorrhage. Two years later, a second girl was born. Post-partum, the patient anticipated fearfully the recurrence of hemorrhage. She became depressed, I believe mildly melancholic, and resumed analysis, which continued for another year. During subsequent years she would return to her analyst for periods of a few months or so. During these years, menstruation became especially distressing. Nevertheless, she gradually became less inhibited by her phobias and began to find more pleasure.

Two incidents had seemed to unsettle her just prior to consulting me. One was a breakdown, I presume schizophrenic, of a friend and neighbor, in the course of which the woman ran away from her home and family. The second was a series of Peeping Tom incidents in the neighborhood, the perpetrator of which was ultimately discovered to be the adolescent son of a neighboring family.

The course of this patient's illness during the initial portion of her analysis with me can be followed by referring to the accompanying diagram (Figure 3). I have arbitrarily divided this fifteen-month period into six phases: A—the phase of recovery from melancholia; B—a high plateau of ego libido, sustained by relatively high doses of medication; C—a less stable plateau unsupported by medication; D—a period of gradual but irregular decline of libido level; E—recovery from the depletion state by resumption of medication; F—high plateau supported by decreasing amounts of medication. The numbers on the abscissa denote individual sessions, each of which is numbered for purposes of record keeping and reference. Administration of medication is denoted by the vertical lines directly above the abscissa in a row labeled "Dose of Energizer." I used Catron, Niamid, and Deaner at various times, and have tried to represent doses comparable in effect by lines of equal length. The scale marked "Ego Libido Content" on the ordinate is the scale described in Chapter III. The dots denote the one or two scale values assigned to each individual session.

CLINICAL COURSE

Phase A: Recovery from Melancholia

Sessions 1, 2. The patient, who has been hospitalized in a private mental sanatorium, indicates by her feelings and somatic symptoms her wish to expel an introject. "I want to expel what's gotten into me." She retches, vomits, and has diarrhea. Libido level 3 (in retrospect, probably 1 or 2).

Sessions 4, 5. She expresses interest in her mother and sister. There are fantasies of homosexual seduction or assault by her nurses. She tells of homosexual play at the age of ten. The patient is reaching out for supporting affection from mother.

Session 6. There is a return of affective feeling. "It feels so good to cry." (I have learned that when a melancholic patient starts to cry, he is starting to recover.)

Session 7. Affective sensitivity continues to improve. "I'm just beginning to let feelings come through . . . I was like in a state of shock." But in the same session, the patient lapses into another mood. "Everything seems to be going down and off of me." (I have encountered virtually the same statement in other melancholic patients. It describes a centrifugal tension which these patients sense. For a more detailed description, see my 1960 paper on depression.) "My anus and vagina seem to let down with slight contractions." She tells of having been refused by her husband when, a month ago, she had spoken of the possibility of having another baby. (Striking fluctuations of mood and libido are not uncommon in recovery from melancholia. Since it is so early—too early to be a drug effect—it is likely a transference response.) For the most part, it is not the husband who refuses the patient, but she who refuses him. She cannot accept love from him or from me, and relapses. Until this point, I had visited her daily in the hospital. Thereafter, she walked to my office from the hospital for her sessions until her discharge for home.

Session 11. When she talks to her husband, the patient feels a sense of bowel urgency. The affectionate demand represented by her husband and the need to protect him against her anger make him a source of distress to her. In a state of depletion, the patient cannot deal with external love objects and virtually introjects them by locating the apparent source of the feelings they engender to a point within the ego. But since encountering a demand which one cannot meet is itself painful, the patient's defense consists of ejecting the introject, using musculature that would be appropriate if she were dealing with an actual physical irritant that had taken a position within her abdomen. This need to eject the pain which seems to arise internally is responsible for the centrifugal tension of melancholics. The anger with the husband, representing her inability to accept his love, applies also to me.

Sessions 11-13. The inability to accept love from any man, husband or analyst, is merely the defense against the longing for their love. As she speaks about the analyst, she is reminded of a past occasion on which she almost had an orgasm during a vaginal examination. "I'm awfully depressed. It's worse than when I was numb . . . I'm beginning to feel better; my husband didn't make me sick last night."

Sessions 14, 15, 16. The birthday of one child and an illness of the other make her feel guilty about not being at home to tend them, and she is somewhat worse. But clinging object relations still strive upward: "I've been troubled by erotic desires today. I have a drawing feeling in the vagina now." The clinging tends to set up a centripetal tension.

Session 17. The craving for affectionate support from husband and analyst continues to encounter resistance and is defensively reflected back into narcissism and autoerotism. She attempted unsuccessfully to masturbate, which she rarely does when well. "My sex feelings are not directed toward you or my husband, just toward myself. I may rape the man in the next cottage." Following the attempt at masturbation, she became more depressed and developed a headache.

Session 20. She accuses husband and father of withholding love, projecting her own withdrawal and coldness. This conflict applies to the transference as well.

Session 21. There is an increase in appetite and in object libido two and a half weeks after the start of medication.

Session 22. Object desires begin to appear with less of the anaclitic quality and more interest in the object himself. "I'm starting to be curious about the other patients [in the hospital]."

Session 23. "I was frightened of a dog while on a walk yesterday. I'm more like normal." The phobia is related to the increase in object libido, but the dynamics are not revealed in the material.

The patient returned to her home after the twenty-third session, three weeks after her admission to the hospital. This improvement came sooner than it usually does in patients treated with drugs alone. The acceleration is probably due to the analytic work.

Sessions 25-28. The material indicates penis envy, and is accompanied by expressions of anger against the husband and the analyst. The husband is excoriated for his premature ejaculation, although her performance is generally worse than his. The indicators at this point justify a libido rating of 7. It would seem that the patient attempts to escape from the Oedipal dilemma by identifying with the man and projecting her sexual inhibition, her castration, upon him.

At this point the dose of Catron was reduced by half to 6.25 mg. Two days later, menses began, always an ordeal for the patient. The repeated menstrual confirmation of the castrated state opposes the patient's desire to maintain the illusion of possessing a penis. The penis envy also represents the wish to retreat from the threatening heterosexual object love by means of narcissism. This defense, too, is repeatedly frustrated by the menses. Following the reduction in dose of Catron, energy level fell to 4 by Session 32. This depletion was accompanied, as before, by a rejection of the affectionate claims of husband and children, and a renewal of oral needs for mother. In an attempt to obtain greater libido support without increasing the net dose, I replaced the daily dose of 6.25 mg. with a dose of 12.5 mg. every second day. (I do not believe that this procedure has any advantage and I no longer use it.) The libido failed to respond. The patient remained unhappy and angry.

Session 37. The penis envy complex, which became manifest in a state of relative plethora, persists in the state of mild depletion. It is now associated with a reassertion of love for mother, doubtless of the anaclitic variety. The connection between these two is revealed by memories from childhood, which emerge in this session. The patient recalls that as a child she would ask her mother repeatedly, "Do you love me?" At other times during her early years she would say to herself, "Mother and I are going to have a baby." It would appear that an identification with father seemed to be a way of terminating her Oedipal love for him and, at the same time, of retaining her anaclitic relation with mother. But she thought about having a baby with mother while she was having a bowel movement. So she is the woman, too. The fantasy may be one of narcissistic identification with both mother and father, from which a parthogenetic rebirth fantasy became possible. The data are not conclusive.

Session 39. With the libido level still at 4, I increased the Catron to 12.5 mg. daily.

Session 41. "I woke up with a fright last night shouting, 'I can't get the light on!' . . . Before going to bed my husband turned out the light in the living room and we necked . . . I remember my father's telling me not to go into a dark room with a boy."

Session 42. "I'm afraid of the dark."

Session 44. There are some phobic anxieties about being injured by exposure to ultraviolet light. In these last three sessions there are expressions of phobic anxieties having to do with light and dark, with seeing and not seeing. Dark means missing the sight of the love object and longing for him, and temptation for heterosexual gratification. It also means blindness as a punishment equivalent to castration. Light means an opportunity to exhibit sexually, but also apprehension by a jealous father and ocular castration. We shall see below that being in the dark, being blind, which here serves as a temptation for sexual gratification, is used not only as a punitive self-castration but also as a means of defending against the tempting love object, via the symptom of hysterical blindness.

Sessions 46-52. In response to the increased dose of energizer, libido level rises to 7. The patient is angry with her husband for his impotence and indulges in fantasies of sexual pleasure with the analyst and with other men, especially young men. Nausea, muscular jerking, and choking appear as hysterical symptoms. They are aversive innervations of mouth, throat, and legs in an attempt to prevent their being used for erotic gratification. Note that whereas we encountered oral material before in connection with ejection of the virtual introject, and then later as an expression of an anaclitic demand for nutritive love from mother, it appears defensively here, in heterosexual impulses presumably of the adult type. The jerking of the legs is an attempt to control them, since they have become libidinized. The patient, her two older siblings, and her father were all expert dancers. The patient enjoyed dancing as child and adult. It will be recalled that the symptoms for which she started analysis at the age of twenty-five included trembling while dancing. Despite her physical attractiveness and her grace in dancing, her gait is rather awkward, doubtless due to hysterical defensive innervation. Following the appearance of these symptoms, libido level declined to 4. We have discussed the theoretical basis for a decline of libido level following repressive abandonment of the object. Of course, the hysterical innervation affords some narcissistic gratification, but this is not sufficient to sustain the ego libido.

Sessions 56-64. Sexual desires and fantasies return. Their inhibition leads to a renewal of penis envy and a wish to identify with father and brother. The result of this identification is winning mother's love. Homosexual fantasies and dreams appear, in some of which the patient obtains sexual pleasure from the bodies of her daughters. She repeats to herself these childhood remarks, "Let's have a baby, mother," and awaking in the morning, thinks, "Kiss me, mother." The former remark is especially apt to appear even now when she is sitting on the toilet. Anal dreams are reported in these sessions. Pregenital and narcissistic regressive defenses are quite evident, but the historical compression continues to obscure the origin and full meaning of these fantasies.

Sessions 68, 69. The husband leaves for a brief business trip. The night before his departure the patient feels shaky while ice skating and has to hold onto him for support. An old fear of becoming insane reappears. In the past, when her husband would go away, she would smell his pillow. As a child she would suck the sheets. She recalls fears of separation from mother when she was eight. It appears that the brief separation from the husband threatens to gratify the wish to detach herself from him, or lends verisimilitude to that wish. Anxiety follows, associated with clinging, oral efforts to retrieve him, following a pattern she once employed in similar situations with mother. It will be recalled that in the preceding chapter we mentioned an important difference between hysteria and anxiety hysteria. In the former, the narcissistic somatic cathexis satisfies the libidinal need, or the enervation that accompanies the withdrawal of cathexis from the object is associated with sufficient depletion, so that object need declines. In the latter, on the other hand, even after hysterical innervation of somatic organs, the yearning for the object continues and attempts are made to retrieve it. It is the separation anxiety, which we see here, that impels these retrieving efforts. Separation anxiety also occurs in the face of impending separation from the anaclitic object. Fear of insanity occurs with fear of losing the object.

Phase B: High Plateau Supported by Energizing Medication

Session 74. There follow a series of efforts to escape the incest taboo by means of sexual relations with degraded objects, such as servants, delivery boys, men who behave badly, negroes, and so on. These fantasies are complemented by fantasies in which she appears as a degraded, anal person. Interspersed in this material are recriminations against her husband and expressions of penis envy, as though her sexual inhibitions with him were his fault.

Session 93. "We had intercourse last night . . . I was worried about getting a bladder infection while my husband was masturbating me." (The patient was seldom able to have an orgasm during intercourse. After his own orgasm, her husband would masturbate her to climax. The sexual experience she describes here is not unusual.) "I had an orgasm when he sucked my breasts. . . . During intercourse I felt nauseated, physically sick, overpowered by his body." The Oedipus complex causes the patient to withdraw psychically from her husband during intercourse and cathect her own body. In this instance, the bladder infection she fears is an expression of anxiety due to this excessive narcissistic cathexis of her own genitals. The intensity of this impulse is too great, in a sense, too hot for her to handle even in this hysterical form, and she reprojects it onto the husband who becomes a large, threatening figure. Since this largeness is a projection, we expect to find that it applies in some way to her self-image. The unusual sensitivity of the breasts is also manifestation of defensive narcissism.

"I drove on the parkway yesterday," she continues. (This represented an advance for her. Her phobias generally kept her off parkways and restricted her to local streets.) "It's narrow. I feel that I can't swerve to get away if I should have to . . . as though I weigh too much." Her car is large and she complains that in an emergency she would have no room for evasive movements. But here we see that we were correct in expecting to find that it was her own sense of largeness and heaviness that she projected onto her husband. The fact that he is a large man only lends verisimilitude to her projection. These attributes seem to derive, at least in part, from defensive identification with her father who was a heavy man and with her brother who was an adult when she was a child. "My father would look like an animal when he got angry. He would shake his hand at my face. . . . My brother used to beat me." These threatening images of the men she loved in childhood were, when they first appeared, already a condensation of introjected images of them and her own sexual anxiety. She repeats this same pattern of sexual desire, inhibition, identification, anxiety, and longing, followed by reprojection of the image which now carries her own anxiety, in her relation with her husband. Incidentally, we now have a genetic root of her animal phobia.

Session 96. The patient again tries the expedient of regression to anality and exposure. "Being exposed to my husband is revolting to me." She recalls that at the age of five, while in a public place with her mother, she defecated on the floor. At about six, she would urinate while sharing a bed with her mother. This defense is characteristic of obsessive-compulsive neurosis but, as we see here, it is not restricted to that condition.

Session 103. Because the patient was in no evident danger of relapse to a state of depletion, I decreased the dose by half again to 6 mg. She responded to this move with fellatio fantasies and a resumption of sucking on sheets and pajama collars. I surmise that these are her response to the fear of relapse—an oral, clinging defense.

Phase C: Plateau Unsupported by Medication

Session 113. Some mild depletion followed the reduction in dose, but after the passing of a menstrual period, that is, by session 115, the libido level had recovered.

Session 118. Catron was discontinued and replaced by Deaner, 25 mg. per day. There followed a resumption of the dynamic processes we have been describing, namely, repeated incestuous thrusts, which were opposed alternatively by repression, regression, projection, or aggression. Occasionally these defenses were associated with slight diminutions of libido level.

Session 134. The patient complains that her right arm is numb. This symptom appeared after a desire to masturbate, which occurred at the time of menstruation. Here we have another root of her menstrual distress, the genital stimulation it causes. At one point while we were talking about penis envy, castration, and menses, she interrupted: "Here come those spots and bright lights again!" She was referring to spots and bright lights and other visual phenomena which were recurrent hysterical symptoms. Evidently she used hysterical blindness, optic and psychic, too, to defend against unpleasant percepts—in this case, castration. She recalls that during her twenties she would dream recurrently about Arm and Hammer Baking Soda. The masturbation, or rather the desire for it, was an attempt to support the defensive narcissism with autoerotism. But it ran athwart the castration complex, and blindness and numbness of the hand had to be invoked to repress the desire. The picture on the box of Arm and Hammer Baking Soda shows a raised arm holding a hammer. It probably represented to her a denial of castration. The patient does not recall actual masturbation during childhood.

Session 141. The patient was aroused by the attentions of a married man at a party. His general behavior was somewhat improper. The following morning she had intercourse with her husband, but she thought about the other man. "I felt like I was swallowing him with my vagina and my mouth. I couldn't have been more open. I felt as if he was going to drown in me. I was really taking him in. I didn't feel any contractions, only a melting—and I made noises, which I never do." By withdrawing from her husband and using intercourse with him to support an anal and oral fantasy, the patient is finally able to break through her inhibitions and enjoy orgastic pleasure.

Session 143. Omit the dose of Deaner every second day.

Session 150. Discontinue Deaner.

As the drug dose is reduced, the material becomes less pressing and distinct, defenses become less intense, and the need for depletion is decreased.

Session 156. "We had intercourse last night. I was very passionate. I had an orgasm during the intercourse. My hands even responded when I touched his back. At night I had a dream: I'm being taken back to the sanatorium. I'm desolate. I felt depressed when I awoke in the morning, exhausted. I'm better off dead. I never should have been born. It's happened before that we've had successful intercourse and then turned away from each other."

This time the patient didn't get away with it. It is as though she were promptly punished by depletion for her illicit pleasure. The patient is now able to see clearly the defensive nature of her withdrawal from her husband. But the relevant genetic material was not forthcoming, despite the obvious reconstruction of its broad outlines.

Sessions 157, 158. There are continuing sexual desires with fantasies about extramarital, degraded objects. The step of regression by degradation increases the distance betwen unconscious impulse and its conscious derivative.

Sessions 159, 160. The patient drove to the analyst's office for the first time. Hitherto she had to be driven. She asks for praise for her accomplishment. "I had a funny feeling in my head as I drove up to the house . . . I feel uncomfortable when my husband praises me. . . . We had intercourse last night, but I was thinking about you and about driving here. . . . As I was driving here this morning, I suddenly felt a film blob in front of my eye. . . . On the parkway you can't stop . . . I'm afraid I'll have an accident. . . . I was very tense and nervous, sick to my stomach while sitting outside [in the waiting room]." The patient attempts to act out her seductive fantasies toward the analyst. Her hysterical defenses, funny feelings in the head, spots before the eyes, fears of not being able to stop, were mobilized by this attempt.

Phase D: Irregular Decline in Libido in the Absence of Pharmaceutic Support

Session 166. In response to repeated interpretations, the patient acknowledges her sexual desires for father and hostility toward mother. Feelings of guilt and some depression are evoked.

Session 172. The patient is overcome by a sense of detachment after receiving an expensive birthday gift from her husband. "My parents visited last night to celebrate my birthday. I was irritated by my father but fond of him. My husband bought me a gold necklace for my birthday. . . . We had intercourse and I enjoyed it . . . I almost had an orgasm . . . I felt some slight nausea. I awoke in the middle of the night with the feeling that I didn't know where I was. It was as though I were sleeping in a cabin in the woods. There was the light of automobile headlights. I had to put on my underpants before I could go back to sleep." On one occasion in her twenties, the patient had been treated to a glass of beer by her father, and had thrown up. "I'd like to come here in my Bermuda shorts, but it wouldn't be proper."

The patient is struggling here with two repressed impulses. One is the impulse to accept a gift from father. The other is the impulse to expose herself to father and to me. The first is aroused by the actual gift from her husband. Accepting gifts from him—and he was fairly generous—always created guilt. The analytic material indicates that the gift is seen as an oral one and the defense is nausea and vomiting. The desire to exhibit, it will be recalled, was interdicted by father. He himself had refused to look when, in childhood, she had exposed herself to him while undressing for bed. She had been hurt and has continued to hold this rejection against him and against her own castrated genital ever since. The gift of jewelry stimulates the desire to exhibit. This is now transferred from father to analyst. This exhibitionistic fantasy had presumably obtained some gratification during intercourse, for the nocturnal anxiety dream seemed to have been trying to carry it further. The automobile headlights were watching eyes. They also represented her road phobia. She had to defend against these spying eyes of father and his superego representation by covering her genitals. It is interesting that she attributes the feeling of guilt for her sexual impulses toward father to him rather than to mother, as though acknowledging hostility to mother were still too difficult for her.

Session 183. After continuing efforts to carry further sexual impulses toward father and deal with guilt toward mother, libido begins to decline. At the time that depletion sets in, the crucial dynamic process is generally repressed, so that the analyst is not able to deal with it directly. We shall see below that with recovery, the repressed wish tends to rise toward consciousness.

Irritability, early waking, eating at night, clinging to the analyst, nausea, retching, headache, castration dreams, and complaints of being dirty and smelly, all indicated further depletion, which was accentuated by menses.

Session 194. When matters seemed to be going too far, I resumed medication—Niamid 75 mg. per day.

Session 195. While she is being masturbated by her husband, the patient becomes frightened. She feels that she is falling into space, that she is losing touch with reality. Defense by detachment becomes more dangerous when the ego is depleted. The depleted ego cannot counteract the detachment, and the latter tends to deplete the ego still further. There are many signs of detachment.

Session 197. Intercourse is painful. After intercourse she asks her husband to serve her milk and bread. The experience of intercourse and the defenses it elicits are enervating and evoke more oral clinging. Niamid dose is increased to 150 mg. daily.

Phase E: Repletion of the Ego by Pharmaceutic Support

Session 198. Increasing libido again precipitates Oedipal conflicts and defensive detachment. There are specks of light and headache.

Session 199. The patient becomes able to drive again. She had not been able to in the state of depletion. Intensified hysterical defenses again evoke feelings of losing contact with reality and suicidal fantasies. Both are methods of dissociation from sources of pain.

Session 206. Alternating thrusts of sexual desire and hysterical defense produce frequent feelings of unreality, dizziness, eye spots, and emotional detachment, the latter disturbing intercourse. Her defensive hostility towards others as well as herself appears in her fear of driving. She is afraid of killing others or of bleeding to death herself.

Session 210. "Driving home was difficult after the last session. I was dizzy and couldn't see the road. At one point, I thought: 'He'll tell me I really want to kill my mother.' Then the road really started looping around. My mother used to get unsteady and dizzy when she was driving. She always wanted someone with her in the car." The analytic work was leading the patient to a confrontation with her hostility toward her mother, in fact, her death wishes toward mother. She defends against this idea, as she does in the case of all unpleasant ideas, by psychic detachment. The psychic detachment takes a number of forms, one of which is an exclusion from vision. What is even more interesting is that in the very way she denies her aggressiveness, she identifies with its object—mother.

Session 213. She stops driving again. "I'll hurt myself if I drive."

*Phase F: Sustained High Libido Level
with Decreasing Doses of Energizer*

Session 220 and sessions following. Oral defenses oppose oral impulses: nausea, numbness of the lips, muscle spasms of throat and jaw, choking, numbness of the tongue.

Session 221. I reduce Niamid dose to 125 mg. daily. The hysterical defenses are becoming too distressing and depressing and are interfering with the analytic work. Decreasing libido level will bring the intensity of the conflict to a more reasonable working area.

Session 225. Reduce Niamid to 75 mg. daily.
Session 231. Reduce Niamid to 50 mg. daily.
Session 235. Reduce Niamid to 25 mg. daily.

There follow a series of sessions in which the patient consistently tries to escape from her incestuous wishes by hysterical re-innervations of appropriate parts of her body, hands, arms, fingers, legs, head, tongue, throat. Penis envy becomes more insistent, and also a desire to have a baby. I suspect that these are both derivatives of the wish to exploit somatic narcissism in support of defensive withdrawal from the forbidden object. If this suspicion should prove correct, it may lend some confirmation to my hypothesis that some cases of post-partum psychosis are based upon the reverse process, that is, upon the danger that arises when a target of narcissistic love—the foetus—automatically becomes the target for object love. This patient, whom I mentioned in our discussion of post-partum psychosis in the last chapter, had suffered a melancholia after the birth of her second child, eight years before she came into treatment with me.

Session 249. The pregnancy solution to the Oedipal conflict is intensified by the approach of Christmas, which has always aroused the patient to strong feelings. A baby is born of a pregnancy which began without a carnal act. "I couldn't sleep last night. I was feeling my blood circulating in my head very fast. I was not dizzy. I could feel a motion in my body, a movement upwards. When I closed my eyes, it got worse." The normal sleep wish to regress to a state of primary narcissism is supported by the neurotic wish to do the same. The narcissistic state becomes too highly charged to permit sleep. As in schizophrenia, primary self-observation obtains, but it is projected out from the ego onto the body: the body moves, not the images. Note that the recumbent position, darkness, and closing the eyes even in the dark, all contribute to this capacity for detachment from reality.

The progressive reduction of medication attenuates somewhat the upward pressure of libido and thereby reduces the hysterical defenses which give rise to the separation anxiety.

Session 260. The patient has been having some distressing abdominal distention, diarrhea, and cramps. She could not tell whether the cramps were uterine or intestinal. What she called diarrhea was actually a frequent urge to defecate, but it had little result. "I think I'm pregnant. It's the twenty-ninth day." The usual menstrual interval was twenty-four to twenty-seven days. She complains of tenseness of the head and neck. "I'm happy at the thought of being pregnant. . . . Last night I dreamed that a snake might bite a little boy. . . . I became frightened when a friend first told me about intercourse [at age twenty-four, just before the exacerbation of symptoms which had led her into her first course of analysis]. She told me she would stretch. I was thinking that my girls might make a sissy of a little boy." The patient's fantasies about becoming pregnant seem to be coming true. There has been no laxity in contraception and a pregnancy would be unexpected. In her head and neck symptoms, she identifies with the baby in the process of birth. As the mother, she is also concerned with being stretched. The baby and the penis, both of which distort her narcissistically overcathected body, are resented. Moreover, if it is a boy, when it is born it will depart taking its penis with it, and leave her mutilated and bleeding as before. She is afraid that she, not her daughters, will castrate him. Like her other hysterical defenses, this too fails, for the narcissistic retreat alone does not attenuate the object impulses which, acting now upon herself, create hypochondriacal anxieties. Moreover, experience has taught her that the confirmation that pregnancy brings to somatic narcissism is ultimately terminated to her detriment. She is worse off after the pregnancy than before, and last time she collapsed under the disappointment. It was another five days before menses returned. I suspect that this may have been a hysterical pseudopregnancy, since it occurred after pregnancy had been proposed as a neurotic solution. Behind this complex there lies the childhood fantasy of having a baby with mother, a fantasy which remains to be analyzed.

DISCUSSION

This case report offers an opportunity to test the usefulness of the clinical criteria and the scale I have proposed in the conduct of pharmacotherapy. The data charted in Figure 3 show a close correspondence between the libido values, which I have assessed solely from psychologic data, and drug administration. In phase A, we see a steady increase in libido level after the energizing drug is introduced. Sessions 30 to 40 exhibit a decrease in libido associated with a halving of the dose. A resumption of the original dose is followed by a resumption of the libido rise. During phase B, the libido is sustained at a high level by continuing pharmaceutic support. In phase C, this support is withdrawn gradually. After a temporary decline (113-124), the libido holds up well. In phase D, however, dynamic disturbances compel an irregular decline. Resumption of medication in phase E is associated with a prompt rise in libido, and, in F as in C, the libido level continues high though the dose of medication is progressively reduced. During the subsequent six months, one or two Deaner tablets a day have sufficed to protect the patient against excessive depletion. It is evident that considerably less drug is required to prevent depletion than to reverse it. While these data alone tell us nothing about what essentially the indicators indicate and the scale measures, they do demonstrate that whatever its nature, it is a reliable monitor of the need for and effects of energizing medication.

Let us turn our attention to the ordinate scale labeled "Mood" in Figure 3 (see p. 195). This is an estimate of whether the patient feels happy or unhappy, appears pleasant or unpleasant, content or discontent. Here the observer's estimate is subjective and is not based upon relatively fixed criteria as libido estimation is. While the scale was originally meant to extend from 0 to 10, centering about 5, it is evident that I have used only the interval from 2 to 7. I should welcome an objective and reproducible set of scale criteria.

We note that the improvement in mood in phase A is quicker than the increase in libido. Mood achieves its maximum value, 7, when the libido has reached a scale value of 7. However, although the libido level holds fairly well at 8 during phase B, with no declines below 5, mood nevertheless varies between 4 and 7. In phase C, the libido level still holds fairly consistently to 8, but the mood now hovers between 4 and 5 with a few excursions down to 3 and up to 6. In phase D, mood descends as low as 2 and rises no higher than 5. With repletion, in phase E, mood improves only moderately and ascends no further in phase F.

The relatively quick improvement in mood at the beginning of treatment may be ascribed to the incipient recovery from the depletion state. However, this improvement in the feeling of well-being, of subjective comfort, should not be confused with mania, which is associated with an increase of libido to levels of 9 or 10. Mania is more than simply euphoria, and the term should not be applied to the feeling of relief which accompanies recovery from melancholia. The subsequent deterioration of mood in Phase C is related to the appearance of guilt and anxiety in response to the sexual impulses that are revived. The guilt and anxiety bring about efforts to abandon the object, detach oneself from it via hysterical symptoms. These, in turn, are followed by further guilt, anxiety, and depression.

Feelings and affects are diminished in two situations—in states of depletion, such as appear in phases A and D due to the loss of libido, and in hysteria, which occurs in phase F due to the hysterical defense of detachment. Both depletion and active detachment effect a subjective separation between subject and object which may be regarded as the basis for the blunting of feeling. Like failure of perception, feeling loss is tantamount to the loss of object, and produces anxiety and depression. Note how happily the patient welcomed the return of affective feeling in phase A (sessions 6 and 7). The patient recalls that in her post-partum psychosis the loss of clitoral sensibility which occurred was the most frightening event. We have commented several times on the fact that loss of sensation is interpreted as a castration.

The occurrence of oral symptoms is denoted on the chart by thin bars extending either up or down from an imaginary central line, the position of which is marked on the ordinate by a dot centered between two arrows pointing in opposite directions. A bar extending downward from this line represents a symptom which expresses a directed outward tendency via the mouth, for example, vomiting. A bar extending upward represents a symptomatic expression of an inward-directed tendency, such as craving for food.

We see that initially, in the extreme depletion state, there are intense symptomatic representations of oral ejection, a feature common to states of moderate and severe depletion. With the improvement of libido to position 5, an inward tendency appears. During phase B there is little activity in this sphere. There are alternating inward and outward vectors in phase C, indicating conflict with respect to the object expressed in oral terms. The conflict is forced by the relatively high libido level. In phase D, the continuing conflict seems to resolve in predominantly ejective symptomatology, with a consequent deterioration of mood and decline in libido. This centrifugal tendency includes hysterical defenses both against oral object drives and against introjection. In phase E, there is a decrease in the manifestations of oral conflict, which comes about because the lifting of the melancholia eliminates the inner pain and drives toward the object have not yet developed. As libido climbs to 8 in phase F, the symptomatic indications of oral conflict are resumed. We infer that these oral symptoms follow the vicissitudes of object relations in general. When object striving becomes so intense that it overcomes dynamic defenses, a regression to orality ensues, and the centripetal tendency toward the object is expressed in oral terms. But this oral object pursuit, in turn, encounters resistance and evoke centrifugal oral defenses. These also appear in states of depletion in order to eject the inner source of pain— the virtual introject. Two questions are raised by this material that cannot yet be answered: Which of these oral manifestations represent actual regressions to oral instincts, and which represent merely oral modes of expression of phallic drives? And what determined the oral fixation in this patient?

Inspection of the incidence of anal symptoms—which are represented in the chart immediately above, and in the same code as, the oral symptoms—discloses a lesser use of that channel and a general predominance of centrifugal as opposed to centripetal tendency, that is, of diarrhea as opposed to constipation. We know a number of derivatives of the anality—for instance, the childhood fantasy of having a baby by mother, which is associated in some way with sitting on the toilet, the fantasy of sexual relations with degraded men, and the anal exhibition with mother. During actual depletion, anal ejection (or dejection) is evoked in compliance with the general centrifugal tendency. The anal material, however, has not been worked out nearly so well as the oral material, and promises to play an increasingly important role in patient's future analytic work.

Above the row of bars on the chart denoting anal symptoms is another row in which hysterical symptoms affecting limbs and muscles are denoted. Excursions downward signify a complaint of numbness, anesthesia, or tingling—that is, sensory disturbances; excursions upward signify complaints of tension, tremor, or spasm—that is, motor disturbances. In session 134, we observed an association of limb symptoms with masturbation, menstruation and teichopsia. I commented, too, upon the libidinization of the patient's limbs. On the positive side, this led to a special joy in dancing. On the defensive side, it led to the interference of tremor during dancing, trembling in bed at night, clumsy gait, fears of falling during ice skating, and an anxiety dream in which she awakened with the sensation that "something was touching my leg." The chart discloses that these symptoms were most active during phase F, when there was an intensification of somatic hysterical defenses expressed in part by the wish to be pregnant.

In the next higher row, I have recorded the occurrence of symptoms relating to the head. A thin bar extending upward from the imaginary baseline denotes the occurrence of headache, while a bar extending downward denotes mention of some other sensation affecting the head. Inspection will reveal a general tendency for headaches to occur in association with relatively low libido levels, while the head sensations are generally associated with hysterical defense occurring during periods of high libido. This correlation becomes more impressive in observing the smaller day to day fluctuations of libido during the course of analytic work. I have observed the correlation between headache and depletion and between head sensations and hysterical detachment in a few other patients, and I have mentioned in Chapter II evidence for the hypothesis that some headaches are manifestations of incipient libido loss.

In the row next above, I have recorded instances in which the patient mentioned specifically the occurrence of genital sensations. Pleasant sensations are represented by an upward excursion from the baseline. Unpleasant sensations, or a complaint of numbness, I have represented by a downward excursion. It will be seen that during the period of recovery from melancholia in phase A, there is relatively little interest in genital sensation. In phase B, as the conflict is re-established and sustained by the medication, it results in genital anesthesia. Positive or voluptuous sensations then predominate in phase C as drug support for libido is withdrawn. These positive feelings may be attributed either to a slight decrease in libido due to the withdrawal of medication, or to the disinhibiting effect of continuing analytic work—perhaps both. As libido declines in phase D, so does genital interest, doubtless due to the loss of object-directed instinctual impetus. A return of genital sensation occurs with repletion in phase E, and in phase F the hysterical defense against sexual desire is manifested by a close intermingling of positive and negative sensations.

Occasions of reported sexual intercourse are recorded by short bars of equal height located on the chart immediately above the record of genital sensation. There is a sharp decrease in frequency during periods of slight to moderate libido depletion.

Reports of remarks about conscious sexual desire or aversion are recorded immediately above by upward or downward vectors from the baseline, respectively. This factor correlates fairly well from genital sensation, which is the somatized expression of the same variable. Conscious desire is absent during periods of low libido level. However, as libido returns (phases A and E) there are sudden brief surges of eagerness for sexual pleasure. During periods of high libido level (phases B and C) positive urges predominate, but in F, hysterical defenses cancel them, despite the high libido level.

The double row of bars to the right of the ordinate label "Object Relations" indicate the degree and direction of instinctual object interest as estimated during the analytic session. Object pursuit is signified by an upward deflection from the baseline, and aversion, by a downward deflection. We see that alternating object pursuit and detachment mark the course of recovery from melancholia in phase A. The positive object relation during periods of relatively low object libido is of the clinging type, while the withdrawal from object is essentially passive, that is, it comes about simply as a result of the ego's enervation, which makes it unable to sustain an object relation. During phase B, object orientation is more positive than negative. However, the reactivated conflicts in phase C are responsible for a turning away. As we learn subsequently, the guilt toward mother discourages object relations in phase D. The repletion of the ego with libido in phases E and F makes dynamic defense necessary, so that both positive and negative manifestations of object desire become prominent, replacing the simple disinterest that obtained during the period of depletion in phase D.

We see here illustrated the group of defenses characterized by abandonment of the object, which was discussed in the preceding chapter. The psychic defense may be given realistic expression by an actual physical flight from the object. The child runs away from home, the husband deserts his wife, and so on. This is the basis for the numerous traveling fantasies and dreams that we encounter especially in hysterics, both conversion and anxiety, and in schizophrenics. A second technique of abandoning the object is withdrawal of preconscious cathexis from the image of the object. This method is common to denial, repression, depersonalization, and derealization. A third technique, which may or may not accompany the second, is a draining of the ego's libido supply or, in more limited defensive maneuvers, an attenuation of the libidinal cathectic charge of the specific id impulse in question.

Three other techniques support detachment from the object. One is a withdrawal to secondary narcissism. Here the subject takes himself as his own object, cultivates and loves himself, and attempts to sustain this self-love by commanding the admiration of others. This creates the personality commonly described as "narcissistic." Primary narcissism is somewhat different. Here the subject withdraws interest from the entire world of objects, including himself seen as an object. All libido returns to the ego, which reverts to the archaic mode of function characteristic of its subhuman or infantile state. Primary narcissism may arise not only in the pathologic instances of libido withdrawal we have just listed but also in physiologic states of libido withdrawal, such as sleep or sensory isolation. Regression to pregenital modes of instinctual gratification, regressive coloring of images of the object or of the ego, and regressive representation of Oedipal objects by degraded current surrogates all put a distance between id instinct and conscious derivative. When hysterical withdrawal does not succeed in containing the upward striving impulse, the technique of projection which characterizes anxiety hysteria and phobia may be associated with regression. This is the basis for the occurrence of oral and anal material in this case.

Returning to our clinical material, we encounter two kinds of separation from the object. First, there is the passive kind of separation which follows necessarily from the depletion process. It makes the patient complain of having no feeling, and it influences her to seek hospitalization, since she cannot respond to the demands for affection or, in fact, to the offers of affection. When object libido is great, the object may have to be discarded as a defensive maneuver. There are many different illustrations in the data. At times the patient denies her desire for the object. Phobic avoidance of the dark and of other sexually tempting situations helps to restrain desire for the object. Oral ejective symptoms attempt to discharge accumulated libido and defend against the forbidden object impulse at the same time, for example, nausea, retching, vomiting, choking, jaw and throat spasms. Hysterical anesthesia renders mouth and genitals insensitive to sexual excitation, and cramps and jerks of the limb muscles impair their libidinized activities, such as dancing. The act of mental dissociation is represented by the numerous expressions of loss of reality feeling, depersonalization, amnesia, fears of becoming insane, and of losing identity. Acts of visual exclusion, such as hysterical blindness, teichopsia, blurring of vision, and distortion of percepts, have a similar effect. Among the most important of these techniques of abandonment is the wish to kill the object or the ego. This may be considered to be a device for achieving physical separation from the object. Withdrawal to primary narcissism is the ultimate outcome of the mental detachment mentioned above. It does not occur here in pathological form as it would if the patient had a weaker ego. I imagine that intensification of the same defensive processes to the point of psychosis would end in paranoid schizophrenia. In the case we are considering, the pathologic process merely intensifies and distorts normal regression to primary narcissism, such as occurs before falling asleep. The patient is a compulsive reader. Compulsive reading, and other forms of preoccupation with active diversions, such as vocation or hobbies, or passive diversions, such as entertainment, are often employed as barriers to preclude object relations. Evidently, the modes of separation from the object are no less varied than the modes of instinct gratification.

The next two rows of markings record some of the phobic behavior of the patient. Under the rubric "Road Performance," I have noted some variations in the patient's driving phobia. A bar extending upward from the baseline indicates more active, uninhibited driving than usual, while a bar extending downward indicates the existence of some anxiety about driving. When the patient drove more freely but at the same time became anxious, the bar extends upward and downward from the baseline. In the row next above I have noted references to animal phobia. Inspection of the data discloses no definite correlation between these symptoms and libido level. I surmise that the appearance of phobic symptoms is a complex function of both energetic and dynamic variables. The patient normally drove her car in the immediate neighborhood of her home. She hesitated to use heavily traveled thoroughfares and could not drive on parkways. Driving to my office was an ordeal that she felt she was not capable of until session 159. Her first attempt was an effort to please me. She gave up driving again when increasing guilt toward mother accentuated inhibition in general in phase D, and forced a depletion of the ego. During the repletion process of phase E, libido was not so low as to prevent driving, nor so high as to create anxiety. As libido built up again toward the end of phase E, anxiety increased and driving came to an end. Animal phobias, not a very prominent symptom during this period of analysis, were most common in phase F when narcissistic, hysterical defenses were invoked against the unacceptable impulses. I assume that the animal phobias arose from the outward projection of the conflict.

In general, there are two situations in which phobic avoidance is encountered. First, there is the situation of avoiding objects which arouse anxiety or guilt. In the case of anxiety hysteria, configurations of topography or of object image acquire the power to provoke anxiety or guilt because various aspects of the object and his sexual contact apparatus, or of the subject and his sexual contact apparatus, are projected out onto these otherwise indifferent features of the natural world (Friedman, 1959). Libidinal cathexis had been withdrawn from the original bearers of these images, object and subject, because anxiety and guilt arose in their erotic relations. The withdrawal fails because the instinctual impulse continues to press for gratification. Reprojection then follows. However, this withdrawal and reprojection, in most instances, does not yet interpose sufficient distance between unconscious impulse and conscious or preconscious derivative to satisfy the ego or superego, and the patient must now avoid the substitute just as assiduously as he avoided the original. Because the avoidance prevents even symbolic gratification, projection becomes more and more widespread, and the patient's inhibitions and constraints become correspondingly more diffuse.

Here are two examples. In session 93, the patient tells how frightened she is of cars on the highway. The night before, she had become uncomfortable during intercourse because her husband's body had seemed so big and crushing to her. Then she recalled that her father used to frighten her by threats and that her brother used to beat her. When her father threatened her, he reminded her of a large animal. To the little girl, overcome by her sexual desire for her father, he becomes a threat rather than a source of love. Affectionate or seductive images of him are concealed behind threatening or overwhelming images. These are withdrawn into the patient's ego by identification, and then projected out again, first onto the patient's husband, then upon cars on the highway. It is likely, too, that the animal phobia arises from the same complex. The process by which an indifferent situation which has acquired a libidinal cathexis becomes a source of anxiety when the cathexis becomes too strong is nicely related by the patient in session 130. "I used to enjoy the motion of the subway. I would watch and listen to people. Then I became afraid. One day, on the way to a date, I felt a man was staring at me. I was very nervous and wanted to get off the train." She has never been comfortable on the subway since.

Some situations become the object of phobic avoidance because they threaten to gratify defensive wishes to separate from the forbidden object, and thus evoke separation anxiety. For example, the patient is afraid of losing her memory, her identity, and her way home. So she is afraid to drive too far from her own neighborhood. She is afraid she might take the wrong exit if she drives on the parkway, and so not find her way home. She is afraid that if she drives rapidly down a ramp, her car may "shoot off into space." She is afraid that by driving she might kill either herself or others. I believe that this discussion applies to traveling phobias in general. The need for a traveling companion, a "hand holder," is based upon the wish to overcome the danger of separation by taking the object or a representative along on the trip. In session 210, for example, the fear of driving signified the fear of leaving the analyst and of killing mother. In session 160, the patient drove to my office for the first time in an effort to please me. "On the parkway you can't stop," she said. "I'm afraid I'll have an accident." This statement actually describes her mounting anxiety about this effort to seduce me. But then the hysterical "film blob" with which she sought to detach herself from me changed the driving situation from one of threatening gratification to one of threatening separation, and this in turn became the cause of anxiety. The dangers of traveling and the separation which it inflicts are sources of anxiety. In session 149, the patient discloses that mother is leaving on a trip with brother and his wife. She expresses concern about a proposed trip of her own. "I was afraid of squashing small cars on the highway today." As a child she feared being run over. Mother's departure with brother reminds the patient that, during her childhood, she and mother used to go on automobile trips together. She is angry that mother is leaving with brother now, and these accident fantasies express her resentment for being so dependent upon mother, her wish to kill mother, and the resultant separation anxiety.

In the case of Little Hans (Freud, 1909b), we see both animal and travel phobias. The pathogenesis in the latter instance is particularly clear. The illness starts with an intensification of the child's yearning for mother. This itself soon evokes defensive fantasies and dreams of separation from mother. Thereafter, actual separation from mother becomes an adequate stimulus for anxiety, and a phobic concern about leaving the house follows.

In contrast to conversion hysteria, one occasionally finds in anxiety hysteria a phobic discomfort focused upon the body itself. My patient was troubled by a recurrent sense of body constriction; her tongue was sometimes too large for her mouth, her clothes felt too tight, she experienced constrictive sensations in the chest. It seems as if she projects object and apparatus images upon the wall of her own body as a first step before projecting them upon the circumambient natural world.

Any of the components of the instinctual desire and its opposing defensive impulse may be projected and become a source of anxiety. While topographic and geographic projections usually represent features of the object's body, generally mother's body, animate targets of projection are less specific. This is true, for example, of animal phobias. First, the feared animal may represent the Oedipal object. In session 93, the patient relates that her father used to seem to her like a threatening animal. In session 223 she says that when a small dog came near her, she felt a pain in the vagina. Here the dog represents the phallus, probably, rather than the man himself. Second, the feared animal may represent the patient. In this case, the patient recalls that she used to bite as a child. Third, the feared animal may represent the punitive superego. Nunberg (1961) points out that remorse literally means the biting of the conscience. She remembers that once mother bit her. In session 17 she speaks of being afraid of dogs and of the old woman next door in the hospital. In the same session, she says of the transference, "This love affair is getting to be too much for me." She denies sexual desire for husband and for analyst due to fear of superego punishment.

Finally, the uppermost markings on the chart denote degree of anger or aggressiveness. During phase A, only an overall quantity was noted wherever specific indication appeared during a session. Starting with session 84, following each session I rated, on a 1 to 5 scale, aggressiveness directed inward toward the self and, similarly, aggressiveness directed outward. These values are denoted by dots placed at an appropriate distance from an imaginary baseline, downward and upward, respectively. Suicide fantasies are represented by bars immediately below. No correlations are evident. It should be noted, however, that suicide fantasies occur both during melancholic depletion and during intense dynamic conflict in the presence of a full quota of ego libido.

I have recorded menses by small horizontal lines located between the libido scale below and the mood scale above. This was done to ascertain whether one can relate a cyclic ebb and flow of libido with the menstrual cycle. If such a relation exists, this patient would seem especially likely to show it, because her menstruation has been distressing to her for years and its occurrence regulates her plans and therefore the family's plans for future activities. Inspection of the chart fails to disclose any covariation of libido, mood, or any symptom with menstruation. It may still be that there is a variation which this method is too crude to detect. (During that portion of the analysis which followed the period reported here, some such tendency did appear.)

I should like to draw attention to another element of symptom formation in anxiety hysteria which is not charted, namely, identification with the love object who has been discarded. The patient identifies with her father in several ways. Both have a bad temper, both are too nervous to drive. Both are afraid of choking. She identifies with mother in the following ways. She becomes dizzy and unable to see, as mother used to when she drove. She has nervous bouts of diarrhea, as mother used to. She shares mother's tendency to defend by denial. When the patient was a child, her mother sent her to Christian Science practitioners who taught her that all was "infinite mind and infinite manifestation." Her traveling phobia she shares with sister. To what extent the common genetic background laid the predisposing basis for these identifications cannot be ascertained.

The purpose of presenting this case was to demonstrate the application of the development of libido theory offered in previous chapters. I have tried to show, not only how the estimation of ego libido content helps to follow the vicissitudes of dynamic and symptomatic changes during the course of psychoanalytic treatment, but also how it can be used as a guide to the administration of medication when it is indicated.

CHAPTER VI

Illustrative Case:

Paranoid Schizophrenia

and Paranoia

IF A PSYCHOTIC PATIENT can be spared the experience of hospitalization, remain at work and with his family, and be restored to self-control and reality testing so that he can participate profitably in the psychoanalytic or psychotherapeutic process, then a remarkable advance in the treatment of psychosis will have been achieved. My second case was selected to illustrate the exploitation of psychopharmaceutic agents for just this purpose. In retrospect, and in the light of subsequent experience, conduct of the drug therapy was rather clumsy. It demonstrates one of the commonest pitfalls in pharmacotherapy—overdosage. By the same token, though, the complementary effects of increasing and decreasing ego libido are clearly discernible, as well as the similarity between spontaneous and chemically-induced changes. Finally, this case illustrates the value of the libido scale I have described for monitoring and recording the course of the illness under treatment.

This second report covers a much more protracted period of analysis than the preceding case—exactly three years. Although the number of relevant variables selected for inclusion on the graphic figure (Figure 4) has been reduced to three—medication, libido range, and mood—it was nevertheless necessary to condense in order to present data derived from three years of daily analytic sessions in tractable form. First, I have found it expedient to divide the graph into three chronologic segments, each segment covering one year starting in July and ending in June. Second, I have entered a single notation for each week of treatment instead of attempting to plot daily points. The entry is a vertical line, extending from the lowest to the highest value which the variable achieved during that week. Along the abscissa will be found the date of the Saturday terminating each treatment week, and directly above that is recorded the serial number of the last session of that week. For example, the second treatment week ended on July 20, 1957, and by that date the patient had been seen in thirteen sessions.

To the right of the note Medication which appears along the ordinate, a horizontal line has been drawn parallel to the abscissa. A vertical line extending upward indicates the daily dose of energizing medication consumed by the patient for the corresponding week noted on the abscissa; a vertical line extending downward, the daily dose of tranquilizing medication.

The numbers 0 to 10 listed along the ordinate immediately above the record of medication, constitute the libido scale. I have drawn a thin line parallel to the abscissa, to the right of a point corresponding to 3½, and another at 8½. The lower line indicates the approximate boundary between pathologic depletion and normality, and similarly, the upper line indicates the approximate boundary between pathologic libido plethora and normality. These two lines define a channel which should contain most fluctuations for nonpsychotic patients. The absence of these data for the very beginning of the case is unfortunate and detracts from its value. In October 1958, I found it necessary to take account of frequent discordance of individual libido indicators for this patient by recording two values wherever the data justified them. The higher number usually represents the mode of ego function in its relation to objects, and the lower represents its function with respect to self-observation. Thus, the patient might disclose a delusional projection of affectionate or hostile intent upon the object, and simultaneously articulate a sense of enervation, pessimism, and guilt. This need for dual notation and its interpretation has been discussed in Chapter III and appears in the illustrative case in Chapter V. Downward-directed arrow wings have been attached

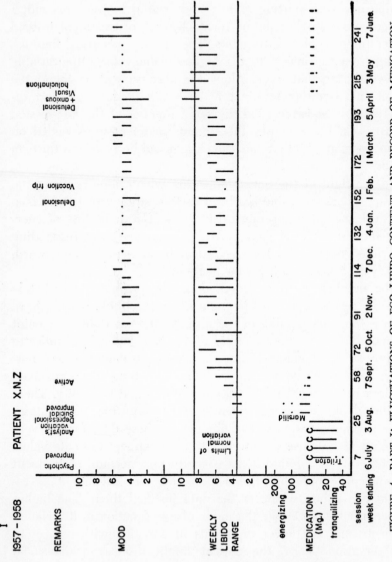

FIGURE 4: PART I: FLUCTUATIONS OF EGO LIBIDO CONTENT AND RECORD OF MEDICATION DURING THE FIRST YEAR OF PSYCHOANALYSIS IN THE CASE OF X. N. Z., A PATIENT WITH PARANOIA AND PARANOID SCHIZOPHRENIA

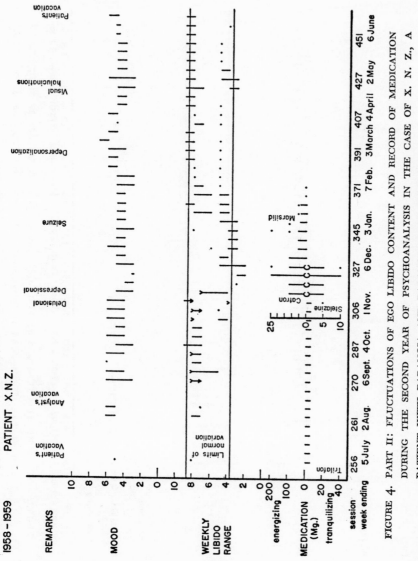

FIGURE 4. PART II: FLUCTUATIONS OF EGO LIBIDO CONTENT AND RECORD OF MEDICATION DURING THE SECOND YEAR OF PSYCHOANALYSIS IN THE CASE OF X. N. Z., A PATIENT WITH PARANOIA AND PARANOID SCHIZOPHRENIA

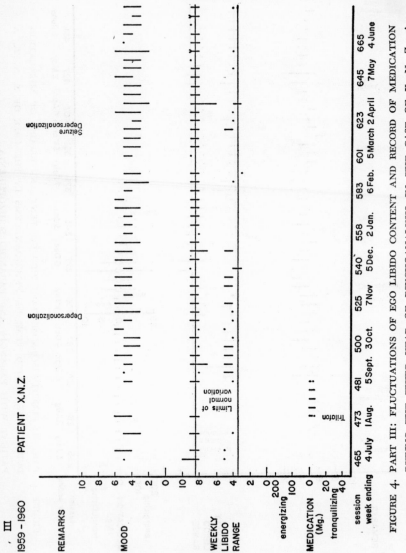

FIGURE 4. PART III: FLUCTUATIONS OF EGO LIBIDO CONTENT AND RECORD OF MEDICATION DURING THE THIRD YEAR OF PSYCHOANALYSIS IN THE CASE OF X. N. Z., A PATIENT WITH PARANOIA AND PARANOID SCHIZOPHRENIA

to the notations whenever a clinging tendency suggested the existence of an opposing tendency of the libido value to fall.

Notations of mood appear immediately above the libido scale. These values represent an attempt to record quantitatively just how good or bad a patient feels during any given session. However, the lack of any definite criteria has made this scale only pseudo-quantitative. The value 5 denotes a neutral feeling, neither good nor bad. Whenever the patient has wept, I have assigned the number 2 to the session. On occasions when the patient's mood has fluctuated appreciably during the session itself, I have designated more than one value.

It will be convenient to present the material in five consecutive phases of illness. Phase A covers the initial illness, the subsequent melancholia, and recovery. It extends from July to October 1957. Phase B, October 1957 to April 1958, is characterized by relative stabilization of libido within the limits of normality. In April 1958, a relapse into schizophrenia occurs. This and the subsequent partial recovery constitute phase C, which extends to September 1958. Phase D is initiated by a second relapse in October 1958, and continues through a period of melancholia and recovery to January 1959. A fairly steady state of controlled paranoia has prevailed from February 1959 through June 1960.

HISTORY

A thirty-seven-year-old married woman, X. N. Z., the mother of three children, was brought to see me on July 7, 1957. For some time she had believed that her husband was having an affair with his secretary. Neither then, nor subsequently, has she ever been able to adduce any cogent evidence to support this accusation, and she has since dismissed the idea. For several days or weeks she had felt that others knew of this affair and were alluding to it in cryptic remarks or gestures. On the day before she consulted me, she decided that she was "confused." She felt that she had retained this insight when she awakened on the morning of the consultation but, "On the way up," she said, "I felt myself slipping." There had been moderate insomnia and anorexia during the preceding three to four weeks. She later told me of feelings of depersonalization and *déjà vu* which had occurred within the same period.

This was the first occurrence of frank psychosis. During her childhood she had occasionally been moody and solitary. At the age of fourteen or fifteen there began a series of episodes of lassitude and tremulousness, each lasting weeks or months. At one point she was put to bed by the family physician for several months for treatment of this condition. The patient has become tremulous at times during periods of depletion in her analysis, and has compared this condition to that which she experienced in adolescence. The patient remembers being unhappy for a period of months during her early twenties. She began to suffer from "migraine" headaches at the age of twenty-six. When these have occurred in analysis, they have usually accompanied an attempt to disengage from reality, and an associated libido depletion. She became pregnant with her first child four years after her marriage and one year after the death of her mother. One day she looked into the mirror and saw her mother's face. Then she "knew" that she was pregnant. Her mother had not conceived until the fourth year of her marriage, and before her death she had predicted that the patient would follow her example. The patient's father died when she was eleven, shortly after she had begun to become affectionate with him.

There was a good deal of mental illness in the family. An uncle had been institutionalized for many years and apparently died in a mental hospital. One sibling of the patient has been hospitalized, presumably with schizophrenia, for twenty years now. Another sibling has had occasional breakdowns, each treated by electric shocks.

Extramarital flirtations began a year or more before the onset of her recent symptoms and she became suspicious of her husband's relations with other women, especially his secretary, at about the same time.

CLINICAL COURSE

Phase A: Initial Illness,
Melancholia, and Recovery

Since the patient was cooperative, her family was in the care of competent help, and her husband was willing to devote himself to looking after her, hospitalization was not necessary. I began treatment with an average of 32 mg. of Trilafon daily. Within two days dystonia set in, and it was necessary to add 4 mg. of Cogentin daily (denoted on the medication line of the chart by the letter C). The patient visited me daily.

On her second visit she volunteered two dreams which she had had during the previous week. "One was a painting of a city that seemed dead—a 'ghost city.' It was painted in black and white and no human or animal figures appeared. All at once the doors of the houses opened and gaily dressed people came out, including my husband and me." This is a typical dream of nascent schizophrenia, a variant of the "end of the world" fantasy. It portrays the defensive wish to detach oneself from the real world, so that the latter seems dead. This invokes a feeling of horrible depression and a wish to revive the dead world by a symbolic rebirth. The dream is essentially one of death and rebirth.

The second dream represented the patient driving very fast in an automobile with her husband. She was afraid of a crash. Suddenly she was resting on a peaceful green meadow. We subsequently learned to recognize these dreams of wild rides as harbingers of psychotic breakdown. They probably represent mounting sexual excitement which the patient can control only by a narcissistic detachment.

The fourth and fifth sessions were unfortunately disturbed by the administration of sedation and Cogentin for the treatment of dystonia, which had suddenly supervened. "My arm and your face are red," she exclaimed on July 11. Such visual illusions and hallucinations have occurred on other occasions when this patient was recovering from psychotic episodes, including one instance (June 22, 1959) when the recovery was quite spontaneous, that is, without pharmaceutic support. Despite the confusion during the first week, the patient became aware of the psychotic nature of her illness, discussed hospitalization, and compared her condition with the other instances of psychosis she had observed in her own family. But alongside the acknowledgment of her illness were the persistent delusionary suspicions and remonstrations against her husband for his neglect of her. On July 12 and 14, there were frank visual hallucinations. She thought she saw her younger brother on the road. (She could not have.) She saw men in black suits following her on the street, and assumed that they were carrying out orders of the parents of her husband's secretary. It is interesting that in the other cases of visual hallucination occurring during recovery from schizophrenia, colors and faces have usually been specified.

Unfortunately, my vacation was scheduled to start on August 2. On July 26, the patient began to talk about separations, and she recalled that after the death of her father she became more affectionate with her mother. On July 27, the first expressions of guilt for neglecting her children began to appear. I did not realize it at the time, but in retrospect it seems to me this guilt marked the onset of depletion. The persistence of delusional ideas with depletion is indicative of a libidinal disequilibrium. This state calls for a reduction in dose of tranquilizing medication. On the following day, "shakiness" and restlessness appeared, that is, akathisia, despite the fact that the patient was taking Cogentin. The patient was quite disturbed to see me leave. Again, in retrospect, I realize that her clinging was exaggerated by the depletion which had already begun.

I saw her for the last time before vacation on Thursday, August 1. She did well on the ensuing weekend, but on Monday she felt "anxious" and called me on the telephone. Misunderstanding the problem, I advised her to step up the medication to 40 mg. per day. On both Tuesday and Wednesday evenings she wired me of increasing distress. I returned to town and saw her on Thursday evening (August 8). She looked depressed. Her face was pale and somewhat bloated. "I have nothing to say to anyone," she said. "I feel I may be a burden to the children. . . . I feel a fog all around me. I haven't spoken to anyone for fear I might say the wrong thing. I've been thinking of my mother recently, humming snatches of her songs." Depletion, at its beginning, induces a regression to an oral relation with mother. "I get these tremors on and off." She compared "these tremors" to those she had experienced during adolescence. Seeing the patient and hearing these new complaints, I realized I was dealing no longer with schizophrenia but with melancholia. I instructed her to discontinue medication at once.

She felt somewhat relieved on the following day, but she complained of lactation, delayed menses, and constipation, common side effects of relatively large doses of tranquilizing medication. She awoke during each of the next few nights agitated and suicidal. On Sunday, August 11, I prescribed Marsilid. By Wednesday, August 14, she was beginning to feel better and her clinging relation to me became stronger. In fact, within a few minutes after she left my office, she returned with her husband because she had become anxious. She embraced him in my presence and said, "Let's stay here." She became more active in the care of the children and in her household duties. Because there were indications of postural hypotension, I cut down the Marsilid from 150 to 50 mg. per day over a period of two days. Friday, August 16, is the first session for which I have recorded a libido value, 3. Over the weekend, the patient became more depressed and on her own initiative increased the dose of Marsilid to 150 mg. She awoke very early Tuesday morning with an acute headache. She called her physician, who gave her Demerol. This failed to relieve her and she called me to come to see her at 7 A.M. She was depressed and agitated and told me she had tried to cut her wrists but had not succeeded. She held my hands. The physician gave her intravenous Seconal and she slept until 4 P.M. She was feeling better when I visited her at that time and held my hands again. The onset of relief occurred much sooner than one would reasonably expect to see the effects of an energizer. The reason was probably that much of the relief came from the cessation of the tranquilizing medication. The sudden relapse on Tuesday was to be attributed, I believe, to the severe, drug-induced headache. This type of physical distress can aggravate a melancholia. On Wednesday she was much better, and she continued to improve thereafter. Headache due to blood pressure volatility is an occasional but very distressing complication of treatment with those psychic energizers that are potent hypotensive agents.

Hitherto, sessions had been conducted vis-à-vis. The patient had remarked about the presence of the couch. On August 22 she asked about it and the next day she volunteered to use it.

As she improved, the patient began to feel energetic. She busied herself less with work at home than with some aspects of her husband's professional activities in which she had always maintained an active interest. He was an unusually successful attorney. Stories about her flirtations during the preceding years occupied much of the session time. It became clear very soon that she envied her husband his success and his popularity. She tried to participate in his activities and to compete with him by testing her ability to interest men. The transference was strong from the first, and was reinforced by the need to cling which was preponderant during the period of depletion. As the latter remitted, the patient tried to convert this anaclitic attachment, the nature of which was revealed in the episode following the session of August 14, into a romantic one. She hoped the relation with me would replace the flirtations which had occupied her so much during the previous year or more.

"I'm more subdued now than before. I haven't been this way in the past eight or nine years," she said on August 25. This remark, based upon primary self-observation, describes the effect of the tranquilizer on the schizophrenic and preschizophrenic personality. She was no longer pathologically depleted, her ego state was that characteristic of a normal libido content. She was already becoming occupied with object pursuit, but remained capable of accurate primary self-observation.

In 1941, she had become disturbed when her brother and a sister became mentally ill at about the same time. Her husband too seemed to her at times like a "day-dreaming, dopey boy." Morbid, autoerotic day-dreaming had been a tendency of hers since advanced latency or puberty. It was the consequence of a seclusive withdrawal associated with ideas of castration inferiority. "Men have their work," she said. "When I'm well, my kids, husband, and home mean the same thing to me." What actually interested her was her husband's work rather than her own. Penis envy became one of the central themes of her analysis.

During the first month of analysis, despite the enervation and fatigue which accompanied her state of depletion, the patient tried to comprehend the course of her illness and to reconstruct the events which constituted the acute psychotic breakdown and led directly into treatment. I have observed this need to fill in memory gaps and to correct misinterpretations in all patients recovering from periods of psychotic or neurotic confusion.

After progressive reduction of dose, Marsilid was discontinued altogether on September 13, at the patient's suggestion. After depletion has been remedied by an energizer, the patient is usually eager to stop taking medication, for it represents a limitation of his self-esteem. In contrast, patients seeking relief by addiction to intoxicants or other symbolic nutriments cannot forgo these substances, for the act of ingestion and the ego intoxication alleviate their pain only temporarily.

As the patient improved, resistance to analysis grew, although she expressed open affection for the analyst. She wanted him to replace the objects of her extramarital flirtations. Meanwhile, the analytic material disclosed, first, a fear of the penis, and second, jealousy of her husband and a wish to participate in his professional activities. She began to dream and talk of the extramarital flirtations and affairs of which she accused him, and it became evident that she was projecting onto him her own homosexual wishes. The complexes which were previously expressed in psychosis began to press upward once more, but reality testing prevailed. The tendency to develop delusions was opposed by my firmness in confronting her with reality. On other occasions enervation occurred spontaneously as if it were a defense. This relinquishment of the psychotic position was accompanied not only by a reduction of libidinal energy but also by a dynamic regression from object relations to secondary narcissism, and from genital to anal sexuality.

It will be noted on the chart that during the week ending October 5, 1957, the libido value climbed to 8. This value was achieved on October 3 when the patient told of having teased her husband about his professional contacts with an attractive woman, and of her own fantasies of a sexual relation between them. Since this is an expression of the fantasy which is the basis of her delusional jealousy, though with intact reality testing, I should probably assign such a session a libido value of 9 at the present time. On the following day, the patient was already somewhat subdued and made an effort to become reconciled with her husband. The libido value for that session was 6. But depletion continued. The following Monday she began: "I've had a gloomy weekend." She told of two dreams. On Saturday morning she dreamed: "I was with my sister G. walking along Fifth Avenue. Suddenly there was all this jewelry on the street. It looked like junk; it was set with stones. We kept picking it up. We were excited about it. G. wanted to go right away to have it valued. She rushed into Tiffany's. There was a man in a small booth. He looked at it. I felt silly about it, about caring what it was worth." On Monday morning she dreamed: "We came back from the country. We'd been away from the house. We came in the back door. My mother, who was later C. [the colored maid] said: 'The door is open. Who could've gone in?' An attractive young Jamaican girl was working there. She'd opened this wicker trunk and all of these bugs and flies were flying about the house. I was protesting bitterly that she'd opened the trunk." As she awakened, she found herself wondering whether the schizophrenic brother was dead or alive. Her association to the dream included a memory of seeing her mother change her younger brother's pants. "He had a load in his pants. I thought the neighbors moved away because of him. Mother had a wicker basket in the cellar. I found a dime bank in it."

Both dreams deal with anal material: the jewelry on the street, the wicker basket in which she had found the coin bank, the back door, the colored women, the little brother with the "load in his pants." In both dreams she is ashamed of the disclosures, of her interest in the cheap, street jewelry in the first dream, and of the bugs and flies in her basket in the second. The man in the booth probably represents the analyst. The thought that the neighbors might have moved away because of her brother's dirtiness expressed her feeling of shame under the analyst's scrutiny. The second dream is a repetition of the classical myth of Pandora's box, which deals with the girl's inability to refrain from masturbation. My patient would often masturbate in adult life, something which she revealed to me later. Masturbation had been associated with overtly homosexual fantasies since the onset of her illness. The dreams express her shame and resistance to analytic examination of her homosexuality, her masturbation, and her anality. The first and third of these became principal, themes of her analysis. The shift from object relation to narcissism, and from genitality to anality, was accompanied by a precipitate decline of libido from 8 on October 3 to 6 on October 4, to 4 on Monday, October 7. The following day the libido value remained at 4. The patient had a dream which again expressed the wish to retard analytic work, to withhold material. "I'm slow at everything. I'm the slowest worker in the state of New York. I dream as I work." When not engaged in the pursuit of erotic object relations, she was prone to retreat to erotic fantasy. Diligent application to solitary work was difficult for her, except for poetry in which she gave expression to her sexual fantasies.

Phase B: Normal Function

Analytic production during this period included frequent ideas and dreams in which mother and sister were disparaged as vulgar, foreign-born, cunning, avaricious, and unscrupulous. These were projections of traits which my patient condemned in herself, mostly anality and greediness.

Let me describe another sequence of mild, spontaneous enervation. On October 15, the patient spoke of a sense of guilt about neglecting her sister. Though a feeling of guilt is often a sign of low libido, the other material of the session indicated a libido value of 7. On October 16 she said, "I feel vague and foggy." Such a remark often discloses a beginning depletion. On both days she recalled the sordidness of her childhood home and family, projecting her own sense of degradation. Actually, she had grown up in a run-down lower middle class neighborhood in Cleveland. The second evening she developed a "migraine" headache. She felt as she had when she was depressed during adolescence. Other people seemed degenerate. She herself wished to be admired.

On the morning of October 17 she had intercourse, but she felt unsatisfied because she had only a vaginal orgasm and not a clitoral orgasm; she usually achieved both. That afternoon she indulged in fantasies of being with me "because I was depressed." Libido values on October 16 and 17 were 6 and 5, respectively. She awoke on October 18 from a dream of caressing vigorously and angrily a young woman who was not responding to her affectionately, and with whom she shared a male lover. She came in for her session at noon saying, "I feel lousy." It was then that she told me of her adolescent masturbation accompanied by fantasies of making love to other young women. The dream was a masturbation equivalent. The triangular love relation which appeared in the dream, and hence the meaning of the transference, was not elucidated by the material. The session rated a libido value of 3 which accounts for the lower extreme of the range recorded on the chart for October 19. This complex of data, of course, led into analytic discussion of her homosexual tendencies and of childhood homosexual experiences. She brought a drawing she had done in adolescence of a young girl, obviously herself, seated at a vanity table and looking sadly out the window. Again she complained about the sordidness of her childhood home. It seemed that her current depressions were repetitions of periods of self-criticism and depression which occurred in puberty and adolescence. In these states she would attempt to find some pleasure in masturbation to the accompaniment of homosexual fantasies. She probably tried then, as now, to project her sense of depravity onto her mother, sisters, and home, so that she ultimately abandoned them in an attempt to save herself.

At this point, late October, another related theme appeared in the analysis. She dreamed of watching a church school party, standing on the sidelines and feeling unwelcome. She recalled that at the age of six she had walked into a church school and attended for a whole summer. She was Jewish but felt that Christians were finer, cleaner people, a distinction which she continued to make as an adult, although ambivalently. Even before the age of six she would wander away from her home to the homes of relatives or neighbors. A favorite place was a house occupied by an elderly, childless Christian couple. The woman would give her good things to eat and allow the child to help her clean. The man fondled her genitals. This dwelling, she recalled, seemed so much cleaner than hers. The tendency to wander from the parental home, in which there was so much Oedipal temptation and projected sordidness, to strangers in the pursuit of exogamy has continued from the fourth or fifth year of life to the present. It was the factor which led her to extramarital flirtations and doubtless contributed much to the transference. Her possessive desire for the husbands of other women appeared in projection as accusations against other women for conspiring to seduce her husband away from her.

The patient's father died when she was eleven. On December 9, she told me that shortly after her father's death she would be gripped by hypnagogic sensations of being lifted by a pair of enormous arms and rocked. These sensations precluded sleep. Clearly, the loss of her father resulted in identification with him and an intensification of narcissism. She would pray that God should be kind to the surviving family, in the absence of father. She always had more love and less awe for God than others did, she said. A poem written at that time speaks of father as living in heaven. A very early narcissistic fantasy, probably infantile, was the image of herself resting on an enormous white surface like a sofa, very safe because the sides were too distant for anyone to approach. She associates this image to God. "No troubles could reach me, and there was plenty of room to explore." This early fantasy expresses, I believe, a narcissistic identification with mother, and the later hypnagogic fantasy expresses identification with the lost father. In both instances, the incorporated object is reprojected as God. There was another childhood fantasy to the effect that she could romantically melt the resistance of a stern, older man. Her tendency to use exhibition as a seductive technique was betrayed in her inability to let herself be seen nude by anyone before her marriage. Her defense against exhibition then took the form of modesty and restraint in dress and manner which have lent her a certain quiet charm.

The latter contrasted with, and often surpassed, the more flamboyant displays of an older sister.

On December 13, the patient presented a dream which expressed her fascination with the penis and, at the same time, her fear of castration by it. This complex had been hinted briefly earlier in the analysis (in September) just before the homosexual material became prominent. On the night of December 12, the patient dreamed: "I was sitting with you on the sun porch and your two little girls were playing there. You and I held hands sweetly. They played with scissors and knives. I said, 'You mustn't.' 'Oh no,' they said, 'we know how.' Then one of them put the scissors in her mouth. I said, 'This is enough.' You said, 'See how harmless this is.' I patted your face but couldn't see it."

The dream is based upon a joke about a young man who became the baby sitter for some small girls. When the parents return they find that the children are playing with his penis. To their remonstrations, he replies, "What do you want them to play with, scissors?" The dream also repeats certain elements of the episode of Tuesday, August 20, when she had tried to cut her wrists with a kitchen knife. I had visited with her on the sun porch which appears in the dream and she had held my hands. There were occasions during her dating periods when she would fear that her escort was becoming too excited. She would put her hand over his penis "to restrain him." In early childhood she saw the erect penis of her insane uncle, who at one point lived in her family's house.

The complex which appears in transference and dream therefore includes the following elements: sexual attraction to the erect penis; the wish to take it in the hand; the fear of being injured, cut, penetrated by it; punishment for the wish by degradation and insanity. The anxiety and guilt pertaining to this Oedipal wish led to her disaffection from her husband and to the reinforcement of homosexual impulses. From this complex, too, issued her frequent efforts to arouse men sexually and then to try to subdue their excitement. By employing seductive techniques, she aimed to gain control over the penis rather than to be controlled—that is, either stimulated or frightened—by it. She never gave up her efforts to excite me, and my resistance to her charms was doubtless responsible in some measure for the firmness of her attachment to me. It will be observed from the chart that the libido level at the time of this dream is well within normal limits.

Thereafter, sexual desire, fantasies, and activity increased. There followed a period in which these were associated with increased concern and guilt toward her husband. A dream expressed the fear that a man might be hurt by black snakes in a tank of water into which he was plunging, that is, a wish to castrate her husband. Childhood memories again dealt with awareness of her brother's erections and their relation to disease and to masturbation. She began to lose sexual interest in her husband, and simultaneously began to think of her old suspicions of infidelity on his part. At the same time, her own extramarital interests increased. She talked about her masturbation. She recalled fondling her own breasts with great joy when her mother stopped sharing a bed with her. During adolescence she had had the impression that her clitoris was too large. Subsequent material continued to deal with the need to separate from her husband. This proposed separation was seen as a repetition of her father's death. It became evident that after the Oedipal disengagement, the father was replaced by her brothers as objects of heterosexual love. These too had to be given up. And now, out of guilt, the husband also had to be surrendered. She disclosed that during her psychosis her husband began to resemble the brother who had become insane, and she feared that her husband might become psychotic too. Although her brother had not become psychotic until she was twenty-two, he had been odd and seclusive for several years previously. She attributed both his illness and her own to the incestuous exhibition that took place between them, and to the masturbation that was excited by and replaced it.

At this point in the analysis (January 1958), the patient developed a vaginal discharge, which recurred repeatedly thereafter. In a dream she related the moisture to sexual excitement that had actually been stimulated by social contact with an adolescent boy on the preceding day. The same dream disclosed competitiveness with an older sister. Thus, to the Oedipal defenses, regression to anality (i.e., the vaginal discharge) must now be added. The competition with her sister for the love of a younger brother repeats competition with mother for father's love. She would often accuse this same sister of attempting to seduce her husband. Sexual intercourse with her husband on the night after her social contact with the boy was unsatisfactory and was followed by the dream. Conscious fantasies of narcissistic withdrawal into indolence and avoidance of sexuality appeared early in adolescence. This clearly arose from a sexual impasse, and foreshadowed her later catastrophic, psychotic break.

When these various defenses against her Oedipal relation with her husband had been run through in analysis—namely, the evocation of anxiety, the desire to abandon her husband, regression to anality, substituting another man, retreat to narcissism and auto-erotism—the patient began to turn more and more to homosexuality. She spoke of herself as having a boyish manner. She recalled living with her sister and dreamed that the two of them ran a house of prostitution. There were dreams in which the homosexual act was manifest although the specific object was concealed. In our discussions of this homosexual material, the patient disclosed that during the period of paranoia preceding her acute schizophrenic break, she had entertained conscious fantasies of homosexual pleasure with one of the young women she believed was her husband's lover. There had been a conscious childhood fantasy of exchanging some kind of physical affection with an old, wrinkled woman. "If I were a man," she used to think, "I'd know how to make love to a woman."

On January 21, there was a dream which introduced what subsequently proved to be a serious complex, hypochondria. "There was a tree like the one in our back yard. It had developed a disease like a fungus. There were nests of insects with cocoons all over it. A doctor was in trouble because he had done the wrong thing. He'd wrapped cellophane about the insect nests to keep them from spreading, but they had already." Menses had begun the previous day, starting with an unusual brownish discharge. The cellophane reminded her of a condom, which was the contraceptive device her husband customarily employed. The dream deals with physical deterioration. The brownish discharge and the reference to the back yard allude to the previously mentioned anal references. The insects and cocoons are standard symbols for unborn children and in this case represent a pathologic form of rebirth.

The cellophane wrapping and its associative referent are derivatives of an isolation complex which appeared on many occasions during the analysis. In anal situations, it is a means of avoiding fecal contamination. It may be employed to protect others, such as her children, against herself whom she sees as soiling; or alternatively to defend herself against others onto whom she projects her own disease. At the genital level, it refers to a detachment from the object or a reduction in the intensity of the object relation. Its infantile predecessor was a fantasy of inserting herself into a suit of metallic armor which she compared to a sardine can. An added masochistic castration element appearing in this early image was the idea that any protuberance of her body which would interfere with a close fitting of the armor would be cut off. Of course, the hypochondria is basically an aspect of the castration complex. At this point, for example, it appeared in response to a sign of genital disease. Note that the hypochondria appears at a time when the patient has withdrawn from direct heterosexual gratification and is about to turn to homosexuality. The shift is not made directly, but via a temporary detour into narcissism.

The hypochondria represents a narcissistic cathexis of the body. The primary focus of this hypercathexis of the body is the genital. Subsequently, other parts of the body come to assume a similar meaning. When the cathexis exceeds a given strength, it causes psychic pain. Thus, the organ which is the object of the cathexis seems to be a source of pain, and when viewed by the conscious ego, it appears to be diseased. The increasing cathexis tends to irradiate beyond the specific organ to other portions of the body, and so the apparently diseased organ seems to threaten the integrity of the entire body. Schizophrenic self-mutilation is a frequent result. The dream of the diseased tree portrays an attempt to contain the disease by setting up insulating walls. The rebirth element signifies that the narcissistic cathecting of individual organs of the body is intended as a method for restoring an object relation which has been relinquished. When the schizophrenic or hysterical woman becomes pregnant, she readily exploits the normal somatic narcissism of pregnancy as the prototype for a pathologic narcissism. When this is a satisfying solution, the pregnancy is enjoyable, and its termination by delivery may be the occasion for depression. When the cathexis of the image of the pregnant abdomen becomes excessive, whether by reason of physical discomfort, distortion of appearance, or because the libido is generated too rapidly to be dissipated, the pregnancy becomes distressing and the woman becomes impatient to be rid of the foetus. Young children represent for the mother a double threat. They evoke both object libido and narcissistic libido at the same time. For the mother who must master a plethora of libido, confrontation with her infant is especially difficult. This was the problem of our patient. She tended to transfer her hypochondriacal sense of decay onto the images of her children, and in subsequent material we shall see that she finds it necessary to isolate and protect them against herself. She dates the onset of her paranoia to the period immediately following the birth of her youngest child. It is not clear just what it is that the dream says I—the doctor—have done wrong. Perhaps it is that I permitted the attachment to me to develop, or, more likely, that by refusing to gratify her desire, I had allowed the libido to become excessive.

The material of the following day demonstrated the reciprocal relation between object love and narcissistic hypochondria, as well as the continuing anal focus and the use of physical isolation as a defense against being soiled. The patient opened the session by saying that she had been "lonely" for me since the beginning of the previous weekend. The term "lonely" betrayed a depressive mood. She then recited the following dream. "I was with mother at our home—outdoors—in the evening. Suddenly the Northern Lights were in the sky, soft and lovely. I said, 'How lovely!' They got more and more colorful and violent. They colored the whole sky. Suddenly it was a great bomb attack with missiles. The sky was flooded with falling objects. I hurried her indoors. We were covered with ash, and incurably contaminated by it. It was radioactive fallout. We got into the house. I tried to wash myself off."

The patient's first association was that the luminous display in the dream reminded her of the formless visual hallucinations which ushered in her headaches. She did have a headache on the morning following the dream, and it lasted for two days. To the skin contamination, she associated the memory that yesterday she had given herself a facial massage since she thought her pores were too coarse. The dream clearly deals with a wish to return to mother. The soft and lovely quality of the Northern Lights characterized her feeling of love for her mother. On the day following the presentation of the dream, she told me that she was always fascinated by the shimmering, luminous quality of human skin. "It must be the way a baby sees its mother," she said. The growing intensification of the visual stimulation represented the increase in libido which was pervading the ego nucleus during the dream. This acceleration of libido flow was threatening, and the anxiety was attributed to the visual representation of the erotic display. The destructive attack in the dream signified the violent instinctual consummation, whose very intensity was itself frightening. What was the nature of the act that was here represented? Color in a dream generally indicated feces. So does bombing. Being covered with ash indicates fecal soiling. The radioactivity and contaminating property of the ash are consistent with this interpretation, and reveal that the shame and guilt and pathologic intensification of body cathexis create the impression of physical decay. To the ash, the patient associated a baby's being powdered by its mother.

The final element of the dream, the washing, resembles the ultimate act of undoing which is common in the dreams and behavior of compulsive neurotics. Obviously it can only be soiling that washing undoes. The dream must be understood, then, to mean that the patient would like to regress to obtain autoerotic pleasure from soiling herself as she had done in infancy. The pleasurable tactile, visual, and olfactory sensations, though self-induced, were attributed to mother by projection. It seemed as though she wished to be defecated upon by mother. This is the violent bombing attack. But in the dream it was she who protected mother, and she who washed herself. Hence the desired object relation is defensively cancelled—the projection is withdrawn and the infant identifies herself with mother. The skin covering which was represented now as radioactive ash and crawling insects, now as protective baby powder and cellophane bandage, sometimes as a mask for erotically-stimulating skin luminescence, sometimes as a metallic armor for her too-delicate skin, was essentially then a *Reizschutz*, a protective barrier. As narcissistic individuals under high libidinal pressure are prone to do, she projected the perceptive surface of her ego onto the surface of her body, and hoped that by controlling the sensitivity of the latter she could protect the former.

The representation of intensity of libidinal pressure by intensity of perceptual brilliance is a characteristic of primary process. We shall discuss in the next chapter the problem of control of perceptual intensity, and the use made by the ego of this control mechanism to defend against prohibited or unsuitable objects of instinctual desire. In this dream, we see how an archaic, libidinal wish that threatens to become excessively strong is blocked by abandonment of the object accompanied by narcissistic identification and the establishment of insulating barriers. The ensuing headache signals the libido depletion that follows from the object loss.

We should not forget that this complex was triggered by menstruation, which implies soiling and which, in many women, creates the temptation and therefore the danger of regression to anal modes of gratification.

During this phase of energetic normality, homosexual material became more plentiful. The patient told of childhood homosexual experiences, of adolescent approaches by homosexual women, and of having shared a bed with an older sister from age eight to age eighteen. Delusional ideas began to make tentative appearances, but the patient recognized these for what they were, and responded with self-criticism, a feeling of needing the analyst (over a weekend), and some depression. As indicated in the chart, ego libido rose to 8 during the last week of January 1958. (By more recent criteria, this material would have warranted a rating of 9.)

Related and confirmatory material appeared in subsequent sessions. There was a desire to expose her breasts to other women and to be fed at their breasts. A dream spoke of powdering naked children to protect them. One of the patient's sisters had a strawberry mark on her face and used a masking paste to conceal it. The patient herself had some adolescent acne and recalls that her sister had a salve made up to treat it. "Mother's skin," she said, "was delicious to touch, creamy and soft." Note how she mixes oral metaphors with words actually appropriate to tactile sensation. What she is describing is probably best called a synesthetic experience. The anal theme was continued with a sudden, brief, unexplained rectal pain followed by an ache. She had had such attacks recurrently over several years dating back to a rectovaginal fistula which had followed her first delivery.

This evolutionary sequence in the analysis was interrupted by a one-week trip to Europe and by the anticipatory apprehension about separation from the analyst. On the night before her departure, she dreamed, "My husband and I were in the back seat of a car. A young couple was driving us at high speed. They were wild kids, perhaps my brother and his wife. The young woman was sullen and depressed and clung to her companion. She wanted to know where they were going, but got no answer. Suddenly she had no clothes on. She hung onto the right-hand door. My husband and I were the older generation. The car was going at a fast clip. We watched and wagged our heads." My patient did not offer sufficient associations for a plausible interpretation of this dream. I give it here because its manifest content, being frightened by an excessively fast ride, appeared on several subsequent occasions at times when the patient was struggling to control rapidly intensifying libidinal impulses. On occasion, this kind of dream preceded a psychotic break. Apparently the idea that things are going too fast, like the idea that stimuli are too intense, indicates excessive libido intensity. Hypomanic patients commonly describe the sensation that their thoughts are going too quickly. Clinging is mentioned twice in the dream. Exhibition is used as a seductive method of clinging. The threat is separation from the object due to excessive libidinal drive. The response is clinging. But to whom? Since she was with her husband, it was not he whom she was afraid of losing. As she left the session that day for this one-week vacation, she shook hands with me and moved towards me as if she wished to kiss me. But whom did I represent?

Upon her return (February 12), the patient recited some traveling fantasies from adolescence. One was the image of herself flying like an angel over the city at night. This obviously is derived from the same instinctual complex that gave rise to the dream of a bombing attack, and confirms our impression that it was she who was doing the dejective soiling. The desire for erectile potency is also implied and relates to her fascination with the erect penis. The second fantasy is the impression of herself riding on an unending trolley trip, watching the scenery along the way. Here the erotic activities of riding and looking are continued as they were in the separation dream, and the sensual pleasure does not stop. Note that these are narcissistic fantasies, and therefore probably accompanied masturbation. While on her trip, she had disturbing dreams about her children, as well as dreams that she was reunited with her entire family. We may guess that the separation which she fears is a narcissistic withdrawal from love objects into autoerotism. Why should such a commonplace event be so threatening to this patient? Probably because in her case the withdrawal tends to pass easily over into psychotic primary narcissism. The narcissism leads not only to psychotic withdrawal and to autoerotism but also to hypercathexis —that is, excessive libidinal investment of the body image. During the last two months of each of her three pregnancies, the patient experienced depersonalization, a rejection of the distorted body image. On the same day that she told me this (February 27), she also told me, "I don't want to believe I was so sick." In other words, her psychotic illness created the same disappointment in herself that the physical changes of pregnancy had.

During the following month, three themes continued to develop. The first was the theme of homosexuality; the love for the other woman was often projected onto her husband. Up to this point, the projections took the form of ideas and fantasies rather than suspicions or beliefs. The second was the tendency toward autoerotic withdrawal. This was often represented as crossing a bridge. Hence it was considered a momentous, hazardous, and possibly irreversible transition. The third was a hypochondriacal concern with physical and mental health. There were dreams that diseased tissues were being cut out and the doctor was at fault, as he had been in the case of the diseased tree. It seemed to me that although she regarded her genital as diseased, she was still afraid of analytic surgery. She continued to desire an erotic relation to me but resisted the analysis.

Phase C: Relapse and Partial Recovery

At the beginning of April, a new complex appeared: concern with her husband's mental health. She complained that his work and associates were putting such pressure upon him that he required analysis. This was clearly a projection outward of her own mental illness. The need to project it away grew out of the hypochondria. This projected hypochondria appeared on the day following an incident in which she began to masturbate while dreaming of being manipulated, and then completed the masturbation upon awakening. At the same time, the ideas of her husband's infidelity —that is, her own projected homosexuality—began to achieve delusional quality. She started to withdraw more and more. On Wednesday, April 9, when her husband began to make love to her, she thought, "I can't let a sick man make love to me." During her session that day, she told me she was so upset that she had thought of calling ahead of time to ask me to set aside two hours for her. Nevertheless, her sessions on that and on the next day were filled with prolix accounts of conversations which were supposed to demonstrate her husband's mental illness. Friday, Saturday, and Sunday were spent visiting a woman acquaintance.

The patient opened her session on Monday with the remark, "I would have broken down this weekend if I weren't in analysis. It was a horrible weekend." She was convinced that there had been a flirtation between her husband and her hostess, and she felt that the hostess reminded her of her sister. The libido rating for that session was 9, although by more recent criteria I think 10 would have been more appropriate, since she was frankly psychotic. She was certain that her husband required treatment, although she retained enough insight to acknowledge that she was in a disturbed state. She confided that her husband hoped it was she who was sick rather than he.

But the projection failed, for the schizophrenic hypochondria continued to agitate and frighten her. The emphasis shifted from concern about mental illness to concern about castration. "I remember that when I was six or seven my mother screamed at my brother when he hurt his nose. I thought she never liked him. She said of me when I was small that my nose was too big, but then I grew up to fit it." Then the emphasis shifted to anality. On the morning of April 18 she awoke terrified after the following dream: "I was at home. C. [her Negro maid] said, 'The water is running out of the bathroom. I can't stop it.' I went in. Dirty water and filth were coming out of the walls and taps. It was disgusting. There was congealed vaginal jelly. I got hysterical and shouted, 'No, No, Stop!'" She was uncomfortable with her husband, frightened in his presence and relieved when he left the house in the morning. Her immediate association to the dream was the fact that following her first delivery she had an rectovaginal fistula and was disgusted by the uncontrolled leakage of fecal material into and out of the vagina. She had told me in a previous session of having seen her mother administer an enema to her brother, the one who subsequently became psychotic.

Further exploration of this subject disclosed a presumably delusional belief that her husband insisted upon using a condom for contraception because he considered her too filthy and refused to come into direct contact with her genitals. This, of course, is an extension of the protective barrier notion whereby she attempted to sequester diseased tissues and prevent them from contaminating other portions of the body. I am reminded here of a practice adopted by some Chassidic Jews, namely, tying a string or cloth belt around the waist in order to separate the clean, upper half of the body from the dirty, lower half. Her delusional conviction of the reality of anal degradation and disease, even though it includes the memory of an actual illness from the past, is a form of, or at least equivalent to, schizophrenic hypochondria. It is the consequence of intense narcissistic cathexis of her own body in which sexual interest has regressed from the genital to the phallic, and finally to the anal, apparatus. This regression is illustrated in an earlier dream of that same night in which she saw a pregnant young woman suddenly appear ill, lose the distended appearance of pregnancy, collapse, and fall into the snow. The patient sees her illness as a loss of phallic erectness and a reversion to anality, since snow often represents feces. This interpretation was confirmed by the dreams of the following night, in one of which she covered her children with transparent cellophane to protect them against the rain, and in another of which her face was covered with a white mud.

Meanwhile, the patient was excited, frightened, and at times depressed. She was excited by her growing libidinal drive. She was frightened by its growing intensity, by the fantasies it evoked, and by the tendency to act them out. She was depressed by the recognition of regressive degradation and by the occasional insight into the damage she was likely to cause if she failed to resist her impulses. She was especially concerned about those fantasies in which she became sexually involved with her children. She began to feel "shaky" and compared this shaky feeling of her sensations during the period of depression in adolescence. Finally, she herself began to talk about tranquilizing drugs. On April 22, I prescribed Trilafon, 4 mg. daily, and on April 25 I increased the dose to 8 mg. On Monday morning, April 28, she felt "infinitely better." I had offered to see her on Sunday if she were disturbed. "I didn't come yesterday," she said, "because I was afraid of what I'd have to tell you—that I've been having hallucinations." She thought she saw men in checkered shirts at various spots in her neighborhood. At the same time, she volunteered that she was apprehensive lest she meet her older, now psychotic, brother someplace near her home.

It will be recalled that she had similar visual hallucinations after receiving tranquilizing medication when I first saw her. The issue was somewhat clouded by the fact that she was then receiving

Cogentin too. However, she took none of the latter drug on this occasion.[1] Her associations indicated that it is her brothers for whom she longs in her psychotic excitement. Her narcissism and autoerotism seem, then, to result from identification with the lost brothers and from repetition of what may well have been incestuous sex play. When a tranquilizer is given, the function of the ego supplement is impaired before the ego nucleus is relieved of its libido plethora, and partial, hallucinatory wish fulfillment becomes possible. Here, apparently, the ego nucleus had already begun to lose some of its charge, for delusional ideas seemed to have lost some of their force, and the libido value did not rise above 9 that week.

On April 28 and 29, the patient took only 4 mg. of Trilafon because she seemed improved. Narcissistic and autoerotic trends continued. Ideas of reference seemed more distinct on April 30 and the dose was raised again to 8 mg. It is interesting to note that as the libido was reduced, the instinctual regression was reversed, and anal fantasies gave way to phallic and genital material. Dreams and fantasies dealt with genital masturbation and genital castration. By the end of that week the patient had regained full insight. With the decline in libido, the possibility of object relations revived and she said she felt more "sexy," although she continued averse to her husband and erotically inclined toward me. There was a fairly typical rebirth dream on May 2: "I was in a room recuperating from measles, in mother's bed. I was better because the shades had been lifted at last. There was a little night table with medicines. There was a feeling of great ease due to the recuperation. I was waiting for my little brother to come in."

Note that the illness chosen to represent the mental disorder was one which affected the skin and the eyes. The skin disorder was an allusion to the anal, soiling fantasies of the psychotic period, and the visual disturbance related to the difficulty in comprehension and to the visual hallucinations. Mother's bed, aside from representing mother, may represent also the analytic couch. Even in recovery she identifies with mother. I am not sure I know the meaning of the awaited arrival of her little brother. It could refer

---

[1] I have discussed the occurrence of visual hallucinations during recovery from schizophrenia in Chapter III, and I have given several case reports in a recent paper (Ostow, 1960e). This patient is included in the latter series, where she is identified as Case A.

to the delivery of her children, since the dream occurred on the morning after the birthday of her youngest son. It could signify that object love evolves from narcissism by a psychic process modeled after a fantasy of rebirth. It could refer to the expectation of growing a penis. That the brother also represented the analyst was clearly indicated by transference associations. One may note parenthetically that the patient suffered slight headache, which has often accompanied her experiences of spontaneous or induced enervation.

From the point of view of psychiatric diagnosis, the reader may be interested in the patient's report of May 7. "Everything seems to be working faster. I feel better. I can do things faster. I've been very productive in my writing." We generally consider this kind of statement characteristic of hypomanic overactivity. In this case, it was the consequence of the relaxation of schizophrenic inhibition and was brought about by a tranquilizer rather than an energizer. She seemed sufficiently improved to permit a decrease back to 4 mg. of Trilafon. The libido value had gradually decreased to 5.

The ensuing weeks were taken up with erotic fantasies about the analyst and impatience with my refusal to comply with her desires. There were dreams about exhibition and concealment and, accordingly, the sessions were analytically rather sterile. Despite the small continuing dose of tranquilizing medication, delusional jealousy gradually began to reappear. The patient was planning to spend the month of July away from the city, and as her departure drew closer, she began to express anxiety about the separation. In view of both of these developments, the dose of Trilafon was increased to 6 mg.

The vacation month of July 1958 passed uneventfully, the patient continuing to take 6 mg. of Trilafon daily. Her suspicions that her husband was unfaithful remained, although without delusional certainty. Upon her return, she expressed concern about being deserted. She told me that as a child she had been afraid that "no one would know who I was. I had it put down on paper. I felt flattered when my father once played ball with me on the beach when I was six." Her dreams contained situations of being deserted and excluded. Then in the second week of August, they shifted to portrayals of competition with her older sister for dates and for father's love. Both of these concerns anticipated my vacation during the latter half of August. The dose of 6 mg. of Trilafon daily was maintained during my absence.

She did well, even though her husband was away on a business trip during the last week of August, but she seemed to be a trifle depressed when I returned. The libido ratings were 7 and 8, but there were indications of a downward tendency, recorded on the chart by arrow wings. This downward tendency, however, only opposed but did not cancel a simultaneous upward thrust. It was not long before the patient disclosed a tendency toward withdrawal from home and family to autoerotic fantasies with occasional masturbation. These fantasies dealt with sexual touching of women. Homosexual desires appeared in dreams, and once more anality began to play a prominent role. It is important to note that whereas I now assign a libido rating of 9 to every session in which delusional projections appear, even when these are not accompanied by full conviction, at that time I often assigned a less extreme value.

Phase D: Relapse into Schizophrenia, Melancholia, and Recovery

The patient continued in much the same way, on the brink of psychosis, during September and October. The attempts to escape from the lonesome autoerotism which threatened to engulf her included erotic yearnings for me, the precise meaning of which was not evident, homosexual desires, and then hypochondriacal fantasies. The latter were associated with an identification with mother. She confided to me (October 6) her belief that "the germs of cancer of the liver" which had killed her mother "are present in me also. I'll probably die of it." Again, the origin of the identification, its purpose, and its significance, except for its lethal implications, were not evident. It will be recalled that in pregnancy, too, she identified with mother. She was four years old when her younger brother was born, and the pregnancy identification may date back to that time. Sexual intercourse was unsatisfying and orgasm impossible, except in response to homosexual fantasies.

On October 14 she said, "I had a feeling of relief when I heard a physicist's opinion that the world will be destroyed." Here we have a foreshadowing of world destruction fantasies, traces of which were evident at the beginning of treatment; in the absence of any other solution, these were slowly developing again. She began to express concern about how well she was attending to the needs of her children. Apparently she found it difficult to spend time with them. She deplored the crowding of her childhood home. On October 17 she actually forgot to call for her daughter at school.

Some allusions to father hinted at the concealed Oedipal relation. There was a memory dating back to age five or six, of defying father and giggling until he begame indignant. "He shook his fist at me. I hid in a corner of my room and covered my mouth." Early one morning, the patient visually imagined father's razor strop. "He used to threaten to use it on my brother." There were fantasies and dreams of stealing money. "The policeman turned out to be the criminal." This related to some vague talk the patient remembered from childhood, from which it appeared that her father had been accused of dishonest dealings. However, the narcissistic retreat from the Oedipus complex and its regressive consequences were too clamorous to permit serious pursuit of the Oedipal material.

Something of the dynamics is revealed by two childhood fantasies. The first was that she lived alone in a very elegant house where she could sit and read at leisure. This was an autoerotic attempt to withdraw from father and her brothers. The second fantasy was derived from the first. The home now became a salon to which "the best brains" were attracted. Here is the return of the repressed. She cannot tolerate the isolation and reaches out to strangers who represent her father.

Toward the end of October, the material disclosed fantasies of parthogenetic pregnancy and rebirth, a hint of narcissistic regression of psychotic proportions. On November 3, I increased the dose of Trilafon from 6 to 8 mg. per day. Nonetheless, she began to quarrel with her husband about his imagined infidelity. This material required a libido rating of 9 (although currently I should probably evaluate it as 10). On November 6 I substituted 5 mg. of Stelazine for the Trilafon. I had to be away from my office for three days until November 10. "I've lost a few pounds rapidly in the past week," she observed. "I woke up at 2:30 in the morning and lay in bed thinking. What would I do with the children in case of a serious atom bomb attack? How could I kill the children so that they wouldn't die a lingering radiation death?" In dreams she saw herself as a little baby, she let her baby roll out of her car, and she fed her husband a food that looked like babies' penises.

Evidently a state of melancholic depletion had set in, caused by an excessive amount of tranquilizer which had probably exaggerated a spontaneous, reparative depletion. Here is the typical early morning awakening, the weight loss, and the orality. She felt that she could not care for her children and wished to protect her narcissism by destroying them. She thought of poisoning them and consuming them. The "babies' penises" which she fed her husband indicated that she felt the state of depletion to be equivalent to a state of castration, which could be repaired by ingesting a penis. There is more than a hint here that she blames her state upon the pills she was getting from me ("the little penises were like almonds"), and correctly so. This state of aggressive orality and destructiveness characterizes incipient depletion, and represents a desperate effort to undo it. The rejection of the children in the state of plethora was the result of a retreat from the world of reality into narcissism. When libido is withdrawn from the ego, the dynamic retreat is reinforced. There is insufficient libido to cathect objects, and what libido remains is attached solely to the ego. It is as though the absolute narcissistic state could not be sustained in the presence of a plethora of libido, and it becomes fixed by the depletion.

The representation of several aspects of the image of herself by the images of her young children is not fortuitous. First, it follows from her fantasies of parthogenetic rebirth. She attempts to escape from narcissism by projecting the admired features of herself onto her children. It will be recalled that she became consciously aware of identification with mother when she became pregnant. Second, as a result of the projection, the children become objects of sexual desire and therefore must be avoided. Third, children arouse erotic instincts in their mothers; to a mother struggling to contain an excess of libido, this additional innervation is painful. Fourth, in the state of depletion, the continuing demands of the children make the depletion relatively more serious with respect to the need, and hence the presence of the children intensifies the pain of the depletion. Fifth, it is not uncommon for patients suffering a state of depletion to attempt to displace the source of the suffering outside themselves. They then attempt to drive away or even kill the projected source, the scapegoat (see Leviticus, Chapter XVI).

I have described this phenomenon at greater length in a paper on depression (Ostow, 1960c). In the case of this patient, since the inner discomfort was aggravated by the perception of the children, their destruction presented itself as the only possible alternative to suicide. In Chapter III, we stated that projection was more common in states of libido plethora than of depletion. There are, as we see here, many exceptions to this tendency. In the phase of clinging induced by incipient depletion, the desire may be projected onto the object. With definitive depletion the disagreeable aspects of the ego may be projected outward. Here we have just such a situation.

In retrospect, I see that the situation clearly called for a reduction in tranquilizing medication. At the time, however, I failed to see that. The patient felt better on the next day, although she was still concerned with the children. She complained that she was neglecting them, that their language was too dirty, that they were too "sexy." Her sister was to undergo a nasal operation, she reported, but she wondered whether it wasn't actually to be a hysterectomy. She attended a dinner party that night (November 11) and was strongly drawn to the hostess, an older woman to whom she felt her husband was attracted; she found herself staring at her breasts. A dream and associations disclosed that she responded as if to her mother's breasts. She awakened at 5 A.M. Had she not already been partially depleted, I believe that this dinner party encounter would have evoked an exacerbation of paranoia.

On November 13, she felt worse. She found it difficult to be alone, especially at night. This intolerance of solitude is a common symptom in early melancholia, that is, in the clinging phase. It also appears in the plethora state of anxiety hysteria, where the detachment from the object, in the presence of a libido excess, leaves the ego helpless. It is most pronounced in states of ego energy disequilibrium, such as that produced by sensory isolation or by mere darkness in the child or delirious adult. Here the perception of the object is needed to support the libido level of the ego supplement, and to prevent the damming-up of libido in the ego nucleus. The loss of the percept tends to encourage the latter and to permit the former to fall, thus increasing the discrepancy between the two. This is the epitome of the situation which gives rise to separation anxiety. On that day, the libido value was 4 (I should describe it now as 2 or 3) so I prescribed a psychic energizer (Catron), 25 mg. to be taken every second day. Since the potential of the tranquilizer for producing disturbing side effects increases in the presence of the hydrazine energizers, I simultaneously prescribed Cogentin. On the following day she told me that she had been thinking all day of melodies her brother used to play before he became psychotic. The tendency to recapture fading object relations is expressed in states of depletion by identification. She dreamed of rebirth. At one point, she felt so bad that she began to pray. On several other occasions I have discerned a need to pray during the clinging phase of a melancholic state in people otherwise irreligious.

The hypochondria which was caused in the state of plethora by a narcissistic reflection of cathexis from the object back upon the body, now reappeared in melancholia as a result of a loss of body cathexis. The patient said she felt withered, in contrast to her sister who was more "virginal." She attributed her own condition to excessive sexuality. She thought that her finger nails were wasting so that they would resemble two shriveled finger nails possessed by her psychotic brother. The hypochondria is usually reducible to a feeling of castration. The concern about a specific organ, such as a finger, is less common in states of depletion than in states of plethora. Hypochondriacal fantasies in the former instances are generally ideas of vague, poorly localized deterioration or decay of imperceptible viscera, while in states of plethora they are commonly applied to discrete, visible, surface organs. By November 17, the libido level had fallen to 3. "I worry that there may be something wrong with my brain," she said. "My mother died of it [i.e., cancer]." Notice that the hypochondria also implies identification with a lost object, identification with respect to defect or disease. It is as though the identification is intended to undo the separation, but it fails because the defect of the object becomes the principle focus since the libido deficiency continues.

She believed that it was the medicine that was making her sick, and she was correct. It has been my experience that when a patient is getting an overdose of medication or the wrong drug, he comes to suspect it himself. It is also true, however, that patients in a state of depletion tend to blame for their illness anything they eat which fails to relieve them. For this reason, schizophrenic patients on the brink of depletion develop delusions of being poisoned. I have learned that in this situation the patient's immediate need is for an energizer, because a tranquilizer will only accentuate the depletion.[2] The state of depletion always brings about a re-

[2] Libido plethora may also cause oral regression, and in defense by projection, the delusion of being poisoned does appear. In that case, tranquilizing medication is indicated.

gression to orality. "When I get to feeling real lousy," my patient said on December 2, "I want warm milk. I've been thinking about mother. When I look at my face in the mirror, I see a resemblance to mother." As the depletion intensified, the capacity to cling diminished and the patient began to resist treatment.

On Monday, November 24, the patient said, "I can't remember things very well. My mind seems sort of numb and useless." In a state of depletion, there is characteristically psychomotor retardation. Intellectual tasks are difficult. The patient will complain that his thinking is slowed and his head is not clear. The true tranquilizers are said not to affect intellectual function. It is true that they exercise little or no toxicity upon the ego; but once they have induced depletion, the depletion prevents proper function of the ego supplement, and intellectual disturbances occur. On that day I doubled the dose of Stelazine, thinking that by further attenuating the pathogenic potential of the instincts I would also diminish the reactive depletion. This principle is unsound. In the presence of depletion, tranquilizers must not be given, unless it is necessary partially to counteract the excessive effect of energizing medication. On November 26, I increased the dose of Catron to 25 mg. daily, thus taking a step in the right direction.

On Monday night, December 1, the patient felt more agitated than ever before. She paced, felt like tearing things, sensed tightness in her muscles and numbness at the back of her neck. She telephoned the next morning. I advised her to take an extra dose of Cogentin, and upon doing so, she felt much relieved. In the session, the libido value was 2. On that day I cut back the dose of Stelazine to 5 mg.

The increase of the dose of energizer and the decrease of the dose of tranquilizer soon took effect. On December 3 she expressed considerable relief and the libido value rose to 5. On December 4 I discontinued the Stelazine and reduced the Catron to 25 mg. every second day. The Cogentin was no longer necessary. Her mood improved, she became more realistic, more affectionate, and more active, and genital interests reappeared. During her recovery, a phenomenon appeared which I have observed in several other patients in one phase or another of depletion-depression, namely, sudden awaking at night, "jumping up." Often upon rising, such a patient will walk into another room, or look into closets. I do not know the meaning of this symptom, although I suspect that it is primarily a manifestation of energy shifts. (See the discussion of clinging in Chapter III). This patient complained at the same time of "jumping muscles." The latter is often seen in patients taking one or another of the hydrazine energizers, and is an innocuous side effect. Aside from their concurrence in this patient, I see no reason to relate the "jumping up" at night to the common myoclonic jerks. I decreased the Catron to 12.5 mg. every second day, starting December 14, and although some feeling of clouding and some hypochondria continued, I decreased it further to 6.25 mg. every second day on December 20, stopping medication entirely on December 23. However, the libido level remained at 4 and 3.

On Monday, December 29, the patient felt so exhausted that she slept through her appointment and she resumed Catron on her own. "I feel like the end of the world. My back aches. My weight has gone down. I have diarrhea and gas, and no appetite. Suddenly, overnight, I felt in the depths of depression again. I don't look good, my clothes don't look good, my house doesn't look good. . . . I've got to get away from people's making demands on me. . . . I want my husband to go to cocktail parties, though I suspected that he had." Here we see a return of primary self-observation and hypochondriasis, extended indiscriminately to external appearance, so that a "pseudo-secondary self-observation" results. "I feel like the end of the world" sounds like incipient schizophrenia, although the patient is not deluded here, and her detachment from the world is due to depletion rather than to dynamic repudiation.

It is interesting that at this point the patient willingly sends her husband to her rivals, whereas in the paranoid state she accuses them of seducing him. The mechanism, I believe, is the same. In the state of libido plethora, the superego silently forces the patient to give up her incestuous object, represented by her husband. She projects this surrender onto her rival and her husband, and feels herself to be the victim of their treachery. At the same time, she behaves so disagreeably toward her husband—accusing him, forcing him to defend himself, criticizing him—that he does become alienated. She may complement the surrender of her husband by retreating into narcissism. When it seems to her that she has lost the object, depletion follows. Then she feels guilty and voluntarily offers as a sacrifice what she previously felt was being taken from her. Thus, the first disapproving action of the superego is to compel the yielding of the prohibited object. This is often ascribed to an "unconscious sense of guilt." After the object has been lost and depletion sets in, consciousness of guilt appears, and the patient offers deliberately what she initially believed was being stolen from her. The mechanism applies here even though she has not lost her husband. The depletion was induced in this case by tranquilizing drugs, but its dynamic effect was the same as if it had followed the actual loss of her husband or a dynamic detachment from him.

Since she had spontaneously resumed Catron and her libido level justified the resumption, I permitted her to continue at the rate of 25 mg. daily until January 1, 1959; then the dose was reduced to 25 mg. every second day. The complex of feeling "let down," nervous, and guilty persisted. She sent a generous gift to some members of her family in less fortunate financial circumstances. On Wednesday, January 7, she told me she was subjectively better, but was concerned about possible toxicity of the several drugs she had been taking. At 7 o'clock on the morning of January 8, while asleep, she had a major convulsive seizure, witnessed by her husband. She could not be roused for fifteen to thirty minutes thereafter. Although she was not seen by a physician until half an hour following the seizure, there seems to be no reason to doubt its organicity. We did not tell her what had happened. On waking, she felt somewhat confused, and complained of a heavy vaginal discharge and a backache. Although I had not known of convulsive seizures as a side effect of Catron, I discontinued the use of that drug at once. I still do not know what caused the seizure. It might have been attributable to the Catron, for I have since seen *status epilepticus* occur in a patient who was taking Niamid and Librium and was suffering some postural hypotension. Seizures concurrent with the use of energizers have also been reported by others (Sharp, 1960). My patient, however, had a second seizure over a year later, in March 1960, six months after all medication with psychopharmaceuticals had been terminated.[3]

---

[3] It is perhaps unfortunate that for an illustrative case I have selected one which was complicated by side effects and overdosage. Yet it is probably inevitable at this stage in the development of pharmacotherapy, because the patients who have been followed long enough to present didactically were accepted for treatment when understanding was even more primitive than it is now. It was through experience with them that we learned the few principles we have already grasped. What is more, no psychiatrist who employs these pharmaceutic agents can altogether avoid similar untoward complications.

During the week or two following the seizure, the patient, who did not yet realize what had actually occurred, was troubled by the muscular aches and pains, and these aggravated her persistent depression. I was reminded of the severe headache of August 20, 1957, which intensified her depression to the point of causing a suicidal attempt. In general, the occurrence of physical distress during a state of depletion intensifies the latter. I had no choice but to replace the Catron with Marsilid, 50 mg. every second day, starting January 9. Although she had taken only two doses of Marsilid, by Monday, January 12, the patient showed clear evidence of repair. "I plan to repaint my kitchen." This and other plans indicated a rebirth tendency. Also, she began to tease her sister, her long-time rival, by telling her of a glamorous party. The libido position was now 7-5. But she associated her misery with treatment, and one element of the rebirth project was to discontinue therapy. Actually, there had been little or no analysis during the period of serious depletion, and little analytic work had been accomplished during the psychotic period immediately preceding. She complained that her sister would flirt with her boy friends, but she also confessed that as an adolescent she used to be affectionate with her sister's boy friends. Quite abruptly, much more suddenly than I had expected, she was thrown back almost into paranoia. That session was assigned the value of 8-5. By January 14, libido had diminished again to 6, and the paranoiac tendency had receded. Simultaneously, her thoughts of terminating treatment disappeared. "After all," she said, "it saved my marriage." I suspect that the abrupt increase in ego libido may have been caused by the seizure. (This turn of events resembles the course followed by the patient I have mentioned, who went into *status epilepticus* while taking Niamid. I had prescribed the energizing drug for relief of a severe postpartum, melancholic depression. Within a day or two after the seizures had stopped, and after the anti-convulsant barbiturates had worn off, it became evident that the depletion depression had given way to a paranoid schizophrenia; this now required treatment by a tranquilizer, to which it responded well. These events are consistent with the hypothesis suggested in Chapter II—that ECT achieves at least part of its therapeutic efficacy by increasing ego libido. See the account of Q. S. T. on page 173.)

By January 15 the libido level had fallen back to 4, despite continuation of the medication, but almost two weeks later she seemed to be on the mend and I decreased the dose of Marsilid to 25 mg. every second day. At times she would think of her husband as a woman, and she told me that during the acute psychosis she had believed that her husband was homosexual. As recovery progressed, anal and also incestuous material appeared in dreams and associations. In one dream, she was about to marry her husband but discovered it was her psychotic brother. The anal regression probably was the result of a retreat from genital, Oedipal fantasies. She felt guilty that she had fine clothes and money to spend. She did not deserve them, she said. This is a common manifestation of Oedipal guilt displaced to the anal level (money symbolizing feces). She believed she would "feel inadequate" entertaining her husband's professional associates.

During much of the time that the patient was taking energizing medication, she complained of severe fatigue. She required naps in the afternoon, and was especially prone to fall asleep at the theater and at dinner parties. "I get very sleepy," she said, ". . . as if drugged. I literally drop off to sleep." I have observed this powerful need to sleep in other patients with similar conditions. During the state of depletion, physiological sleep is the least demanding state and the patient often has the idea that he requires sleep to sustain his strength. Insomnia, in the form of early morning waking, also is common in melancholic depression, and it leaves the patient with a sleep deficit. The energizing drug itself may cause insomnia, and patients even when improving will suddenly find themselves overcome by sleep during the day. These "sleep attacks" are most likely to occur in late afternoon or early evening. At times, too, one has the impression that by falling asleep the patient is attempting to withdraw from the object relations to which he feels himself urged by the increase in libido—that falling asleep is a mode of detachment from a prohibited object or an unwelcome percept. It is probably not irrelevant that the patient remembers her mother sleeping much in the afternoons.

As she continued to recover, the original Oedipal conflict began to appear once more. There was a renewed effort to obtain my love. This transferred attachment to me contributed strongly to her efforts to analyze and to continue treatment. On February 6 she brought in the following dream, which I present here because it illuminates the Oedipal constellation so nicely: "M. N. was making love to me. There were people about. He had his arms around me, he was being very affectionate. His wife was there. She came over and warned us that people were looking. I assured her it didn't mean anything. M. was going to buy a poem of mine for $10, but he said, 'I promised you I'd do it once a week. I'm going to Europe and can't keep it up. You take these black tights.' I couldn't, and said, 'Don't think about it.' We walked around together and sat on a low couch or on the floor. His wife came over and started to cry. I turned from him and put my arms around her to comfort her. She had long black hair. I said, 'I understand, and I know how you must feel.' I understood that this was her homosexuality. M. was telling her she mustn't be so upset."

M. N. was an older, married man whom she admired, and with whom she had flirted during her illness. She had once sold a poem of hers for $10 to a beau of her older sister, the sister who, she complained, would flirt with her dates. Her father used to give her candy or trinkets once a week. "He left me a small diamond ring. I was to have it when I graduated from high school. I never cared for it, so I gave it to Mother to keep for me." It was mother who had long black hair. The dream discloses the incestuous desire for father, which is consummated by an exchange of gifts. First her mother and then her sisters were her rivals. Remorse compels her to give up her father to placate her suffering mother. She turns instead to mother as a love object, but projects the homosexual desire upon her. The black tights and mother's long black hair probably represent the same fetishistic object, and the money and diamond ring may be other images of it. We know from other cases that fetishistic objects often signify feces, and considering the strong anal component in this patient's illness, it is likely that here, too, the gifts exchanged may have the same significance. I wonder whether, in regression, the man himself may represent a fetishistic gift to be exchanged with the loved woman. This patient is not clinically a fetishist. She does take pride in her possession of interesting rather than expensive jewelry and enjoys exchanging gifts.

The libido value for this session was 8-5. On that day I discontinued the Marsilid. I had been permitting the patient to use dexedrine and meprobamate *ad libitum,* and she has continued to use these whenever she has been uncomfortable.

During subsequent weeks, there was an increased concern with money matters and an excessive interest in her husband's business activities. In some dreams fecal symbols, smokey air, and new-born babies represented the fetishistic object. Gradually the fetish came to represent her phallic genital. For example, it appeared in dreams as a box of animated toys for children, and as a wet, roughed-up cat. At the same time, masturbation resumed, accompanied by fantasies of being masturbated by the analyst, and of masturbating her daughter. The masturbation was entirely clitoral. Sexual intercourse, even when it brought about clitoral orgasm, did not allay the need to masturbate—in fact it increased it. But with the narcissistic retreat appeared the fear that detachment might go too far. It was not long before the image of the genital became contaminated again by anal fantasies, and this regression facilitated the tendency to withdrawal. The anality had a phallic significance. She recalled a dream or memory from childhood that her brother was sitting on the toilet and told father that something was hanging out from his back (that is, his anus). "Father said, 'No,' then looked and said, 'You're right!'" The anal regression also led the way back to object love. Father used to greet her and her younger brother by asking them whether they had had a bowel movement that day. She recalled seeing her mother administer an enema to her brother. Pregnancy fantasies and dreams appeared at the same time.

Phase E: Controlled Paranoia

Toward the end of February, the patient's concern with her husband's activities and her suspicions about him began to assume psychotic proportions. But now she was able to recognize this tendency for what it was. She attempted to control it by thoughts of leaving her husband, by fantasies, expressed only in dreams, of the destruction of the world, and finally by disparaging herself for being psychotic. This last involved a decrease in self-regard, and, at times, depersonalization. It facilitated the tendency to depletion, and thus helped to achieve a spontaneous correction.

One of the features of her marriage that displeased her was her husband's love for her. "He seems too attainable. . . . I almost like it better when he's aloof, when he doesn't try too much to please me." This was the opposite of the fantasy she had entertained since childhood, the fantasy of seducing an older man and overcoming his resistance. This type of relation she found in the transference. "I think about you too much and it bothers me. And you have the goddamndest poker face I ever saw in my life."

This complex probably represented a pattern of turning away from her brothers, who were too available to her, and setting her cap for her father, who was in a sense a safer Oedipal object because he resisted her. "I had the feeling that father loved me best of all, that only I could overcome his reserve."

She began to accuse her husband of being dirty, constipated, smelly, oafish. "During periods of contemplation he would look moronic, or as if he were about to masturbate." She recognized that some of these accusations might be projections of her own anality, which seem to have colored her sexual fantasies about her brothers, or, perhaps, her actual sex play with them. I have no evidence that it was a displacement onto her husband of anal features of her brothers to which she responded. The immediate trigger for this anal material was a persistent brown vaginal discharge. However, the sense of dirtiness was also the result of superego condemnation. Immediately after telling me a story about touching someone's penis, she recalled being told by her sister that her fingers were dirty. She then revealed that she was not at ease handling her husband's penis. "I suddenly become very conscious of myself instead of being lost in lovemaking."

"I was thinking that your wife must be concerned to see us together," she said on March 25. "When I was eight or nine, I overheard a quarrel between my parents. The next day I sat on father's bed and put my arms about him. I said, 'You shouldn't be angry with mother.' I felt very embarrassed and shy. I couldn't let him do this to her. I felt I could stop this. He was gentle. He was giving me the affection he should have been giving to mother. I felt mother was alone in the kitchen at this point. . . . I felt that father should be affectionate with me, not with mother . . . as if she were the grandmother. I was always very respectful of mother. I never kissed her or showed affection to her until after father's death, although I remember caressing her breasts when she lay down with us when I was six."

Thereafter, there followed a period characterized by a tendency to withdraw from love objects. There were dreams of uncontrollable floods, to which the patient associated uncontrollable psychosis, and fiery enemy attacks. There was a tendency to masturbate and to identify with mother. The narcissistic identification with mother led to an autoerotic increase in breast sensitivity reminiscent of her adolescent breast masturbation. She revealed that she had on occasion responded with full genital orgasm to caressing of her breasts. There was a longing to touch me, which she compared to her touching the hands of her psychotic brother.

The tendency to narcissistic withdrawal alternated with a paranoid tendency occasionally approaching delusional intensity. She struggled to retain perspective and insight, often succeeding, sometimes failing. Temporary success was often accompanied by mild depletion subjectively felt as misery and depression. Headache was a common component of the depletion syndrome. In one dream, she revealed that the idea of her husband's having an affair with her girl friend disturbed her because she wanted the girl herself. In this connection she recalled fury with her mother during childhood, and "socking" her sister. "If I were able to, I'd have killed her." She angrily accused her sister of erotically stimulating her children. The paranoia grew out of her homosexual love for her sister and mother.

At this point, an interesting episode occurred. On April 22 she complained of diarrhea, bloated abdomen, and a bad taste in her mouth. "The bloatedness is depressing, as if it were in my head instead of my stomach. . . . When at fourteen, I'd had a sleepless night, I'd wake up with a running stomach. . . . I've had a feeling today that I've been sicker than you realize or I realize. I've had the feeling that people's faces were distorted. . . . I occasionally got this kind of stomach attack when I had to go down to parties at M's [one of her favorite rivals]. . . . I used to make up prayers: I used to tell God that I loved him though lots of people were afraid of him. I felt this was bold of me. After father's death, I dreamed of father in heaven and coming to visit me in heavenly robes. After mother's death, I had a dream of two short Hebrew words. I thought it was a revelation; I felt that the earth was only a temporary place, that I'd soon join mother in heaven or wherever God was." A dream accompanied this material. The rabbi who had introduced her to her husband and had officiated at the wedding ceremony was embracing her and assuring her husband that it was all right, that it was only tender, brotherly love. She hesitated, she said, to tell her children the Passover story of the Egyptian plagues, especially the story of the slaying of the first-born.

What had happened here? The retreat from paranoia was accomplished via a mild depletion, possibly associated with an actual infection—there was a slight viral gastrointestinal epidemic in her neighborhood at the time—or possibly giving rise itself to a disturbance of intestinal motility. The ego supplement depletion was sufficiently marked this time to bring about distortion of visual perception. This corresponds to the luminous visions which appear in this patient's dreams of world destruction, frequently followed by headache. Visual hallucinations and illusions appeared previously in this case in association with recovery from psychotic states, but in each instance, the recovery followed the administration of tranquilizing drugs. On this occasion, the visual disorder accompanied spontaneous depletion.

There are several references to death in this session. I believe that they express the patient's effort to escape the homosexual temptation by killing herself and her love object. However, the idea of death carries with it the possibility of re-establishing the original Oedipal love for father which was abrogated in the interest of the love for mother.

That night (April 22), the patient was disturbed by stories of hostility and destruction in the Passover Seder readings. She was somewhat depressed the next day. She told me that at the age of three she had seen a mother beating a teen-age girl. "I couldn't leave. I assumed she'd misbehaved the night before. . . . Spanking troubled me. There was a mixture of carnal pleasure and revulsion. I used to get upset when I saw a mother spanking a baby. I'd enjoy the fantasy of identifying with the mother." Here we see the emergence of a sadistic tendency. Two roots are suggested. One is that the desire to eradicate the love object is itself erotized. Therefore, she was afraid to tell her son the legend of the destruction of the first-born. The second is that the return to an incestuous relation to father invites an erotized punishment by mother.

Thereafter, the analysis continued with the patient on the brink of paranoia or actually in a paranoid state. Abrogation of reality testing was never extended beyond the specific ideas of jealousy, and it could usually be reversed by confrontation in analysis and analytic work. There were frequent periods of depression accompanied by minor temporary depletion. Such depletion had the effect of restraining the upward tendency of libido and, occasionally, of reducing it. The depressive episodes were induced by two factors. One was the pathologic tendency to relinquish the husband out of Oedipal guilt. Since the alternative homosexual position was never gratified, and narcissism was discouraged by the analytic work as well as anxiety and shame, the patient was left without an object. Depression was the response to the lack of object. Second, when confronted with her own tendency to become deluded, to misjudge and to retreat into ineffectual narcissism, the patient experienced a sharp diminution of self-regard, which also served to evoke depression. The patient used meprobamate and amphetamine *ad libitum* to alleviate the depressive symptoms, but between February 1959 and the time of writing (June 1960), it has not been necessary for me to prescribe any tranquilizer or energizer. The patient herself resumed Trilafon medication during vacation (4 mg. per day) in July 1959, but I was able to discontinue the drug within a week of resuming treatment with no adverse effects.

The chart of ego libido for the third year of treatment shows that its level has remained fairly steady without medication. Often the patient has entertained paranoid ideas, but almost always with some residual reality testing. The actual improvement of the third year over the second half of the first and over the second is obscured in the chart. My criteria have become refined somewhat during these years, and states that I earlier recorded as 8 or 9, I now record as 9 or 10. Hence consistent application of the more recent criteria would have shown a greater prevalence of values of 9 and 10 in the earlier period, so that the actual improvement would be more evident. From a practical point of view, the improvement means that this patient is no longer as erratic in behavior, provocative toward her husband, mercurial toward her children, and inaccessible to the voice of reality and reason as she had been. At the time that I am writing this, there remains much analytic work to do, but the improvement ascribable to the analysis rather than to medication is impressive.

I should add parenthetically that on March 26, 1960, the patient had a second major convulsive seizure just before her usual waking time. According to her husband, it was essentially similar to the previous one. There was no evidence of focal or lateral origin. Full physical, neurologic, roentgenographic, and electroencephalographic examinations were negative. The patient was taking no medication at the time of this seizure. There has been no recurrence since. From an analytic point of view, the experience accentuated her tendency to hypochondria, and for the next two months the analysis was devoted almost exclusively to it.

CHAPTER VII

Epilogue: On Human Unhappiness

AMONG THE MOST CONTROVERSIAL of Freud's writings are those in which he attempts the elucidation of the problems of society and civilization by applying to them the psychologic insights wrung from clinical work. I have in mind such papers as *Totem and Taboo, Future of an Illusion, Civilization and Its Discontents,* and *Moses and Monotheism.* Religion especially held Freud's interest, comprehending as it does so many of the eternal problems of mankind and man's attempts to solve them. Above and beyond the resistance which all psychoanalytic speculation and inference arouse, this domain possesses special difficulties which do not apply to clinical material. First, it is difficult, perhaps impossible, to check one's hypotheses by observation, and second, the practical application of one's conclusions is remote. Nevertheless, the intellectual challenge of applying hypotheses derived from one kind of data to a different realm of knowledge is not easy to suppress. And besides, we have no right to abstain from any investigation which might even ultimately contribute to the strengthening of human culture and civilization against the destructive forces which claw at it unceasingly. It is in this spirit that I venture to append an essay which will explore the implications of energy theory for group and cultural behavior.

THE MECHANISMS OF
DEFENSIVE DETACHMENT

In our discussion of energy distribution, we have had to confine our remarks to conditions obtaining within the ego, since we have no access to data derived directly from the other two psychic institutions. We still have no alternative to occupying ourselves essentially with ego psychology. Let us examine, then, the function of the archaic ego. I consider the ego of the lower vertebrates and of the human infant to be what Nunberg calls the ideal ego, that is, an ego which operates only to execute the demands of the id, interposing no restrictions or inhibitions (Nunberg, 1955, p. 126). It is represented in the adult human by an ego nucleus which strives to perform the same function—subject, however, to regulation by another portion of the ego, which exists only in higher vertebrates and is hypertrophied in the human (Ostow, 1959a). The functions of the archaic, animal ego, if we follow von Uexküll, are completely determined by the strength of the instinctual impulses presenting at the moment (von Uexküll, 1934). When a given drive is activated, the ego becomes selectively sensitive to the perceptible configurations of the external world, including other members of the same species, that must be found and dealt with in the instinctual act. For example, the male fish under the influence of a mating drive becomes especially susceptible to the sign stimuli, the releasing configurations, emitted by receptive females on the one hand and intruding males on the other. He responds to both with a vigor provided by the impelling drive. At other times, when that drive is inactive, he fails to respond to these same triggers. In other words, the instinct operates partly by sensitizing the perceptive end of the mental apparatus to relevant triggers and simultaneously desensitizing it to irrelevant percepts. The perceptible world of such a creature must vary from season to season, in fact, from day to day and from hour to hour, depending upon the instinctual drives which wax and wane.

This is an admirable device for securing the promptest gratification, especially suited to that segment of the biological world in which an oversupply of all elements is produced so that successful instinctual interaction of only a fraction of the population suffices to carry on the life of the species. In the case of man, however, precision of regulation substitutes to a certain extent for oversupply. The human parent has fewer children than the animal, but cares for them more attentively and over a longer period of time. The human, too, does not rely upon finding in nature the object of his desire when the desire arises. He attempts to anticipate his needs and to plan for their gratification whenever they should occur in the future. This he does by forming a microcosmic image of the external world and its contents. It is in this process of constructing an inner replica of the universe that the concept of an instinctual object as a separate being first becomes possible. This is equally true of the individual's capacity to view himself as an independent person. The microcosmic replica can now be employed to solve problems, to predict future events, and to project one's behavior realistically into the future. It resembles an analogue computer, which solves problems by reproducing within itself the pertinent forces and letting them act upon each other, or a model airplane in a wind tunnel, whose behavior can be used to predict the behavior of its large prototype in flight. I have called this predicting, planning, problem-solving, phylogenetically new segment of the human ego, the ego supplement.

Obviously the information provided by a perceptual apparatus which is influenced by a varying array of drives is useless for such a supplement; the latter must impose a corrective regulation of perception so that the perceived image corresponds in a constant reliable way to the objective world. Klüver speaks of "homeostasis of the *milieu externe*" (Klüver, 1951). We may say then that it is the ego supplement which imposes upon ego function the reality principle, and also reality testing, its principle agent.

How does this ego supplement achieve perceptual constancy? It must oppose variations in perceptual parameters produced by fluctuations in drive intensity. A percept which an active drive renders intense, close at hand, large, familiar, and satisfying, must be corrected so that it appears that much less intense, more distant, smaller, less familiar, and less satisfying. The ego supplement must organize percepts so as to form realistic images. It must distinguish between the real and the illusory. Yet a perceptual view which encompasses in full fidelity all of impinging reality must lose the forest for the trees. A faculty of selective attention exists whereby a large portion of perceptible reality is excluded from conscious notice so that the maximal mental work may be done upon a relatively small segment.

There is some fairly good evidence to support these specula-tions. A temporary dissolution of this hypothetical mechanism may be seen in some of the events of the normal mental life. In dreams we find what Freud has taught us to be evidences of the operation of primary process in perception, namely, condensation of images, co-existence of opposites, visual representation of abstract concepts, fragmentation, distortion, and alterations in intensity of percepts (Freud, 1900a). Here, quite evidently, the corrective, realistic modi-fication of the ego supplement fails to operate, and perception, be-sides regressing to hallucination, also becomes responsive exclusively to drive intensity and to inhibitory influences. In the dreams of obsessive patients, the image of the desired but forbidden sexual object not infrequently undergoes a visible change in quality from attractive to ugly. Or a homosexual object which first appears in the dream as a pleasure-giving, friendly image, becomes a fierce, mur-derous enemy. Evidently inhibitory forces can influence the percep-tive function of the ego nucleus just as primary drives can. Even in waking apperception, the instinctually determined affect usually colors the percept. The less structured the percept, the more oppor-tunity there is for the intrusion of instinct into apperception. This is the basis for projective tests, which encourage the projection of unconscious drives into suggestive percepts.

A similar dissolution of the image-stabilizing function of the ego supplement can be induced by organic changes. The illusions and hallucinations of delirium illustrate the escape of primary proc-ess tendencies into perception. Irritation of the temporal lobe creates illusions affecting the several parameters of perception individually or in groups. These include size, distance, intensity, familiarity, real-ity, and benignity. Often the affect which corresponds to these dis-tortions becomes conscious at the same time. The hallucinogenic drugs have a similar effect. Hyde (1960) found that the specific direction of the illusional distortions produced by LSD was deter-mined in each case by affective prejudices. Thus a disliked individ-ual was distorted so as to seem ugly. We may infer from these data confirmation of our hypothesis that the perceptual fluctuations com-pensated by the ego supplement are not random, but are determined by the presenting drive impulses. Alles (1959) points out that under the influence of an hallucinogenic drug, perceptual intensities are distorted, so that faint sounds originating at a distance seem loud and insistent. This effect resembles the effect of listening to a tape recorded conference. Fortuitous sounds, produced by passing traffic or originating in an adjacent room, obtrude into the recording with annoying intensity. We assume that the intensity of the recording reproduces the actual relative intensities of all impinging sounds, but that participants in such a conference spontaneously screen out adventitious percepts. The hallucinogenic drugs impair this mechanism for selective attention. The observation that these effects are reproduced by discharge phenomena of the temporal lobe, together with the converse finding that extirpation of both lateral temporal cortices in the chimpanzee obliterates the effect of lysergic acid, leads to the inference that one or more of the temporal lobe structures are essential for this apperceptive smoothing of perception (Baldwin *et al.*, 1959).

A discussion of perception inevitably proceeds to a discussion of defenses. It has doubtless not escaped the reader that even in the brief mention we have made of apperception we were not able to avoid mention of defense. In the primary process apperception executed by the ego nucleus, an inhibitory influence is expressed by distortion of the unacceptable drive. The object which is instinctually desirable is made to seem visibly ugly and degraded. This defense, which includes elements of projection and regression, is especially characteristic of obsessive-compulsive neurosis and of paranoia. Since the degradation and ugliness are often associated with anal material, we may speculate that such distortion of the object or of the self is a primary defense against anal instincts, which may perhaps precede even the primal repression.

The adult human is frightened by the impact of naked percepts untempered by the modulation of the ego supplement and uncorrected for intrinsic distortions of the ego nucleus, such as synesthesia, and for the distortions caused by drive impulses and inhibitions (Bercel *et al.*, 1956). These modulating, tempering, and compensating activities of the ego supplement, therefore, may be considered defenses against anxiety. The institution of these defenses could correspond to the primal repression which Freud postulated as a necessary, biological defense against the very power of the sexual instincts. Repression, says Freud, consists essentially of keeping an idea away from consciousness, or of weakening its intensity, which has a similar effect: "The psychic changes which accompany this process of cultural change are striking and not to be gainsaid. They consist in the progressive rejection of instinctive ends and a scaling down of instinctive reactions. Sensations which delighted our forefathers have become neutral or unbearable to us" (Freud, 1933b). In this ego supplement residing, at least partially, in the temporal lobe, we have a mechanism with the power to control instinctual impulses by attenuating their conscious representatives, possibly by excluding them from consciousness altogether, and by making them seem unreal or unfamiliar. Under what circumstances is this mechanism used as a defense rather than as a device for the stabilization of percepts? I suppose that it is used as a defense when impulses become too strong to be handled easily by the ego.

But I think that we can go one step further and propose that the attenuating function of the ego supplement is brought into play not merely to tame the wild instincts in the interest of regulating relative intensities in the psychic systems but also in the service of the superego. The superego, when it develops, gains access to pre-existing methods of defense and uses them to give effect to the ideals which it enforces. It exploits both the more archaic, object-retaining defenses, whose *modus operandi* is aim modification, and the object-abandoning defenses.

Turning away from the object and attenuating the strength of the attraction are categories of defense that are perhaps broader than the psychic maneuvers usually specified as defenses. These object-abandoning defenses include repression, denial, negation, doubting, catatonia, negativism, withdrawal, sleep, depersonalization, derealization, and illusions of unfamiliarity. They also include actual flight, killing the object, suicide, and self-mutilation. More normal expressions are absent-mindedness, ignoring, misestimating; autoerotic activities such as smoking, nail biting, and nose picking; and compulsive reading, playing, or working. While some individuals use smoking as a form of addiction—that is, as an oral, narcissistic, symbolic, repletion device—I suspect that more use it as an auxiliary discharge maneuver. By indulging this autoerotic activity, they drain off both interest and energy from the principal object of attention. If the latter is a piece of mental work, smoking drains off accumulating energies which are distracting. If the principal activity is an object relation of some kind, the smoking helps to attenuate it by absorbing some of the libido autoerotically. All these maneuvers imitate and supplement the defensive activities of the percept-attenuating mechanism. A young man reports that when he becomes anxious in a heterosexual relation, he moves away from the girl and lights a cigarette. A young woman who has isolated herself in a hysterical way from social and sexual contacts ignores this isolation by continuous, compulsive reading. At the risk of laboring the obvious, I should like to emphasize that such distracting, attenuating activities are prevalent and taken for granted in everyday life. We become aware of them clinically only when they are exaggerated or pinpointed temporally.

So far our discussion has led us through metapsychologic speculation, but we have yet to encounter the central problem of our concern, the problem of human unhappiness. Our last remarks lead us directly to it. We have drawn a picture of man as a creature whose ego is too delicate to tolerate naked percepts and naked affects. And whatever dilute instinctual pleasure his cultured ego might tolerate is encroached upon by the increasingly demanding superego, which is not content with interdicting direct Oedipal gratification, but even pursues Oedipal substitutes through several steps of transformation and displacement. Man is left with accumulating libido and inadequate means of satisfaction. He develops a restlessness, a longing, a *Weltschmerz*, an unfocused yearning, with no awareness of what it is that he wants and what can possibly give him a profound, penetrating satisfaction.

Sadism and masochism remain puzzles despite all the psychoanalytic work which has been done. I should like to suggest that one root of these may be an attempt to circumvent the blankness, the nothingness, that follows the destruction of object relations, by libidinizing the process of destruction. Killing and degrading the love object or oneself, not only defends against intolerable gratification, but itself becomes a source of sexual pleasure. A derivative of this sadism and masochism is a readiness for adventure, a search for new forms of sensation, a welcoming of danger, even war. As an aging man whose taste is becoming blunted begins to use more and more condiments, the detached, the affectively blunted, man seeks new sensory experiences and thrills.

Nor is this partial disengagement from the real pleasure-giving world the whole of the trap. Man's unhappiness also has another, more urgent, source. Freud (1915e) taught us that repression has two separate components. First, there is the removal of cathexis from the preconscious image of the object, a process which is equivalent to the attenuation of images which I have described above. Second, the impulse of the instinct is blocked, and its energies are excluded from the preconscious. I believe these energies are no longer available to the ego. The difference between denial and repression is precisely this: in repression the energy of the instinct is excluded from the ego; in denial it is not (Freud, 1927e). I would guess that whenever the image of an object loses its preconscious cathexis, a tendency to exclude the energies of the associated impulse follows closely. The exclusion reinforces the defensive process, reduces the tendency of the instinct to achieve a substitute gratification, and alleviates the painful pressure upon the ego caused by an ungratified instinct. In a sense, then, every object-abandoning defense tends to follow the pattern of repression.

I repeated in Chapter II a hypothesis to the effect that since the amygdaloid nucleus is structurally a component of the basal ganglia, and is topographically and functionally a component of the temporal lobe testing and aversion mechanism, it might be concerned with the device for reinforcing defense by excluding from the ego the energetic impulse of the instinct whose object image has lost its preconscious cathexis. These newer speculations concerning the method of removing preconscious cathexis—namely, by attenuating the intensity of a perceived image—takes us back to the temporal lobe and adds support to our guess about the energy-depleting function of the amygdaloid nucleus.

The exclusion of the energies of a single impulse from the ego may not be crippling. However, if at a given time most of the instinctual energies are concentrated on a single drive, as is the case with a person in love, or if most of the individual instincts have the same object, as is the case with the young child, abandonment of that object and the loss of all of the energies pertaining to it leave the ego with no opportunity for activating instinctual gratification and, indeed, with no impetus to do so. We conclude that when defense against instincts extends far enough over the range of currently available objects, it may leave the ego seriously depleted.

But, we may ask, does this depletion mechanism operate in the case of object loss in the service of defense? Is the defense two-pronged, both reducing the object cathexis and blocking its energy, or is it serial, the energy depletion being a consequence of the object loss? I shall not presume to answer this second question, but I think we can answer the first, which is more limited. We do know that depletion follows a fortuitous loss of object. We may speculate, therefore, that object loss tends to be followed by depletion of the ego no matter what its cause—superego protest, ego intolerance, or external necessity. Our metapsychologic speculations about how object loss causes depletion have led us nowhere, but the facts support the generalization that it does.

OBJECT LOSS AND HUMAN UNHAPPINESS

To what extent is this state of affairs peculiar to our own times? We often assume that because of advances in medical care in the past century we are less frightened about crippling and total illnesses than our grandparents were, or than man was two or more centuries ago. Statistics are reassuring, but protection is far from absolute; while the objective probabilities of succumbing to an illness are lower than they were, I doubt that there is much of a difference in subjective apprehension regarding illness. The tendency to hypochondria is determined by psychodynamic influences, not by the objective probabilities of illness. In the absence of hypochondriacal tendencies and in the absence of immediate threats to health, we all assume a sense of invulnerability and ignore actual dangers. Note the widespread indifference to what are probably real hazards to health and life expectancy arising out of smoking. The savage was no less immune to death by violence than we. The security of our food supply, the reliability of shelter and clothing and warmth, the reduction in the amount of physical labor required of us, all make us more comfortable, but we rapidly become accustomed to a changed condition and merely operate from a new baseline. The additional leisure provided to us challenges us to find ways to pass the time which will be pleasurable and yet harmless. There are few humans fortunate enough to have sufficiently broad interests so that time freed from obligation readily increases the amount of pleasure. Leisure time activities in periods of prosperity attain a quality of intensity and desperation which reveal that they are actually serving instinctual needs which have been intensified as a result of the abstention from work. And the competitiveness among individuals which is no longer required to secure the essential necessities of life reappears in play with no loss of earnestness. We have achieved the capacity to make it physically possible for each man to sit quietly under his fig tree in his garden, but few men enjoy doing so, and some who do not enjoy it find it necessary to challenge and fight those who do.

It is my impression that the physical conditions of life are limiting, but that the limits they set are relatively broad. The limitations inherent in the nature of the human ego and imposed by the superego are far more compelling. The man whose ego is at peace with his superego can find pleasure under a fairly broad range of living conditions. When the superego is critical and severe, a man cannot enjoy the most opportune circumstances. There are fluctuations in the ideals of a given society from period to period, depending upon its political and economic experience, but we have no evidence that there has been any change in the severity of the individual superego during historical times.

Freud takes note of the interesting fact that people are prone to interpret misfortune, even when it is of obviously external origin, as a punishment for guilt (Freud, 1915e). The tendency to displace cathexis from one idea to another that is associated with it, is a mode of function characteristic of primary process and therefore of all unconscious psychic activity. Even when there are two or more possible causes for a given event, the need for causality demands only that a single cause be found. Primary process permits us to assign responsibility to that event which is least offensive or most congenial, with no regard to reality. Since both accident and superego are, at different times, proper causes for misfortune, it is to be expected that under the influence of primary process, responsibility for a given mishap can be assigned to either. But if it is not reality that is to determine the assignment of responsibility, what is? We cannot answer this question without taking note of another fact. Just as it is true that we may on some occasions attribute to the superego misfortunes that are actually accidental, on other occasions we may attribute to fate what is actually a self-punishment. I have mentioned (see p. 91) a patient (R. L. X.) who, in a state of libido plethora, mutilated her face as a punishment for her Oedipal desires and claimed that the resulting disfiguration was caused by physical disease. She refused to acknowledge that she was the agent of her destruction. On the other hand, in a state of mild depletion, she insisted that she was to blame for her husband's business difficulties. Of course, the acknowledgment of guilt in the latter case, although partially true, was irrelevant to, or at least distant from, the actual pathogenic conflict common to both abnormal states.

But here we have one answer to the question of what determines the tendency to ascribe the responsibility for mishaps now to fate and now to conscience. It is the libido supply of the ego. All events that affect us are attributed to an external agency when we are in a state of libido plethora. In a state of libido deficiency, even fortuitous events are attributed to the superego. What actually has initiated the sequence of object loss followed by depletion is of little consequence to the ego in its need to establish causality for affectively significant occurrences. If psychic outcome is limited to object loss, the cause is seen as external; when it continues to depletion, the cause is imputed to the conscience.

Object loss and libidinal depletion of the ego are the twin sources of psychic pain in modern man as well as in the primitive. Both might be caused by external necessity, by the hypersensitivity of the ego, or by the intolerance of the superego. (Object loss, as I use the term here, includes narcissistic loss—that is, a disappointment in oneself following illness, accident, or failure.) I have already spoken of the distress caused by object loss in the presence of persisting ego libido. The loss of libido is an additional and potent source of misery. We assume that the normal function of depletion is to reduce the disequilibrium which results from dammed-up libido in the absence of object. Reducing the disequilibrium should reduce anxiety, allay fruitless but increasingly desperate attempts to find substitute objects, and attenuate the continuous libido build-up with its deleterious consequences for ego function. Therefore, the initial depletion—which is commensurate in degree with the extent of the loss—should provide relief from anxiety. I suppose it might actually do so, perhaps more effectively among normals who do not come for treatment than in those who become patients, precisely because the defensive maneuvers of the latter are either excessive or inadequate. Certainly the initiation of depletion, whether spontaneous or drug induced, in a patient with libido plethora brings about visible relief, subjective as well as objective.

When does libidinal depletion of the ego become painful? Patients who have previously suffered severe melancholic depletion syndromes become sensitive to its early signs, and for them incipient depletion arouses signal anxiety, even when it is a salutary correction of a pathologically intense libido level. Patients who have had no previous experience with serious deficiency do not begin to complain until the appearance of the initial signs of impairment of ego supplement function—namely, confusion, difficulty in thinking, in making decisions, and in becoming interested in events outside the ego, and susceptibility to illusory and in some cases hallucinatory distortion of reality. This partial depletion, affecting primarily the intellectual functions of the ego supplement and leaving the libido content of the ego nucleus relatively intact, offers minimal relief and accentuates the disequilibrium before a broader depletion alleviates it. Sometimes akathisia, often associated with insomnia, is the first sign to betray the onset of depletion. The full depletion syndrome, as we know, is an intensely painful state which may go on to suicide.

This full depletion syndrome, melancholia, is a pathologic state; but early, mild, or threatening depletion is a condition which often falls within the range of normal, and it is this, I believe, that is responsible for much of the free-floating, unexplained unhappiness that prevails in so many people. When there has been a broad disengagement from potential love objects, and a beginning but not fully commensurate depletion, the combined pain of the object loss and of the depletion may fall within the limits of normal variation, but may be the reason for the "lives of quiet desperation" which so many men lead.

To many, the pain of libidinal depletion of the ego is a serious threat, often sufficient to evoke anxiety. It is my impression that when some people speak of a fear of death, it is a fear of depletion that they have in mind. Alternatively, it may be a fear of detachment from the love object or from all of reality. In most instances, it is probably the combination that is called the fear of death. More often, the fear of detachment is expressed as fear of insanity, and that too is accentuated by an accompanying depletion. Free floating anxiety—anxiety that cannot be associated with any specific fear—is probably often the anxiety aroused by incipient depletion. Anxiety which develops in a state of ego plethora is likely to be assigned to an external threat, whether such an assignment is realistic or merely a projection.

The chief point of this speculative excursion is that, first, much of human misery may be attributed to object loss and enervation of the ego; and second, many symptomatic acts of individual neurosis as well as group activities and cultural attitudes are designed to overcome this dual threat. To describe all the varieties of individual and group expressions of distress originating from this source, and all of the varieties of defensive efforts to counter it, would require a major scholarly investigation. It is my intention here merely to restate this old problem of impending doom with the innovation I have suggested and to list some of its more common derivatives and the defensive activities mobilized to oppose it.

REPARATIVE EFFORTS

First we must acknowledge that it is not always easy to determine whether a given defensive act is actually undertaken to combat the threat of object loss, or whether it is a response to the threat of libidinal depletion. Addiction to food is, I believe, a clear-cut example of an effort to resist the threat of depletion. Clinging to the love object, on the other hand, may be a similar attempt, or it may be a direct defense against impending loss of the object. More often than not, vigorous clinging with an aggressive component represents an effort to prevent an object loss which is known to be followed promptly by depletion. Certain intoxicants may have the effect of impairing the ability of the temporal lobe ego supplement mechanism to remove percepts to a greater distance. Their intoxicating action either appears to restore the lost object, or, in larger doses, accentuates the detachment by impairing perception while simultaneously intensifying sensations of internal origin so as to diminish the sense of isolation from the world. Such an action would tend to combat the impact of object loss and so deter or perhaps even reverse depletion. This could be an adequate basis for establishing addiction. Many problems obviously remain to be solved.

Can we attempt to distinguish between independent, individualistic defenses and group or cultural defenses? We shall find that it is impossible to draw a sharp line between the two. Some defensive acts are asocial or idiosyncratic, others are essentially cultural phenomena, and very many partake of both elements.

There is a familar set of activities which provide for gratification of object-directed instincts with little likelihood of encountering repression due to ego or superego protest. These are group activities. By acting as a member of a group, either in some collective performance or in a coordinated program, the individual obtains instinctual gratification. The mode of gratification is identification. Since little or no physical contact is involved, and since the group prevents excessive intimacy, there is not much occasion for the production of anxiety. Further, a group can largely supersede the individual superego, and to that extent, whatever is done as a member of the group is exempt from superego criticism. When group relations are sustained over a long period of time—as, for example, in an employment situation—exclusive, two-party object relations and triangular situations emerge and tend to disrupt group loyalty. A study of the cohesive and dispersive factors in group relations is beyond our area of interest. What is important to us is that group activities offer opportunities for instinctual gratification which can, to a certain extent, replace individual relations and thus expend libidinal energy. Pathologic accumulations of libido are thereby precluded, limiting automatically the potential intensity of emergent two-party relations.

Similar in some respects to group activity is a working relation in which two or more individuals participate jointly. Interest in the common task facilitates group formation by identification. The work itself absorbs instinctual energy and thus permits an attenuated object gratification, which in turn tends to drain off whatever surplus libidinal energy might be accumulated in imperfect, two-person object relations.

In both sublimated and unsublimated object relations, that is, the social and the sensual, a degree of attenuation can be achieved by interposing an extraneous activity which absorbs part of the libidinal energy generated. Dynamically it also distracts the participants from their principal concern with each other. If the extraneous activity is some common work, we have essentially the same situation described above. The substitute activity may be a variety of narcissistic autoerotic behavior such as smoking, nail biting, fidgeting, or picking at oneself. These are autoerotic, grooming activities, reminiscent of the displacement activities of animals. The latter are instinctual movements, often reflexive, which animals perform when an instinctual tendency has been aroused, but the impulse is denied discharge by some interfering tendency; it is as if the displacement activity served to drain off the mobilized but undischarged instinctual energy.

The use of intoxicants in social groups might be mentioned

here. We have already discussed three possible modes of satisfaction afforded by intoxicating drugs. First, they anesthetize the ego against painful affects, notably anxiety and depression. Second, they provide symbolic nutrition to counteract the ego depletion. Third, they weaken or cancel the distance obstacle interposed by the temporal lobe—that is, the ego supplement interposed between ego and object image. We can now suggest a fourth mode of satisfaction. When intoxicants are used in social groups, as is often the case with alcohol, the group relation itself becomes an auxiliary source of gratification.

At this point we may take note of some techniques for securing surcease from pain mentioned by Freud in *Civilization and Its Discontents*. These fall, he said, into three categories: diversions of interest, substitutive gratifications, and intoxicating substances. Other methods the individual adopts to obtain pleasure and avoid pain consist of regulating the degree of his participation in the affairs of the world. He may attempt to achieve unbridled gratification of his desires. He may isolate himself and so procure protection against unhappiness arising in relations with others. He may join with others in a cooperative endeavor.

Freud's remarks about intoxicating substances is sufficiently interesting in the light of our point of view to warrant quotation here: "The crudest of these methods of influencing the body, but also the most effective, is the chemical one: that of intoxication. I do not think anyone entirely understands their operation but it is a fact that there are certain substances foreign to the body which, when present in the blood or tissues, directly cause us pleasurable sensations, but also so change the condition of our perceptivity that we become insensible of disagreeable sensations. The two effects not only take place simultaneously, they seem to be closely bound up with each other. But there must be substances in the chemical composition of our bodies which can do the same, for we know of at least one morbid state, that of mania, in which a condition similar to this intoxication arises without any drug being absorbed. Besides this, our normal mental life shows variations, according to which pleasure is experienced with more or less ease, and along with this goes a diminished or increased sensitivity to pain. It is greatly to be regretted that this toxic aspect of mental processes has so far eluded scientific research. The services rendered by intoxicating substances in the struggle for happiness and in warding off misery rank so highly as a benefit that both individuals and races have given them an established position within their libido-economy."

One may attempt to avoid pain by subduing the instinctual impulses themselves. Extreme self-abnegation is a teaching of some religions. More commonly we attempt to keep our instincts satisfied with a relatively small amount of gratification. Disappointments, with such a technique of self-control, are fewer and less painful than with the attempt to deny instincts completely.

Sublimation facilitates a diversion of instincts, from sensual object relations which can give rise to pain, to creative and investigatory intellectual work, artistic and scientific. This protective device is not available to the multitude and it fails when somatic disease overtakes the body. A similar function is performed by every man's daily work, which can discharge both libidinal and aggressive impulses and provide narcissistic gratification.

Substitutive gratifications may be found in the enjoyment of works of art which offer the illusion of satisfaction. This is only a mild and temporary refuge. A step beyond this is the mental reconstruction of reality to resemble a satisfying fantasy. When this fantasy loses the stamp of unreality it becomes a delusion, and religion, says Freud, is just such a mass delusion.

A life which makes the enjoyment of love its goal possibly comes closer to the achievement of happiness, Freud continues, than any other. But its intrinsic hazard is that it renders the individual so vulnerable to disappointment, frustration, and misery. The enjoyment of beauty, the esthetic attitude, offers little protection against suffering, but it can compensate for it.

Neurosis and psychosis are the final resolution for individuals who can make no other compromise with reality.

All of these devices catalogued by Freud are intended to prevent or mitigate the frustrations, disappointments, and pains of living. When successful, they avoid the need for object abandonment and the neurotic and psychotic regressions by means of which the abandonment is accomplished. Beside these stand the pathologic techniques of abandonment which Freud included in his list, namely, the turning away from the world of love objects into narcissism and the retreat into illness.

Let us return now to the expedients we have already mentioned for opposing incipient or threatening libidinal depletion of the ego. In some instances, there is first an intensification of whatever object or narcissistic activity may be current. The intensification consists of increasing demands upon objects or self, or increasing speed and extent of performance. In addition, the energies of the death instincts are invoked and add an aggressive component to the activity. What may have been an affectionate object relation now becomes a hostile clinging one in which more and more is demanded of the object and in which he is abused and reviled when even his best efforts fail to stem the depletion. When depletion has begun as a result of the inner neurotic conflict, the object is, of course, unable to arrest it. A common form of clinging is speech. The individual prevents the object from departing by talking at length, being afraid to terminate the conversation. Children often show this behavior when a separation from the parent is impending. They always have one more thing to say at bedtime. Under threat of depletion, the jeopardized object relation now becomes an anaclitic relation.

The reader will recall, from our discussion of abandonment of the object as a type of defense, that if the act of abandonment becomes libidinized, it can itself become a mode of object relation and instinctual gratification. This mechanism is comparable to that employed by the paranoiac, who simultaneously abrogates his homosexual love and reinforces it by changing its quality from affectionate to hateful, its expression from devotion to persecution. The projection of initiative, which is a regular component of the paranoia complex, does not always accompany the libidinized abandonment or destruction of the object, although it may. The addition of the aggressive energies of the death instincts, invoked by the pain which has brought about the need to abandon the object, is chiefly responsible for this conversion of an affectionate to a sadistic relation. Similarly, when incipient libidinal depletion of the ego threatens to cause pain, the defensive energies of the death instincts which are then evoked transform the jeopardized affectionate relation to a hostile, clinging one. To whatever extent this hostile, clinging attachment affords pleasure, it becomes sadistic. In some instances a love relation takes the form of masochistic enslavement to the object, or self-sacrifice in its favor. When even such a relation is threatened, either by the object or by dynamic influences arising within the ego of the subject, it too acquires an aggressive, clinging component which, in reflexive form, augments the masochism. If the self-sacrifice or enslavement is newly created by the need to cling, the latter initiates the masochism. Our energetic studies have thus led us to propose two roots for sadistic and masochistic behavior, above and beyond those now known. We propose that sadistic or masochistic behavior can come about when a defensive abandonment of the object (or reduction of self-esteem, or injury to the self) is libidinized, and when, under threat of libidinal depletion of the ego due to impending object loss, the jeopardized object relation is reinforced by the addition of the energies of the death instincts.

The relation between object loss and sadism is trenchantly presented in some of the writings of Albert Camus. Caligula, the youthful Roman emperor, is the subject of an early play (written in 1938) entitled simply *Caligula* (Camus, 1960). At the beginning of the action, Caligula's whereabouts are unknown; he has disappeared from his court without a trace. It is rumored that his disappearance is related to the death of his beloved sister, with whom he has consummated an incestuous relation. Caligula returns in a state of physical neglect and reports that he has been searching for the "moon" but cannot find it. Thereupon he embarks upon a series of vicious, sadistic acts directed against his nobles. He robs them, humiliates them, has them executed without cause, strangles them with his own hands, rapes their wives in their presence, and perverts their sons. As the action proceeds, Caligula displays increasing megalomania and bizarre behavior. One of his last acts is to dress as the goddess Venus and demand the worship of the populace. When an attempt is made on his life, he kills himself by jumping from a high point.

This play can be interpreted as a Greek tragedy—that is, as the acting out on the stage of a common intrapsychic process. As a result of the incestuous guilt, the superego decrees that the object must be given up. The subject suffers great pain and at first denies the loss of the object. He wishes only to die, for the pain of isolation is too great for him to tolerate. Then the sadistic behavior seems to provide him with some respite. As we see, the respite is only temporary; in the end, he does kill himself. Moreover, it appears that his provocative behavior is inviting retaliatory destruction. Even in the sadism itself, the superego exerts a self-punitive influence. But what is the meaning of the sadism here? In one sense it is clearly an attempt to deflect outward the superego's punishment. It has another aspect, though, which pertains to this discussion. Unable to tolerate the real loss or abandonment of the object, Caligula proceeds to re-treat to a narcissistic position. He identifies with his lost sister and so undoes the loss, and then loves himself as he had loved her. He becomes megalomanic. But he complements this withdrawal by in-tensifying his detachment from the world of real people and real love. This he effects by attempting to eradicate the world of people, to which he is still attracted, but which also increases his pain by re-minding him of his lost love and his Oedipal guilt. We have seen, however, that the schizophrenic retreat cannot be sustained unless there is ego depletion, which seems here to advance only to the phase of clinging. In its absence, the schizophrenic clings with his left hand to the object he pushes away with his right. It is my im-pression that Caligula libidinizes the destruction of his nobles, thus obtaining erotic instinctual gratification even while he is destroying them. Again, his destruction of his intimates is a self-destruction in several ways. First, we have noted that it is a provocative invitation to assassination. Second, he is destroying his own court and his own people. Third, the megalomanic schizophrenic finds his way back to love objects by projecting himself onto them. This projection is indicated in the play, for example, by Caligula's accusing a noble of wishing to poison himself, that is, he projects his own suicidal wish. Caligula promptly strangles him. I have brought this illustra-tion to show that sadism can grow out of a need to abandon and to cling to the object at the same time. The combined murder of the object and suicide that we encounter at times in schizophrenia is an abbreviated version of the same process. In addition, in these cases, the simultaneous death is seen as a reunion and as a rebirth. In other writings of Camus one sees a preoccupation with the prob-lem of psychic detachment from love objects and the destructive, immoral behavior that often results. The fact that this destructive immorality is the consequence of relinquishing the love object in obedience to the superego is ironic. But we are familiar with such irony in our patients, and we call it a "return of the repressed," which describes Caligula's case too.

We have already mentioned the virtues of intoxicants for afford-ing the narcissistic illusion of sustenance. Addiction to foods and beverages and the accumulation of possessions of various kinds af-ford a symbolic repletion. From a social point of view, the use of al-cohol, while publicly condemned, is actually sanctioned by most of American and European society. Alcoholic socialization offers the drinker the repleting influence of social affection to supplement the chemical effect of the drug. Excessive eating, however, is often done in solitude, and the resulting obesity tends to reduce the individual's self-esteem even further and so to exacerbate his isolation from love objects.

There is a semi-social phenomenon, similar in some respects to a craving on the one hand and to hypochondria on the other. It is the eagerness of large segments of the population to subscribe to pseudo-preventatives or pseudo-medical remedies for nonspecific ailments. Generally these are oral activities of one kind or another. Dietary fads are one example. Another is the use of vitamins by large segments of the population without medical advice. Here an active agent, which is therapeutic under certain circumstances, is used magically to combat the inner pain of incipient or partial depletion. Other medicaments used in a similar way, patent "tonics," often contain alcohol and so surreptitiously provide the comforts of the latter to people who might refuse to indulge in frank intoxicants. The extent of this behavior is astonishing. The amount of money spent annually in the consumption of such preparations may perhaps be taken as a measure of the prevalence of misery, which I believe is essentially the consequence of incipient, early, or partial depletion.

What maneuvers can be employed to replete an ego which has already suffered a significant degree of depletion? This is a serious question of great therapeutic importance. We have learned that the psychic energizers can do this job, but we still have no idea what it is that determines whether and when a pathologic state of depletion will spontaneously come to an end. In the case of mourning, Freud suggested that depletion continues until the mourning work —the realistic review and dissolution of affectionate ties to the lost object—is completed. Is there a similar process which must be accomplished in the case of melancholia? Is a shift of endocrine balance required to make the individual once more responsive to opportunities for object love? Is it now a psychologic and now an organic factor which is operative? It will be important in studying this problem to investigate the brief, mild, reversible depletions that we often see in analytic work. We might attempt to determine what it is that makes a depletion reversible and what factors make it irreversible. These data are still to be accumulated.

I think it is true that certain mild states of depletion are readily reversible. I have seen spontaneous resolution occur especially easily in patients with obsessive-compulsive neurosis. While serious depletion is relatively infrequent among such individuals, it does occur—particularly under the impact of object loss, to which they are more sensitive than others. Here a return of the object or its replacement with a substitute is often sufficient to correct the depletion.

LIBIDO SUPPLY AND GROUP MORALE

I think the problems of object ties and libido fluctuation we have been discussing relate to the general question of morale. What seems to be involved is the phenomenon of hope as opposed to despair. In the presence of a serious personal blow, one attempts to prevent the demoralization of the victim by sustaining in him the hope of future gratification. This hope, it is expected, will retard the depletion and perhaps prevent its progress to the point of irreversibility.

Let us take note of the fact that we now know of three criteria which distinguish normal depletion of the libido supply of the ego from a pathologic deprivation. First, normal depletion may follow object loss due to the exigencies of reality or the preference of the object; pathologic depletion is consequent to abandonment of the object out of neurotic needs. Second, normal depletion drains both the unsublimated drive energies of the instinctual impulses and the sublimated, tonic energies of the ego supplement *pari passu;* pathologic depletion decreases one more promptly than the other, so that a disequilibrium results. Third, normal depletion tends to reverse when a substitute object appears, or in any case, within a few days or weeks; pathologic depletion resists reversal and may persist for weeks, months, or years.

To revert to the question of morale, the influence upon it of the group is well known. Group support for a single individual or a small number who have suffered some catastrophic loss may limit the degree of demoralization, or at least hasten recovery from it. But what happens when an entire population faces an impending disaster or has just sustained one? Natural causes as well as human agents conspire to produce such events now as in the past. Famine, flood, and epidemic are better controlled in the more advanced countries than they were, but war, captivity, enslavement, genocide, and tyranny are more devastating than ever, and more than cancel whatever respite has been obtained from the former. Our generations have not been spared mass tragedy. I have no new data to add to the subject of individual and group panic, but we can say a few things about despair.

Elie Cohen (1953) has described the behavior of individuals in the concentration camps of Nazi Germany. The immediate response to incarceration with its attendant horrors and tortures was, in many instances, fright; in others, it was a sense of depersonalization or loss of reality feeling. There followed for most people a phase of "apathy" characterized by inertia and retardation, which lasted a week or two. It was succeeded by a period of depression and mourning, extending from three to six months. This initial sequence was the most traumatic phase of the entire concentration camp ordeal, because most of those who succumbed did so then. The immediate depersonalization and loss of reality sense were evidently the same defenses against acknowledging a painful reality that we have already discussed. The apathetic phase, judging from Cohen's description, comprised both a dynamic detachment from reality and a libido depletion. In the state of apathy, the prisoner took no interest in his surroundings or even in protecting himself. The "mournful, depressive" attitude signifies, in my opinion, the beginning of a gradual restoration of libido and an attempt to acknowledge and surmount the full extent of the catastrophe. It is common clinical experience that the appearance of sadness and weeping in melancholia usually heralds recovery.

Concentration camp inmates who learned to endure their ordeal and survived exhibited three principal patterns of behavior. One was a desperate clinging to life, although in many instances it meant a betrayal of the individual's personal standards and morals. The quest for food was a principal concern. Cohen and others consider this the result of the grossly deficient diet provided to the prisoners. I do not doubt that starvation alone can cause such behavior, but in this situation, I believe the metabolic requirements of the body were powerfully reinforced by the oral, clinging efforts to combat libidinal depletion. The latter was attributable to numerous factors, including the loss of family and possessions, the threat of pain and death, the loss of self-esteem due to degradation, and, of course, the inadequate nutrition and excessive physical demands. The state of partial or severe depletion was responsible for the absence of genital eroticism even when the acute fright and the period of grief had passed. The pursuit of food was matched by the avoidance of danger. These two preoccupations, in most prisoners, overrode all other considerations of loyalty, friendship, compassion, and morality.

A second form of behavior seen in surviving prisoners was a readjustment of immediate interests and aims to conform to a realistic evaluation of possible gratification within the world of the concentration camp. The prisoner attempted to extract a maximum of pleasure from a narcissistic cathexis of somatic and psychic sensations.

A third form of behavior was characteristic of those prisoners who seemed to tolerate their incarceration most effectively; it was, in fact, more of an attitude than a behavior pattern. Two separate components often concurred, though not always. One was a persistent concern with a group ideal—a political, religious, or national ideal. Most writers on the subject agree that an idealistic orientation strengthened the individual's tolerance of the rigors of concentration camp life. The second was an ability to view oneself in a detached, condescending way, from the viewpoint, so to speak, of the superego. The people who adopted such an attitude often were able to evince a sense of humor with respect to themselves and their plight. We would say that they did not take themselves too seriously. Cohen, in fact, quotes Freud's 1928 paper on humor in which he relates the capacity for humor to the ego's ability to view itself from the viewpoint of the superego. Both of these attitudes originate, as do the two forms of behavior mentioned above, in a deflection of erotic interest from the world of outside objects to the ego—in other words, a shift to narcissism. These first two behavior patterns cathect the coenesthetic and affective sensations of the ego; in contradistinction, the narcissistic foundation for the third attitude consists of a cathexis of the superego by object libido.

I do not question the observations of Cohen and the others whom he quotes. I wonder, though, whether it is correct to say that these people survived *because* they retained their ideals or their sense of humor. In so doing, we are merely displacing the problem of individual fate one step farther; we have not specified what it is that makes one man more idealistic or tolerant than another. I suspect that we can only state that these are modes of survival, but that we cannot determine why these modes are available to some and not to others. It is legitimate to infer, though, that in each of the three cases there was a mobilization of psychic energies, and that this mobilization probably played an essential role in survival. In the first instance, there was the clinging type of mobilization in which the energies of the death instincts reinforce the residual libido. In the second and third instances, there was sufficient energy to obtain narcissistic gratification, but not so much as to constitute any great plethora of object libido. The lack of any consistent sexual desire demonstrates the dearth of object libido. Moreover, we have seen in Chapter III that the ego gives voice to the superego only in states of relative ego dearth. The fact that the voice of the superego in the state of humorous, detached self-observation is not the harsh, painful voice that castigates the ego in melancholia, indicates that the libido level is relatively low but still above painful, pathologic levels.

Paul Friedman (1948, 1949) has reported his observations of survivors of German concentration camps and other displaced persons. The psychic disturbances he encountered were those persisting after liberation, although some of the people he examined had been reinterned in the detention camps of Cyprus under conditions little different, except for the absence of the threat of murder, from the Nazi camps they had left. Most of the complaints dealt with disturbances of somatic function—gastrointestinal, cardiac, and muscular—and also headaches, dizziness, and so forth. These represented narcissistic redirection of libido and were accompanied in many instances by depletion of the ego. Friedman says that they were usually accompanied by anxiety states and occasionally panic, confusion, disorientation, and hallucinations.

All of the children displayed a fatigue beyond anything that could be explained by their physical condition. Some of the adolescents showed a marked sleepiness, so extreme at times as to warrant the term narcolepsy. This condition is often encountered among hysterical and schizophrenic patients who are artificially maintained at a high libido level by the administration of an energizing drug. Since this chemically-stabilized energy state precludes the recourse to depletion as a defense, a dynamic aversion must be invoked, and enforced sleep acts as such. I have encountered this mechanism in three of my patients—R. L. X., X. N. Z. and K. N. X. The tendency to sleep may also present simply as fatigue, though the latter com-

plaint may also refer to the subjective appreciation of ego depletion. Marked apathy and emotional shallowness in many of these
adolescents indicated a psychic detachment from those experiences
which, in small doses, would evoke horror and grief.

Depression with guilt appeared in many adults. The guilt was
attributed by these individuals to the fact that they alone had survived when so many others hadn't. I cannot comment upon the
validity of this explanation, but I would attribute the conscious appearance of guilt to ego depletion. The latter also accounted, in my
opinion, for the pronounced loss of genital sexuality which Friedman reports, an absence of genital fantasies, conscious desire, masturbation, nocturnal emission, erection, and even cessation of menses.

"In all the survivors of the Nazi camps, one might say, the self-
preservative instinct became so dominant that it blocked out all the
other instincts. Indeed, it would seem that the whole libido had to
be withdrawn from the outer world and focused on the struggle for
survival. One might also speculate on whether this narcissistic withdrawal created a vulnerable area in the psyche, which, later on,
would account for the appearance of those psychosomatic ailments
so general among the survivors of the concentration camp" (Friedman, 1949).

It was difficult to organize and direct these people. Just as many
depressed patients are hostile toward their therapists, so these survivors from disaster were resentful of their rescuers and leaders. It
seems that once depletion has occurred, it is not easily reversed by
promises of future gratification unsupported by current relief. Depleted egos do not readily respond to offers of affection, nor do they
readily associate to form groups. According to Friedman (1949),
effective leadership of these survivors was difficult to achieve.

A different view of the problems of group morale may be obtained from religious literature, particularly prophetic writings.
These are of two distinct varieties, prophecies of consolation and
prophecies of denunciation. The purpose of consolation seems to be
a "remoralization," encouragement, inspiration. Prophecies of de-
liverance from ongoing affliction are apparently intended to re-
mobilize libidinal energies, for one of the methods of increasing ego
libido is to promise gratification. Temptation, for example, which is
an immediate promise, intensifies libidinal pressure, often to the
point of overcoming inhibition. Denunciation has the intention of
discouraging libidinal gratification when the latter has begun to

override superego protest. Doom is predicted as the ineluctable punishment for illicit pleasure. The individual is exhorted to surrender his hedonistic delights voluntarily, lest he lose them in catastrophic retribution. To whatever extent denunciation is effective, it acts to forestall the self-destruction which is ultimately invoked by the offended superego, and the ensuing libidinal depletion; it disarms the superego.

A third kind of religious appeal exploits the feeling of guilt that accompanies libidinal depletion, whether the latter is caused by a loss dictated by the superego or simply by fate. If even a fortuitous disaster can be rationalized as a punishment for guilt, then the power to overcome it seems to lie in the hand of the victim. In other words, accepting the responsibility for all the misfortunes one suffers is a form of narcissistic megalomania. It differs from the megalomania of libido plethora where omnipotence is attributed to the ego; in the megalomania which ascribes all adversity to guilt, the omnipotence is attributed to the superego. Since the superego is a representation of the parent, and the child knows that he can influence the parent, a confession that misfortune is due to guilt represents an attempt by the individual to take his fate into his own hands. Religion has established techniques of atonement for guilt. New religions, sects, cults, and whole new religious systems have come into existence when the methods of older, accepted religions have failed to improve group morale in the face of continuing adversity. If their advent is accompanied by incidental relief, or if their promises, their sanction of group illusions, or their reinforcement of group ties actually effect a "remoralization," then they achieve the status of a legitimate component of the superego of each member of the group. Having achieved such status, they acquire even greater power to sustain the libidinal vigor of the group.

Among the arguments presented in this chapter, several points have lent themselves to illustration from religion. Freud noted that the religious life was chosen by some as a path to happiness, although he deplored this choice since it was essentially illusory (Freud, 1927c). In a recent paper on religious worship, I proposed for investigation the hypothesis that many forms of religious worship act to sustain the level of libido in the ego. The beliefs which Freud deprecated certainly have the function of supporting morale. However, there is more to religion than belief. Living in a Christian culture, we tend to think of religion as a system of convictions. It is true that to question items of faith is blasphemy, but when we analyze a patient we refuse to be limited by his rules in conducting the investigation. The fact that religion tells us that belief is central does not mean that it is. In Judaism, for example, belief is considerably less important than it is in Christianity. Judaism has no canonized credo, and one drawn up by Maimonides was never granted full authority. In fact, it is not entirely clear from Talmudic literature just what a Jew is expected to believe. Virtuous behavior is considered more important than belief, even when it is not performed in the name of religion. Religions share forms of worship to a greater extent than they share beliefs.

If we turn our attention to these worship performances, we shall find it easy to support the hypothesis I have suggested. "The power of religion over life," said Robertson Smith in 1894, "lies . . . mainly in its influence on the general tone and temper of men's minds, which it elevates to higher courage and purpose, and raises above a brutal servitude to the physical wants of the moment. . . ." And again, "The sacrificial feast was not only an expression of gladness but a means of driving away care, for it was set forth with every circumstance of gaiety, with garlands, perfumes and music, as well as with stores of meat and wine" (Smith, 1956).

Writing of animal sacrifice, Smith asserts that it served to strengthen the tie among the members of the clan and between them and their god by virtue of participation of both sacrificers and god in the same meal. The meal consisted of the flesh and blood of a totem animal which was kin to both. We recognize the psychic mechanism of this strengthening of group ties as identification by oral incorporation, a defense against object loss, and one which Freud said was employed by the ego to replenish a failing libido supply (Freud, 1933a). Ancient animal sacrifice is the prototype of ritual meals which exist in modern religious practice and which tend also to become established in nonreligious groups. I have observed that even among those of my Jewish patients who have abandoned religious observance almost completely the Passover Seder still exerts a powerful pull. We may deprecate as illusion the idea that by the ingestion of the sacrificial victim, or his representation in modern practice, the participant acquires the strength and vigor of the god of the clan. It is not illusory, however, that a sense of renewal or rebirth, an increase of ego libido, does result from the experience of participating in a ritual meal. This innervating influence arises both from the symbolic act and from the cohesion introduced into the group by this activity.

The requirement of sabbath abstention from labor may seem strange if we regard religion merely as an authority which restricts pleasure in the interests of morality. But if we are willing to consider its influence on the regulation of psychic energy, we notice that sabbath observance is a means for strengthening affectionate family bonds by companionship and intimacy. Love between husband and wife and between parents and children is usually attenuated, inhibited, and distorted to some extent by the factor of primary repression of sexuality and Oedipal guilt. The effect of these inhibiting influences is to induce people to seek erotic gratification outside the family, in the associations formed in work, at school, in social and community organizations. If this deflection of tender love to individuals outside the family becomes too extensive, family life will suffer, sensual drives will be distorted or frustrated, and the extrafamilial relations will acquire a sensual component which may, in turn, exert disruptive effects on the community and incur superego protest and punishment. No system can consistently support ego libido and sustain morale without providing for some instinctual gratification. Inhibitions can be tolerated only when some channels for satisfaction remain open. Hence, by encouraging family pleasure, religion tends to offer a compromise between an adequate minimum of gratification and, on the other hand, instinctual satisfaction so free that it would incur internal resistance and agitate the social organization.

Religion has not disdained to use intoxicating beverages in its efforts to restore and support morale. In the religions we know most familiarly, wine which "gladdeneth the hearts of men" is used ceremonially. Other intoxicants are said to play a role in the less well-known, more exotic cults.

It is easy to understand that from influencing group behavior in the interest of sustaining morale, religion advanced to the regulation of social behavior. At first its requirements were relatively coarse, dealing with sexual and status taboos. With the development of civilization and the progress of culture, religious restrictions and admonitions became more extensive and more subtle. Law was supplemented by morality, and morality by ethics. Today, by formulating specific sanctions, restrictions, and prohibitions, religion permits the individual to come to grips with his superego on a conscious basis. The superego, as we have seen, is a potent factor in the determination of the level of ego libido. When the superego is satisfied, the ego is proud, its self-esteem is increased, and its libido supply is raised. When the superego is dissatisfied, self-esteem falls and libido dwindles. If the requirements of the superego are not consciously known, they cannot be taken into account in planning. We have seen, too, that under the pressure of libido excess, the tendency to pursue instinct gratification is not restrained by acknowledgment of the superego's jurisdiction until the latter, in a corrective protest, forces the individual to relinquish his pleasure and thus to lose libido. The code offered by religion makes the requirements of the superego conscious, so that the response of the superego to any action or wish may be anticipated and reckoned with. Optimally, the operation of the code should have the effect of sanctioning a program of minimal but adequate pleasure, and of precluding an intensity of gratification that would be likely to incur superego protest.

These are illustrations of the influence of specific features of religion upon libido economy. One of the most consistent and important of these is the fact that it promotes group cohesion. Robertson Smith points out that the ancient Semitic religions were primarily "an affair of the community rather than of individuals." Today, some of the practices, petitions, and regulations of religion are formally individual communications between the worshipper and God. Yet in most cases the act of affirmation of belief, the recitation of prayer, brings the individual into a definite relation to the religious community. I indicated before that personal relations develop in group working situations. They then have the advantage of escaping ego or superego objection since they are only incidental to the consciously known and laudable purpose of work, and since they are necessarily attenuated because of the absence of physical intimacy and the participation of the whole group. Similarly, personal relations evolve in religious organizations, and these not only escape protest for the reasons I have mentioned but actually acquire superego sanction. This strengthening of group organization may be the most important single influence of religion upon the libido economy of the individual.

The relation between religious worship and individual libido level is fortunately open to clinical investigation. Certain observations are there for the making. For example, I have found that some patients (for example, X. N. Z. and M. T.) who have had no religious interests suddenly began to give voice to guilt, to appeal to God, and to promise restitution when they were suffering libido depletion. But these were just expressions of wishes, unaccompanied by any acts of worship or any interest in the religious community. Other patients, not depleted, who had always been pious and observant, participated in worship and preferred group to individual service, but expressed little or no guilt or self-observation. At times a rebellious attitude toward authority would lead to a temporary cessation of performance, but no essential change in its form was attempted and, unless there was an accompanying depletion, no guilt ensued. Such observations should be checked and extended. The availability of energy-increasing and -decreasing drugs makes possible an almost experimental investigation of the effect of ego libido on worship behavior.

The political organization of the community, no less than its religious organization, may be conceived of as both influencing and responding to the level of group morale. It is legitimate to ask the reason for the overall trend toward increased democracy in Western Europe and the Americas in recent centuries. Under what circumstances of libidinal economy do the people welcome an absolutist government under a single leader, and under what circumstances do they find an absolute leader oppressive? What is the effect on individual libido and on group morale of arduous conditions of living on the one hand, and of prosperity on the other? When do men tend to conserve traditional forms and values, and when do they depart from them? Are there characteristic states of group and individual morale which favor war? We have seen that nations and peoples tend to repeat old destructive patterns as consistently and blindly as do individuals. These are all current issues of the greatest practical importance. I believe that there may be sufficient correlated historical and biographical data available to enable us to study the relations among history, group morale, and individual libido level.

In summary, the chief occasions for human unhappiness lie in loss of object, loss of self-esteem, and loss of ego libido. These troubles may be effected by external influence or they may be the outcome of inner conflict. The social group offers opportunities for sublimated or attenuated instinctual gratification which tends to weaken the destructive conflict. Also, when disaster of external origin has shaken the individual's equilibrium, society can offer certain forms of consolation and compensation which help the individual to surmount his difficulties. The effective social group in any given case may be the family, the clan, the working team, the religious congregation, the neighborhood, the local community, or the nation. Family, religious, national, or political ties may be exploited in the interest of group remoralization. Study problems suggested by these considerations include the mutual interrelation of individual ego libido and group morale, and the relations between these and current religious, philosophic, economic, and political systems.

APPENDIX

The Pharmaceutic Agents

Iₙ ᴛʜɪꜱ ᴀᴘᴘᴇɴᴅɪx I shall describe the several groups of pharmaceutic agents which are useful in psychiatry. I shall not attempt to assess the value or toxicity of the individual members of each group, first, because my experience does not provide such data, and second, because the selection of one among the various agents in each group is far less important in any clinical problem than deciding which pharmacologic group is indicated.

Let me state parenthetically at this point that I am not proposing to give a complete list of all the available psychically active agents, nor am I proposing to evaluate any of them. Omission does not imply disapproval, but only that I am not familiar with a particular drug. I wish to repeat, too, that all the information needed to use any given drug will not be provided here. I propose merely to indicate the specific psychic effects of the various substances to the extent that I know them. This information should help the psychiatrist to select from among the various categories the type of drug which will produce the effect he desires. Where there are several chemicals in a single category, the selection of one rather than another is often a matter of indifference. If the information is available, one should select that drug which is least toxic, has the fewest undesirable side effects, and requires least frequent administration. In general, I favor a drug which has been in use for several years over one which is not well known. There is also something to be said for becoming very familiar with the actions and idiosyncracies of one or a few members of each category rather than trying them all.

The problem of nomenclature for the newer drugs is complicated by the fact that there is no general agreement about their mode of action and their therapeutic potency. "Tranquilizer" was perhaps the first name to gain currency; I shall retain it in this book, for I consider it appropriate for some of the drugs to which it has been applied. The term "psychic energizer" was applied to other drugs (Ostow and Kline, 1959; Loomer, Saunders, and Kline, 1957) in accordance with the theory presented here. Other terms such as ataractic, neuroleptic, psycholeptic, thymoleptic, psychotropic, and psychopraxic have not found general acceptance and offer nothing to classification. At the present time so many psychically active drugs are available that a large volume would be required to contain an account of the chemistry, pharmacology, clinical action, toxic effects, and recommended uses of each. While a handbook of this type would have some important advantages, it is not my purpose to compile this information. What I propose to offer in this appendix is only the view of the psychic effects of these drugs which has crystallized out of my own experience with them, and the indications for, and manner of, administering them.

Of the pharmaceutic agents that possess therapeutic potency in mental illness, a large number act by altering the ego's content of libido. Another group acts without affecting ego libido significantly. Among the former we can distinguish two principal varieties —those that decrease ego libido and those that increase it.

THE TRANQUILIZERS

In the category of tranquilizers I include those drugs whose principal action is to decrease the libido content of the ego. In general, the tranquilizers ameliorate mania and incipient schizophrenia, and aggravate melancholia. They retard most behavior in animals, spontaneous and conditioned, and from the clinical observations I have seen in the literature, I think it would be fair to infer that their primary action is to diminish instinctual impetus. The tranquilizers decrease vital functions such as blood pressure and body temperature, and seem to favor parasympathetic tone. They may prevent menstruation or interfere with the normal cycle. Given long enough or in high enough dosage, they elicit evidences of basal ganglia disorder, either hypomotility (Parkinsonism) or hypermotility (dystonia, tics, spasms, akathisia). At present, we know of three chemically distinct groups of tranquilizers—the phenothiazines, reserpine, and tetrabenazine.

THE PHENOTHIAZINES

The agents in this group have in common the phenothiazine nucleus, and differ from each other only in the prosthetic groups R_1 and R_2. Not all derivatives of phenothiazine have a strong tranquilizing action. Most of these drugs oppose nausea and vomiting and are sometimes used as antiemetics. Annoying side effects which are commonly encountered are visual disturbances due to impaired accommodation, dryness of the mouth and throat, and,

THE PHENOTHIAZINE NUCLEUS

occasionally, swelling of the breasts with slight mammary secretion. Some instances of seizures have been reported, occurring either during medication or after withdrawal. While all the phenothiazine tranquilizers seem to have essentially the same therapeutic effect, other pharmacologic properties divide them into two groups, the chlorpromazine type and the prochlorperazine type (Freyhan, 1958).

The Chlorpromazine Type

Chemically, chlorpromazines are characterized by a chain of three carbon atoms followed by a nitrogen, in the R_2 position. Pharmacologically, these agents are less potent than the prochlorperazine type; they require daily doses of the order of 100 mg., whereas the latter are efficacious in doses of the order of 1 to 10 mg. The former combine an immediate sedative effect with their tranquilizing action, which ordinarily requires days or weeks to become manifest; the latter lack this sedative effect and in fact may produce insomnia. Administered in therapeutic doses, chlorpromazine-type drugs are somewhat less apt than the prochlorperazines to evoke extrapyramidal effects, and when they do, these effects are more likely to be of the hypokinetic rather than the hyperkinetic variety. From a therapeutic point of view, we know of no specific preferential indication for one of these two groups over the other. However, the immediate sedative effectiveness of the chlorpromazines may be used advantageously in the treatment of disturbed and excited patients, who in any case will not obtain the specific tranquilizing action for several days.

Chlorpromazine (Thorazine: Smith, Kline and French). Chlorpromazine was the first of the phenothiazines to be used successfully in mental illness, and it has become a standard to which all others are compared. The syllable "chlor" in its name denotes the fact that the R_1 position on the phenothiazine nucleus is occupied by a chlorine atom. The R_2 position is occupied by the chain:

$$-CH_2\,CH_2\,CH_2\,N\,(CH_3)_2$$

By now there has been a great deal of experience with this drug. Its action is gentle, reliable, and constant. Its chief drawback is its occasional toxicity. Severe and sometimes fatal blood dyscrasias have been reported, including agranulocytosis, hypoplastic anemia, and leukopenia. Jaundice is also seen and should be watched for. Orthostatic hypotension makes its use difficult in patients with low blood pressure and sclerotic vessels. Dermatitis and photosensitivity are distressing side effects, but readily reversible. Chlorpromazine potentiates the action of barbiturates, narcotics, general anesthetics, and alcohol.

Promazine (Sparine: Wyeth). Promazine is identical with chlorpromazine, except that the hydrogen in the R_1 position is not replaced. It has been especially recommended for the treatment of acute alcoholic excitement and for delirium. Barsa and Kline (1957) found promazine to resemble chlorpromazine in its clinical effect on chronic schizophrenic patients, but to be weaker than the latter, milligram for milligram, in both therapeutic and toxic potential.

Mepazine (Pacatal: Warner-Chilcott). Mepazine, like promazine, has no prosthetic group in the R_1 position, but three carbon atoms in a chain are affixed at one end to the terminal nitrogen of the R_2 chain, and at the other end to the second carbon of the R_2 chain, forming a ring. Bowes (1956), and Sarwer-Foner and Koranyi (1957) found its tranquilizing action similar to that of chlorpromazine, but it is less sedative and possesses atropine-like, parasympatholytic side effects. Its toxic potential also seems to resemble that of chlorpromazine.

Triflupromazine (Vesprin: Squibb). The structure of the triflupromazine molecule resembles that of chlorpromazine, except that the R_1 position is occupied by three fluorine atoms rather than the single chlorine of chlorpromazine. Its properties are essentially similar to those of chlorpromazine.

Thioridazine (Mellaril: Sandoz). Thioridazine is a more recent substance and differs from other phenothiazines by the introduction of a thiomethyl radical (-SCH_3) into the R_1 position, where the others have a halogen or no prosthetic group. Also, a chain of four carbon atoms is attached at one end to the terminal nitrogen of the R_2 chain of promazine, and at the other end to the third carbon of the R_2 chain, forming a ring. Data distributed by the manufacturer suggest that thioridazine resembles chlorpromazine in its therapeutic potency, but is considerably less toxic and has fewer side effects. Kinross-Wright (1959) concurs.

Methoxypromazine Maleate (Tentone: Lederle). Methoxypromazine maleate is one of the newest of the chlorpromazine-type drugs. It differs from the latter only in bearing a methoxy group (-OCH_3) in the R_1 position. It is said to be somewhat less potent than chlorpromazine, but also less apt to produce side effects.

The Prochlorperazine Type

Chemically, the prochlorperazine type of phenothiazine differs from the chlorpromazine group only in the R_2 side chain. Whereas in the chlorpromazine type the terminal nitrogen bears either two methyl groups or one methyl group and a three- or four-carbon chain which doubles back to attach a more proximal point on R_2, in the prochlorperazine type, the terminal nitrogen belongs to a

$$-CH_2CH_2CH_2N\diagup^{CH_3}_{\diagdown CH_2 - R_3}$$

THE R_2 SIDE CHAIN IN THE CHLORPROMAZINE SERIES

piperazine radical. Thus, the R_2 side chain of a chlorpromazine-type drug appears as shown above.

Here R_3 may be a hydrogen atom or a chain of two or three CH_2 units which is also attached at another point on the R_2 chain. In the prochlorperazine type, the R_2 side chain appears as follows:

$$-CH_2CH_2CH_2-N\bigcirc N-R_3$$

THE R_2 SIDE CHAIN IN THE PROCHLORPERAZINE SERIES

As I have noted above, members of the prochlorperazine group are effective in smaller amounts, they do not possess a sedative action as the chlorpromazine type compounds do, and they are more likely to produce extrapyramidal disturbance, especially of the hyperkinetic variety. The Parkinsonian symptoms of rigidity, masked facies, tremor, and salivation are well known. The hyperkinetic syndrome includes spasms and tics involving face, jaw, and tongue; torticollis; dystonias; myoclonic twitches and spasms of the long trunk and limb muscles; hyperextension of the neck and trunk; and oculogyric spasms. These may be accompanied by sweating, pallor, and fever (Freyhan, 1958). Since this extrapyramidal hyperkinesis is very distressing to many patients, it is wise to prevent it by prescribing an anti-Parkinsonian drug whenever a moderate or large dose of a prochlorperazine type of phenothiazine is given. Any of the anti-Parkinsonian drugs will do. I have been recommending a 2 mg. tablet of benztropine methanesulfonate (Cogentin: Merck, Sharp and Dohme) to be taken at bedtime, since it has a sedative effect; if necessary, it may also accompany a morning dose of tranquilizing medication. Unfortunately, the atropine-like action of the anti-Parkinsonian drugs reinforce the visual disturbance and dryness of the mouth and throat often produced by the tranquilizer. The piperazine compounds seem to be less toxic to blood and liver than the chlorpromazine group, and perhaps they are not toxic at all. Among the piperazine drugs as a group, I know of no important clinical criteria for choosing one over the others. I list them in order of increasing potency, although differences in potency are not of great clinical significance. The more potent agents, given in large dose, can exert maximal therapeutic influence, but their greater potency also makes them more difficult to regulate, especially in cases where only a small or moderate effect is required.

Prochlorperazine (Compazine: Smith, Kline and French). Prochlorperazine is one of the first of the piperazine phenothiazines to have been used clinically. Like chlorpromazine, it has a chlorine atom in the R_1 position. The R_3 position in the piperazine side chain is occupied by a methyl group.

Thiopropazate (Dartal: Searle). Like prochlorperazine, thiopropazate too has a chlorine atom in the R_1 position. The R_3 position on the piperazine structure is occupied by an acetoxyethyl group ($-CH_2CH_2OC(=O)CH_3$). It is effective in doses approximately equivalent to, or slightly less than, prochlorperazine.

Perphenazine (Trilafon: Schering). Trilafon, like the two drugs mentioned above, has a chlorine atom in position R_1. It differs from them in having a hydroxyethyl group ($-CH_2CH_2OH$) in the R_3 position on the piperazine radical. It is somewhat more potent than the former two.

Trifluoperazine (Stelazine: Smith, Kline and French). By replacing the chlorine atom in position R_1 with three fluorine atoms while retaining the prochlorperazine structure otherwise intact, a compound with considerably greater tranquilizing potency has been obtained. I would guess that, milligram for milligram, it is of the order of five times as potent as prochlorperazine.

Fluphenazine (Permitil: White; and Prolixin: Squibb). The most powerful of all the phenothiazine tranquilizers, more powerful than stelazine, is fluphenazine. It resembles stelazine in having three fluorine atoms in the R_1 position, but like Trilafon, it contains an ethyl hydroxide side chain on the R_3 position of the piperazine radical.

How do the phenothiazines work? What do they do? Three elements enter into this question. First, what is their psychic action? Second, on which somatic structures do they exert their influence? Third, how do they affect these structures? The psychic actions of all of these pharmaceutic agents, and their exploitation for therapeutic purposes, was the central concern of this book. At this point I shall merely call attention to the fact that I have placed the phenothiazines in the group of "tranquilizers," a term I employ to designate only those substances which, in my opinion, decrease the amount of libidinal energy available to the ego. It is important to bear in mind that there are few, if any, chemical substances that affect only one functional unit within the body and no others. As therapists we tend to think of the action we aim to obtain as the "specific action" of the drug; other effects are considered either side effects or toxic effects, depending upon whether they are innocent or noxious. For example, some of the phenothiazines, in addition to their energy-depleting effect, also possess an antiemetic action and an antihistamine action. The agents in the chlorpromazine series exert a sedative influence. This sedative influence is frequently confused with the energy-depleting action. The former is a quieting effect like that produced by the barbiturates. It may alleviate the excitement of mental illness temporarily by reducing the level of psychic activity, but it has no specific anti-psychotic action. The tranquilizing action is anti-psychotic. These differences will be developed below.

The substances in the prochlorperazine group are prepotent as tranquilizers, although they have no sedative effect whatever, and in fact tend to cause restlessness and insomnia. Physicians may prescribe chlorpromazine for a condition in which not a tranquilizer but an energizer is called for. Although the sedative effect of the drug may make the patient more comfortable for a while, his symptoms may increase after some time. If the dosage of medication is correspondingly increased, the physician will be puzzled to find that the patient becomes sicker. Chemists, physiologists, and psychologists seeking central correlates of drug action have seldom isolated the several discrete psychic actions that a single drug may exhibit in their experimental procedures. This confusion has made basic pharmacologic research more difficult, and its data more puzzling than necessary.

The actual tranquilizing action of the phenothiazines—and this is true of reserpine too—usually requires days or weeks to become demonstrable and therapeutically effective. On the other hand, the sedative action of the chlorpromazine group appears promptly upon administration: within five or ten minutes if given intramuscularly, and thirty to sixty minutes following oral dosage. Why does the tranquilizing influence take so long to become established? Part of the reason may be that effective local concentrations of either the drug itself, or of some metabolic product which accumulates as a result of the drug action, require days or weeks to accrue. We shall find that the therapeutic effects of the energizers follow a similar time course. In the case of those energizers that inhibit the action of monoamine oxidase, it has been demonstrated (see discussions by Teller and by Resnick of paper by Udenfriend, 1960) that unoxidized amines accumulate in the body slowly, requiring almost two weeks to reach significant values, and that they persist two to three weeks after the drug has been withdrawn. In this case, it is not clear whether the limiting factor is the slow decrease in the effective concentration of the oxidase or the slow accumulation of the unmetabolized amine. Another reason for the slow development of the therapeutic effect of psychopharmaceuticals may be that the shift in ego libido supply to a normal level cannot instantaneously repair a damaged ego. Repair of the ego which has suffered from a plethora or a deficiency of libido is a spontaneous process impelled only by the *vis medicatrix naturae,* probably associated with the ego's own synthetic power. It can occur only after the energy derangement has been corrected, but it is not effected directly by the drugs. There is considerable variation in the rate of this functional restoration among patients, depending upon a factor which we may call the "resilience" of the ego.

What is the locus of action of the phenothiazine drugs? This is still an unsolved problem. Acute as well as chronic administration to animal preparations of varying degrees of intactness have been found to cause changes in electrical function of a number of different brain structures. Just which of these alterations produces the tranquilizing effect has not been established. One method of study which seems especially promising is the method of investigating the influence of these drugs on the pattern of self-stimulation of the brain. It has been shown that when cats and other animals are given an opportunity to deliver a gentle electrical stimulus to certain loci in the brain by depressing a lever, they will do so repeatedly over long periods of time without other motivation (Olds, 1958, Lilly, 1959). Olds and Killam have investigated the effects of reserpine and chlorpromazine on self-stimulation cats. With reserpine, self-stimulation by means of electrodes placed in front of the anterior commissure is unaffected. In the case of more posteriorly situated electrodes, however, the rate of responding is much decreased, as it is also for electrodes placed in the hippocampus and in the amygdaloid nucleus. Self-stimulation by electrodes placed in the septal region remains unaffected. When the animal is given chlorpromazine, self-stimulation delivered to the amygdala, the lateral hippocampus, or the caudate nucleus, is diminished. Rates of stimulation to the hypothalamus and septal area are erratic (see Olds, 1957; Olds, Killam, and Bach-y-Rita, 1956). I suspect that these findings would be more consistent and more focused if the effects of chronic rather than acute administration of the drugs were studied.

In a paper written in 1956, Kline and I (Ostow and Kline, 1959) suggested that the site of the tranquilizing action of chlorpromazine and reserpine might be the striatum (see also Saunders, 1959). The principal reason for this localization is that both drugs, though structurally different, produce extrapyramidal effects, usually one or more components of the Parkinsonian syndrome. It has turned out that all of the more recently introduced phenothiazine drugs which are effective tranquilizers—and now a quite different molecule, tetrabenazine, which also appears to act as a tranquilizer—have significant influence on extrapyramidal function. It has so far been impossible completely to dissociate the tranquilizing action from the extrapyramidal influence.

How do the phenothiazine tranquilizers exert their effect on the central nervous system? The chemical pharmacology of all of the newer drugs has attracted a great deal of interest and industry, but no hypothesis has yet been able to command general acceptance.

RESERPINE

Reserpine is an alkaloid isolated from the root of certain species of Rauwolfia. It is one of the first of the true tranquilizers to have been studied and used therapeutically. Like the phenothiazines, which it preceded in clinical use, it seems to decrease the amount of libidinal energy available to the ego. It also has certain other effects upon the ego, including an ego-intoxicant and an hallucinogenic action. Like the phenothiazines, too, it tends to decrease spontaneous activity in man and animals. Its use impairs the establishment of conditioned responding, and the performance of conditioned behavior that has already been established. Vital functions are diminished: hypotension and sinus bradycardia are encountered fairly consistently, often pronounced in degree. Because of this property, reserpine is widely used for the treatment of essential hypertension. Like chlorpromazine, it exerts a mild sedative action over and above its tranquilizing action, but the two effects are quite

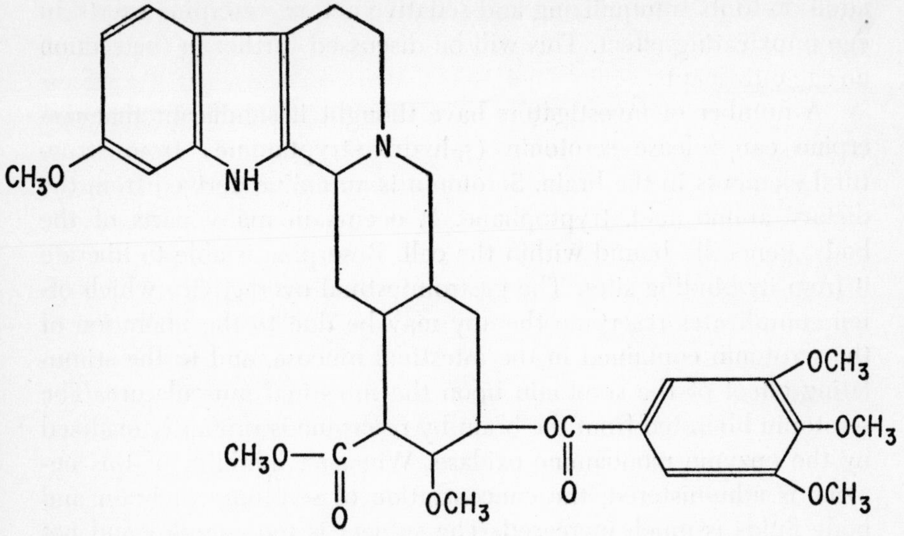

CH_3O—

CH_3O—C

O

OCH_3

N

NH

OC

O

OCH_3

OCH_3

OCH_3

RESERPINE

distinct, the former appearing immediately after administration and the latter only after days or weeks of chronic administration. Reserpine has been found capable of resolving acute schizophrenia and mania, while in at least some individuals it can elicit a melancholia. Side effects include nasal stuffiness, increased gastrointestinal activity, distressing dreams, and, as we have noted above, a Parkinsonian syndrome. It appears to be free of the potentiality of causing jaundice or agranulocytosis, a hazard in the use of some members of the chlorpromazine group.

While the action of reserpine resembles that of chlorpromazine in several ways, there are three conspicuous differences. First, the schizophrenic patient recovering with the aid of reserpine is more likely to experience a period of "turbulence" during the first few weeks than a similar patient under treatment with chlorpromazine (Barsa and Kline, 1956). Second, patients treated with reserpine often describe weird, horrifying dreams from which they awaken slowly, finding it difficult to distinguish waking reality from dream reality. Third, tranquilized to a similar degree, the chlorpromazine patient's conscious content is relatively constricted and limited, while in the case of the reserpine patient, his thoughts and dreams are likely to be more flagrantly erotic or aggressive than usual. Kline and I have pointed this out earlier and suggested that in addition to its tranquilizing and sedative action, reserpine exerts an ego intoxicating effect. This will be discussed further in the section on ego intoxicants.

A number of investigators have thought it significant that reserpine can release serotonin (5-hydroxytryptamine) from structural elements in the brain. Serotonin is an amine derived from the dietary amino acid, tryptophane. It occurs in many parts of the body, generally bound within the cell. Reserpine is able to liberate it from its binding sites. The gastrointestinal overactivity which often complicates reserpine therapy may be due to the liberation of the serotonin contained in the intestinal mucosa, and to the stimulating effect of the serotonin upon the intestinal musculature. The serotonin liberated from the brain by reserpine is promptly oxidized by the enzyme monoamine oxidase. When an inhibitor of this enzyme is administered, the concentration of serotonin in brain and body fluids is much increased. The subject is too complex and not sufficiently relevant to justify my reviewing here all of the hypotheses that have been proposed, and the data and arguments for and against them. Suffice it to say that, thus far, it has not been generally accepted that the tranquilizing action of reserpine is mediated via its release of serotonin (see Editorial, A.M.A., 1956; WHO Report No. 152, 1958; Brodie, 1960). A final resolution of the problem will have to take account of the fact that norepinephrine and other amines are released from the brain by reserpine in addition to serotonin, and also that the phenothiazines, which exhibit the same tranquilizing capacity, do not liberate amines from the brain.

TETRABENAZINE

(Nitoman: Hoffman-La Roche)

Tetrabenazine is a new drug which is currently being tried experimentally. It is presumed to be a tranquilizer because it seems to be most effective in schizophrenia. Like reserpine, it releases serotonin and norepinephrine from the brain. Its pharmacologic action comes on more quickly than that of reserpine, and also subsides more promptly after the drug is withdrawn. Like reserpine and chlorpromazine too, it produces Parkinsonism. It also induces drowsiness, but not hypotension. Assessment of its therapeutic value

$$O$$

$$-CH_2CH(CH_3)_2$$

$$CH_3O-$$

$$N$$

$$CH_3O-$$

TETRABENAZINE

waits upon further reports (see Heise, 1960; Stackhausen, 1960; Smith, 1960; Brodie, 1960; Voelkel, 1950).

THE PSYCHIC ENERGIZERS

In 1956, Kline and I prepared a paper, "The Psychic Action of Reserpine and Chlorpromazine," in which we proposed the hypothsis that the anti-psychotic effect exerted by both of these drugs lay in their ability to deplete the psychic apparatus of libidinal energy. Partly to test the clinical applicability and validity of the theory, partly as an intellectual exercise, we posed the question: What would be the clinical properties of a drug which facilitated the generation of psychic energy, if such a drug could be found? We predicted that: "It would relieve simple depression and at least the sadness and inertia of melancholia when aggression was present. It would reduce the sleep requirement and delay the onset of fatigue. It would increase appetite and sexual desire and increase behavioral drive in general. Motor and intellectual activity would be speeded. It would heighten responsiveness to stimuli, both pleasant and noxious, not by improving the function of apperception, but by increasing the readiness to respond to percepts that release instinctual behavior. The plethora of id energy would make large amounts of energy easily available to the ego so that there would be more than enough energy available for all tasks. Such a situation would result in a sense of joyousness and optimism. As the dose was raised to the point where id drives threatened the integrity of the ego, anxiety would appear. If the dose were raised still further, one would expect the id pressure finally to cause a rupture of ego defenses so that clinical neurosis or psychosis would ensue, depending upon the specific ego weakness which would determine its line of fracture."

This paper was read before the American Psychoanalytic Association in December 1956, but it was not published until 1959. At that time Kline added the following footnote: "This paper was written before the identification (by N. S. Kline) of iproniazid as a psychic energizer; with minor exceptions the predictions have proven correct." On the basis of these theoretical considerations, when the psychic effect of iproniazid was discovered, it was called a "psychic energizer" (Loomer, Saunders, and Kline, 1957).

The psychic energizers as a group tend to undo melancholia and to bring about mania or schizophrenia. Like the tranquilizers, their therapeutic effect requires weeks to become established, partly, perhaps, because the build-up of critically important amine substance is slow, and partly because the spontaneous reintegration of a disrupted ego takes some time. Energizers tend to increase vital functions, especially temperature, although simultaneously they induce a hypotension of some degree. While their physiologic effects can be duplicated in some animals, their behavioral effect, other than an increase in locomotor activity (Irwin, 1960; Irwin and Tabachnick, 1961), has not been elicited in animal studies (Pletscher, 1959). However, when iproniazid is administered to animals before reserpine, the latter induces excitement rather than sedation.

Three varieties of psychic energizer are currently in use: (1) monoamine oxidase inhibitors, (2) iminodibenzyl derivatives, and (3) deanol.

THE MONOAMINE OXIDASE INHIBITORS

The monoamine oxidase inhibitors are thought to achieve their energizing effect by inhibiting the enzyme which normally oxidizes some of the amines produced in the course of the degradation of amino acids. The evidence for this is not conclusive. It is based upon the observations, first, that among the substances used, the clinically effective dose varies inversely with potency for enzyme inhibition and, second, that the time required for clinical recovery and relapse are comparable with the time needed to build up and dispose of brain amines. The chief difficulties with this hypothesis are that similar anti-depressant effects can be obtained with drugs that do not inhibit monoamine oxidase; and conversely, some drugs that are potent oxidase inhibitors have only slight anti-depressant effects (Zbinden, Randall and Moe, 1960; see also discussion by O. Resnick of the paper by Udenfriend, 1960). Most of the monoamine oxidase inhibitors currently in use are hydrazines—that is, they contain the double nitrogen group—NHNH—. However, there are monoamine oxidase inhibitors other than hydrazines.

Hydrazines

Iproniazid (Marsilid: Hoffman-LaRoche). This is the first of the psychic energizers to have been used therapeutically after its anti-depressant action was identified as a side effect in the treatment of tuberculosis (Davis, 1958). Loomer, Saunders, and Kline and G. E. Crane and A. L. Scherbel apparently all began to work with it in 1956. While it remains one of the most effective energizers,

IPRONIAZID

it was soon replaced by other hydrazines, because some patients treated with it developed hepatic necrosis with jaundice, and there was a small but disturbing mortality rate. Vascular hypotension is a distressing side effect in the use of iproniazid, but all of the energizers, the monoamine oxidase inhibitors and the others, too, share this difficulty. Localized or diffuse edema is another side effect of iproniazid which is encountered less frequently in the use of other monoamine oxidase inhibitors. Constipation, difficulty in urination, difficulty in erection or achieving orgasm, headache—are all unpleasant complications. They are all reversible and do not call for terminating treatment. I interpret the impairment of genital function as the result of peripheral autonomic dysfunction, rather than as the result of a decrease in libido. It often occurs along with an increase of sexual desire.

The following drugs are in clinical use, and are effective energizers when given in adequate doses. Their toxicity is considerably less than that of iproniazid, but it is not zero. Troublesome side effects may be encountered, including postural hypotension, muscular cramps and spasm, edema, constipation, urinary sphincter disturbance, and impotence. These are all easily reversed by withdrawing the drug.

Beta-phenylisopropyl hydrazine (Catron: Lakeside). Since

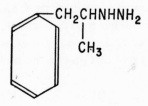

BETA-PHENYLISOPROPYL HYDRAZINE

the preparation of this monograph, the manufacture of Catron has been discontinued. Some patients to whom it was administered suffered distressing visual loss, which proved reversible.

Phenelzine Dihydrogen Sulphate (Nardil: Warner-Chilcott).

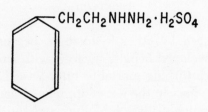

PHENELZINE

Nialamide (Niamid: Pfizer).

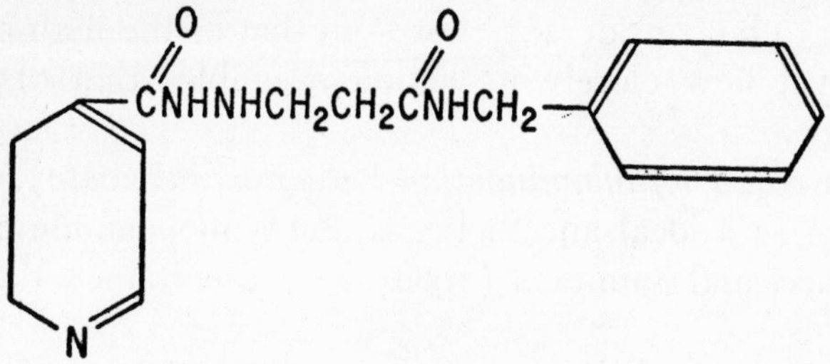

NIALAMIDE

Isocarboxazid (Marplan: Hoffman-LaRoche).

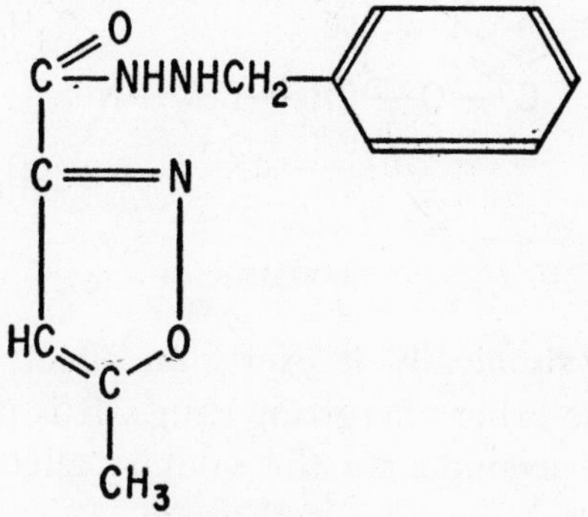

ISOCARBOXAZID

Amines

Tranylcypromine (Parnate: Smith, Kline, and French). Tranylcypromine is a monoamine oxidase inhibitor, but not a hydrazine. In structure it differs from amphetamine only in that the three carbons

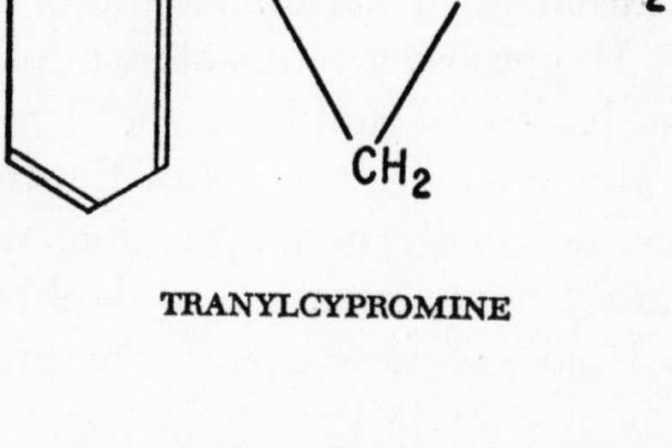

TRANYLCYPROMINE

of the straight aliphatic chain of the latter are here linked to form a closed triangular ring. Hence its toxicity, at least on initial investigation, seems to be considerably less than that of the hydrazines. It is not clear yet how closely its action resembles that of the other energizers.

Procaine (2-Diethylaminoethyl-Paraaminobenzoate). Procaine, well known as a local anesthetic, is also a monoamine oxidase inhibitor. Bucci and Saunders (1960) have ascertained that when it

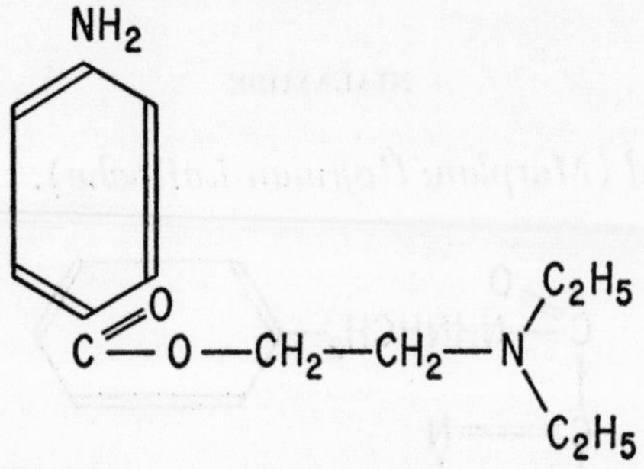

PROCAINE

is administered systemically it exerts an effect essentially identical with that of the other energizing drugs. It is probably this energizing action that accounts for the salutary effects of systemic administration reported from Eastern Europe.

IMINODIBENZYL DERIVATIVES

There are two drugs which have an energizing effect essentially similar to that of the monoamine oxidase inhibitors, but which resemble the phenothiazines in molecular structure. They are imipramine and amitriptyline (see the illustrations). Probably as a result of this structural similarity, these substances often cause side effects reminiscent of those induced by the phenothiazines: dryness of the mouth, disturbance in accommodation, tremor, skin eruption, and jaundice. Hypotension, characteristic of both phenothiazines and energizers, is also encountered.

The literature abounds with reports of the therapeutic efficacy of these substances, especially of imipramine, which has been in use for several years. I have no reason to doubt these reports and in a few instances I have witnessed their energizing potency. It is

my impression, however, that these drugs actually have two separate and distinguishable effects. The energizing effect appears after
three to six weeks of administration, as it does in the case of the
monoamine oxidase inhibitors. But within minutes or hours of the
first dose, some patients begin to feel a sense of detachment, of being
removed, of being cushioned against stimuli impinging upon them.
In greater doses or in more sensitive individuals, the sense of detachment becomes a frightening feeling of loss of contact with reality. Hence I have observed that patients inclined to hysterical
or phobic defenses often find the first effects of these drugs intolerable and refuse to continue with medication. I would expect that
patients who are anxious because of excessive involvement in object
relations might welcome the feeling of distance created by the
medication. I would also expect that in the rebound state of libido
plethora which the energizing drugs induce, this distance from the
libidinal object might retard the evolution of manic and schizophrenic states. However, I would not recommend the use of these
phenothiazine-like compounds for patients with hysteria or phobia.
The initial sedation might be more welcome in psychotic patients.
If an adverse therapeutic effect does not develop and it is desired
to substitute a monoamine oxidase inhibitor, an interval of several
days should ordinarily be interposed between the withdrawal of
imipramine or amitriptyline and the initiation of the monoamine
oxidase inhibitor. Administering the two kinds of drugs together
incurs some risk of serious toxicity—organic psychosis, seizures, and
autonomic crises. It is not clear whether there is an advantage to
combining them.

Imipramine (Tofranil: Geigy). Imipramine, or Tofranil, is the

IMIPRAMINE

older of the two compounds, and it has earned a considerable amount of enthusiasm among psychiatrists. Many have reported that it is especially efficacious with the elderly.

Amitriptyline (*Elavil: Merck, Sharp and Dohme*). Amitriptyline is chemically similar to imipramine and is reported to exert a

AMITRIPTYLINE

similar energizing effect (Barsa and Saunders, 1961). It is the investigators' impression that this drug is more potent than imipramine and less likely to impel the recovering melancholic into schizophrenia. Initial reports suggest that it is less apt to have toxic side effects than imipramine.

DEANOL
(Deaner: Riker)

Deanol is a useful drug to know about, for it is gentle, reliable, and virtually nontoxic. It is reported to cause an increase in vigor and alertness and to diminish the need for sleep. From my own limited experience, I would say that Deaner is an energizer, although a weak one. It is not sufficiently powerful to dispel a melancholia. However, it can be used for long-term administration to deter a relapse into melancholia. Its lack of toxicity makes it more suitable for prolonged use than even a small dose of any of the more potent energizers.

Deaner's pharmacologic chemistry is no less puzzling than that of the other energizers. Only that part of the molecule to the left of the central dot is active; the para-acetamidobenzoic acid portion

$$HO-CH_2-CH_2-N \overset{CH_3}{\underset{CH_3}{}} \cdot \quad \overset{O}{\underset{HO}{C}} - \overset{}{} -NH-\overset{O}{C}-CH_3$$

DEANOL

is supposed to be pharmacologically inert, but forms a stable salt with the amine (2-dimethylaminoethanol). The deanol is assumed to be a precursor of brain acetylcholine, and it passes through the blood-brain barrier, whereas choline, which is similar to deanol but bears an OH group and an additional CH_3 group on the nitrogen, cannot traverse the barrier. Headache, muscular tenseness, insomnia, and postural hypotension are infrequent and reversible side effects (see Pfeiffer *et al.*, 1957, and Pfeiffer in discussion of paper by Heath, 1959).

EGO INTOXICANTS

In this category, I include all those agents whose effect is achieved by impairing ego function in one way or another. Among them one would place all anesthetics, narcotics, somnifacients, sedatives, analgesics, and hallucinogens. It must be obvious that I can make no serious attempt to discuss or even to mention all of these drugs in this book. I shall deal with only a few of those substances which have recently been introduced into psychiatric therapy.

How do the drugs in this group compare with the tranquilizers? In theory, intoxicants act by directly impairing ego function in one or more respects. Tranquilizers, however, do not directly affect the ego, but diminish the amount of libidinal energy available to the ego so that its overall functioning is retarded. (There are instances, when the depletion of ego energy seems to affect some portions of the ego sooner than others. When this occurs, the clinical manifestations resemble those of intoxication, including confusion and hallucination.)

The effect of intoxicants is obtained within minutes after the drug is administered, while the effect of tranquilizers is seen only after days or weeks of administration and persists for days or weeks after the tranquilizer has been withdrawn. It might be objected that if a drug relieves a patient of distress and facilitates a return to usual function, it should not be called an intoxicant. The use of this term is meant to imply not that a substance is harmful or dangerous, but that the beneficial results it evokes come about only via the relief of pain. Such a drug may be compared in its action to a local anesthetic, which, by impairing sensory function in a diseased area, permits the rest of the organism to resume normal behavior. Of the two, though, the tranquilizers may be thought of as operating one step further upstream than the intoxicants, for while they do not remove the precipitating cause of the illness, they do correct the disturbed energetic balance and so permit the impaired ego to reintegrate itself. The intoxicants, on the other hand, act directly upon symptoms, and whatever ego reintegration is achieved results only from the relief of distress.

MEPROBAMATE
(Miltown: Wallace; Equanil: Wyeth)

Meprobamate has in the past few years become one of the most widely used pharmaceuticals in this country. It is often referred to as a tranquilizer, since in many instances it does ease a disturbed patient, but it is not a tranquilizer in the sense that I have used the term in this book. Meprobamate effectively and relatively safely undoes anxiety. Its anti-anxiety action is obtained with small doses, too small to sedate. Sedation may be achieved with somewhat larger doses and the drug may also be used as a somnifacient. In small amounts, meprobamate seems to anesthetize the ego to painful affect, producing little or no other defect in ego performance.

The anti-anxiety effect of meprobamate affords great relief to patients suffering from anxiety syndromes and mild depression, but it does not act to repair the psychic lesion. If used too liberally, it will permit the neurotic patient to delude himself into thinking that he requires no psychotherapeutic assistance. On the other hand, given in small amounts opportunely, it will help the distraught patient to collect himself sufficiently to exercise self-control and participate usefully in therapy.

The structure of meprobamate is simple. It is relatively nontoxic. Compared to the very large quantities of the drug used, the number of reports of serious toxicity is rather small. Reversible

$$CH_3 \diagdown$$
$$C(CH_2-O-\overset{\displaystyle O}{\overset{\|}{C}}NH_2)_2$$
$$CH_3CH_2CH_2 \diagup$$

MEPROBAMATE

skin rash is perhaps the most common disturbing effect. The risk of addiction appears to be low. Occasional seizures have been described upon abrupt withdrawal of the drug when the patient has used large amounts of it over a long period.

RESERPINE

In the earlier discussion of reserpine (see p. 306), I noted chemical, pharmacologic, and clinical differences from chlorpromazine, although both are principally tranquilizers. The molecule of reserpine is considerably larger, more complex, and bears more groups that are chemically active, so that it would appear that *in vivo* its characteristic effect may be exerted by one or more of its breakdown products. Reserpine has the power to liberate serotonin, norepinephrine, and other amines from the brain and other tissues where they are bound. When reserpine is administered to an animal after iproniazid, the amine content of the brain is found to be increased and the animal becomes excited. These results are not obtained from the administration of reserpine alone, or reserpine followed by iproniazid. Chlorpromazine has no direct influence upon the liberation or breakdown of amines, and its effect is not altered by premedication with iproniazid. Clinically we have noted, first, that reserpine seems to broaden the content of the patient's conscious thoughts so that they become more openly erotic or aggressive than usual; second, that reserpine makes dreams more weird and more realistic; and third, that the clinical course of a schizophrenic patient recovering with the aid of reserpine is more likely to be interrupted by a "turbulent phase" than in the case of chlorpromazine. We concluded that above and beyond its tranquilizing effect, reserpine must exert an ego-intoxicating effect.

There is still another clinical difference between reserpine and chlorpromazine that has been called to my attention by Kline.

When reserpine is given to a melancholic patient along with a hydrazine energizer, he says, it acts synergistically with the latter, rather than opposing it as one would expect. Chlorpromazine does oppose the effects of an energizer, although it does not cancel it, as was already noted (p. 151). Those who believe that reserpine's effect is accomplished by its mobilization of amines, especially serotonin, from the brain, explain its action as follows. Given alone, reserpine empties the brain of serotonin so that its concentration in intracerebral fluids is diminished. Given after a hydrazine energizer, it flushes amines out of their storage places in the brain into intracerebral fluids where, in the absence of oxidase, their concentrations increase to high levels (Brodie, 1960). It seems to me that the chief difficulty here is that the individual clinical actions of reserpine have not been clearly dissected out and their time courses identified so that the pharmacologist can relate the chemical and physiological events to them.

There is evidence to suggest that some fraction of the reserpine molecule, perhaps the trimethoxybenzoic acid, exerts an ego-intoxicant effect similar to that of the hallucinogens. Those chemicals that induce perceptual illusions and hallucinations render the individual much more sensitive to external stimuli than he normally is. They seem to remove an intrapsychic wall with which the individual protects himself against the impact of meaningful perceptions (Bercel et al., 1956; Elkes, 1957; Cohen, Fichman, and Eisner, 1958). Isbell and Logan (1957), in acute experiments, observed that while chlorpromazine ameliorates the mental state induced by LSD-25 in man, reserpine aggravates it. However, Giberti and Gregoretti (1955), who gave their subjects one or the other tranquilizer for "several days" before the experiment, observed that both chlorpromazine and reserpine reduced the effect of LSD-25. Even then, reserpine was less active than chlorpromazine in undoing the perceptual disturbances induced by LSD-25, in contrast to the behavioral disturbance. In other words, the immediate effect of reserpine is to reinforce the toxic action of LSD-25, while its long-term effect opposes it, as a tranquilizer would. (Tranquilizers oppose the effects of hallucinogens by reducing the instinctual pressure upon the impaired ego.) It may be this ego toxicity that is responsible for reserpine's synergistic action with hydrazine energizers in the treatment of melancholia. If, like the hallucinogens, it can weaken the melancholic ego so that the ego becomes more responsive to love objects and less completely bound to the self-observation of inner pain, it may induce some temporary symptomatic relief from misery. Of course. I cannot exclude the possibility also that reserpine facilitates the therapeutic power of the hydrazine energizers by flushing active amines out of their storage depots within the body. These two actions are not mutually exclusive. (Although theoretically interesting, the anti-depressant action of reserpine is not sufficiently impressive to warrant clinical use—probably because it is so readily overcome by its depleting action.)

CHLORDIAZEPOXIDE
(Librium: Hoffman-LaRoche)

Librium is one of the most recent of the psychically active drugs. Chemically it differs from other agents currently in use.

CHLORDIAZEPOXIDE

Its spectrum of clinical utility has yet to be precisely defined for the initial reports fail to establish it. It is said by the manufacturers to be able to "tame" monkeys, and its administration to animals tends to elevate the threshold for seizures, to relax musculature, and to increase appetite. Clinical reports indicate that Librium counteracts feelings of anxiety and depression. Some say that it is helpful in hysterical and dissociative reactions, while others say that it may precipitate an hysterical or dissociative reaction. It is reported to help some schizophrenics and to make others worse.

My own experience with Librium is limited, but I have seen it act rapidly, within hours, to relieve the misery of mild to moderate melancholic depression: the desperation, the suicidal drive, and the hypochondria. It does not affect the energy supply to the ego; it acts promptly upon ingestion, and its action does not persist for more than a day following the final dose. But why consider it a toxic rather than a tonic agent? Because its therapeutic effect is often limited by a disturbing sense of detachment or depersonalization which it may induce—drowsiness, ataxia, and confusion. Some patients derive only these disturbing responses and no beneficial effect; other patients suffer these unpleasant symptoms in addition to experiencing relief. In many, the beneficial effect wears off after a few days or weeks, leaving only the troublesome side effects.

The drug seems not to affect the basic illness, but to afford only symptomatic alleviation. I recall one patient with a severe postpartum melancholia who improved markedly within twelve hours after starting to take Librium. She seemed well and happy. However, in a therapeutic session, when she started to think and talk about herself, it became evident that the melancholia was still there. After two weeks the relief gradually diminished and gave way to a progressively increasing confusion. (Cf. patient Q. S. T., p. 173.)

It is my impression, at this point, that the drug acts to weaken the ego so that it cannot be entirely fixed and absorbed by the pain of the melancholia; part of it can still be attracted and gratified by suitable objects. In this respect the action of Librium seems to resemble a part of the action of the hallucinogenic drugs. The comparison, I believe, is not so far-fetched. Some observers have reported that the drug is not suitable for schizophrenia. In those cases where it has been found helpful in the management of schizophrenia, I suspect it is simply the sedative effect which is useful. I administered Librium to a melancholic patient who, under the influence of relatively small amounts of the hydrazine energizers, developed hypochondriacal delusions, and who was, I inferred, probably basically schizophrenic. These delusions were absent while she was depressed. Twenty-four hours after starting to take Librium, she returned to my office, still depressed, with her delusions as florid as ever, and with the additional notion that her skin condition was now spreading to her children. It seemed to me that the drug had acted to weaken her ego in such a way as to permit psychotic projection of her sense of psychic defect onto her skin and onto the skin of the love object. Within hours after Librium was withdrawn, the delusions disappeared. (Patient R. L. X.)

Librium is an interesting drug which deserves further close study. I would recommend it especially to provide some quick relief to melancholics during the interval of three to five weeks before an energizing drug can provide more definitive therapy.

EGO TONICS

In the category of ego tonics I include those substances that improve ego function fairly promptly upon administration: caffeine, for example, and the various amphetamines. There are others, too, but I have had no personal experience with them. These substances may be utilized to strengthen the ego when its function is impaired by toxins, by physical illness, by sleeplessness. They provide relief to some melancholic patients, although others respond to them with increased agitation. In the case of those melancholics that do respond—to dexedrine, for example—the ego tonic seems to hasten the definitive relief offered by an energizing drug. I believe that the use of ego intoxicant and ego tonic drugs to supplement and complement the action of agents that directly affect ego energy supply invites study.

THE AMPHETAMINES

The name "amphetamine" denotes alphamethyl phenylethylamine. It is chemically related to several active amines, some of which are found in the body, such as epinephrine and norepinephrine; others are used only medicinally, such as ephedrine, while still others are potent toxins, such as mescaline. Slight variations in molecular structure determine significant pharmacologic differences, principally whether the drug acts more peripherally or more centrally, and what its duration of action is.

A full and well-written discussion of the known properties of these substances will be found in Chauncey Leake's excellent monograph, *The Amphetamines, Their Actions and Uses*. Leake states that the amphetamines increase visual and auditory activity, increase the capacity for mental work, decrease the sense of fatigue, and promote wakefulness, alertness, attentiveness, and euphoria. Large doses may produce headache, dizziness, agitation, apprehension, confusion, fatigue, and mental depression. They may also exert a slight analgesic action, increasing the efficacy of morphine analgesia. Given in very large amounts, they evoke restlessness, dizziness, tremor, tenseness, irritability, confusion, delirium, anxiety, and hallucinations. Depression may follow the stimulation induced by the drug. There seems to be some question whether genuine amphetamine addiction occurs. Paranoid symptoms may follow prolonged, consistent dosage (Askevold, 1959).

It is evident that I have made no attempt to discuss all the chemical substances that have useful psychic effects. Moreover, I realize that new drugs are being introduced constantly. The chief contribution of this appendix is to present a classification of the several drugs—or rather of the several drug actions, since a single agent may have more than one effect. I have tried to distinguish between an influence upon ego function itself, and an influence upon the energy supply to the ego. I should like to suggest that newer drugs may be understood better if it is not assumed that they have only one influence, and if laboratory investigation is planned to conform closely to mode of clinical usage. Animal studies will be more illuminating if ethologic modes of observation are employed—that is, observation of spontaneous behavior in an environment simulating natural habitat.

BIBLIOGRAPHY

ALLES, G. A. 1959. Some relations between chemical structure and physiological action of mescaline and related compounds. In H. A. Abramson (Ed.), *Neuropharmacology: Transactions of the Fourth Conference*. New York: Josiah Macy, Jr. Foundation.

ASERINSKY, E., and KLEITMAN, N. 1955. Two types of ocular motility occurring in sleep. *J. appl. Physiol., 8:* 1.

ASKEVOLD, F. 1959. Paranoid incidents, delirium, and amphetamine. *J.A.M.A., 170:* 1453. Reprinted from *Acta. psychiat. et neurol. Scandinav., 34:* 145.

AVOL, M., and FOGEL, P. J. 1955. Treatment of delirium tremens with reserpine (Serpasil). *J.A.M.A., 159:* 1516.

AZIMA, H. 1961. Psychodynamic and psychotherapeutic problems in connection with imipramine (Tofranil) intake. *J. Mental Science, 101:* 74

AZIMA, H., AZIMA, F., and DUROST, H. 1959. Psychoanalytic formulations of effects of reserpine on schizophrenic organization. *Arch. gen. Psychiat., 1:* 662.

AZIMA, H., and VISPO, R. H. 1959. Effects of imipramine (Tofranil) on depressive states. *Arch. Neurol. Psychiat., 81:* 658.

BALDWIN, M., LEWIS, S., and BACH, S. 1959. The effects of lysergic acid after cerebral ablation. *Neurology, 9:* 469.

BARBEAU, A. 1960. Preliminary observations on abnormal catecholamine metabolism in basal ganglia diseases. *Neurology, 10:* 446.

BAROODY, N. B., BAROODY, W. G., REED, A., and MEAD, W. R. 1960. Management of delirium tremens. *J.A.M.A., 172:* 1284.

BARSA, J. A., and KLINE, N. S. 1956. A comparative study of reserpine, chlorpromazine, and combined therapy. *Arch. Neurol. Psychiat., 76:* 90.

BARSA, J. A., and KLINE, N. S. 1957. Promazine in chronic schizophrenic patients. *Am. J. Psychiat., 113:* 654.

BARSA, J. A., and SAUNDERS, J. C. 1961. Amitryptiline (Elavil), a new antidepressant. *Am. J. Psychiat., 117:* 739.

325

BEACH, F. A. 1948. *Hormones and behavior.* New York: Hoeber.

BERCEL, N. A., TRAVIS, L. E., OLINGER, L. B., and DREIKURS, E. 1956. Model psychoses induced by LSD-25 in normals. *Arch. Neurol. Psychiat., 75:* 588.

BEXTON, W. H., HERON, W., and SCOTT, R. H. 1954. Effects of decreased variation in sensory environment. *Can. J. Psychol., 8:* 70.

BIBRING, E. 1953. The mechanism of depression. In P. Greenacre (Ed.), *Affective disorders.* New York: International Universities Press.

BLEULER, E. 1924. *Textbook of psychiatry.* A. A. Brill, trans. New York: Macmillan.

BLEULER, E. 1950. *Dementia praecox, or the group of schizophrenias.* J. Zinkin, trans. New York: International Universities Press.

BOWES, H. A. 1956. The ataractic drugs: The present position of chlorpromazine, Frenquel, Pacatal and reserpine in the psychiatric hospital. *Am. J. Psychiat., 113:* 530.

BRAUCHI, J. T., and WEST, L. J. 1959. Sleep deprivation. *J.A.M.A., 171:* 11.

BRESSLER, B., SILVERMAN, A., COHEN, S., and SHMAVONIAN, B. 1959. Research in human subjects and the artificial traumatic neurosis: Where does our responsibility lie? *Am. J. Psychiat., 116:* 522.

BRODIE, B. B. 1960. Biochemical sites of action of psychotropic drugs. In H. A. Abramson (Ed.), *Neuropharmacology: Transactions of the Fifth Conference.* New York: Josiah Macy, Jr. Foundation.

BUCCI, L., and SAUNDERS, J. C. 1960. A psychopharmacological evaluation of 2-diethylaminoethyl-paraaminobenzoate (Procaine). *J. Neuropsychiat., 1:* 276.

CAMUS, A. 1960. *Caligula.* In *Caligula and three other plays.* S. Gilbert, trans. New York: Knopf.

CHAMLIN, M. Personal communication.

CLITES, M. 1935. Certain somatic activities in relation to successful and unsuccessful problem solving. *J. exper. Psychol., 18:* 708.

COHEN, E. 1953. *Human behavior in the concentration camp.* New York: Norton.

COHEN, S., FICHMAN, L., and EISNER, B. 1958. Subjective reports of lysergic acid experience in a context of psychological test performance. *Am. J. Psychiat., 115:* 30.

COHEN, S., SILVERMAN, A., and SHMAVONIAN, B. 1959. Psychophysiological mechanisms of stress responsivity. Semi-annual report to Air Force Office of Scientific Research. Nov. 1959B. Unpublished.

COUNCIL ON DRUGS. 1960. New and non-official drugs. Methoxypromazine maleate. *J.A.M.A., 172:* 1519.

CRANE, G. 1956. The psychiatric side-effects of iproniazid. *Am. J. Psychiat., 117:* 494.

DAVIS, G. D. 1955. Locomotor hyperactivity and the caudate nucleus. *Federat. Proc., 14:* 35.

DAVIS, G. D. 1958. Caudate lesions and spontaneous locomotion in the monkey. *Neurology, 8:* 135.

DAVIS, W. A. 1958. The History of Marsilid. *J. clin. exper. Psychopath., 19* Suppl.: 1.

DEMENT, W. 1960. The effect of dream deprivation. *Science, 131:* 1705.

DEMENT, W., and FISHER, C. 1960. Dream deprivation. Read before the N. Y. Psychoanalytic Society, March 1960.

DEMENT, W., and KLEITMAN, N. 1957. Cyclic variations in EEG during sleep. *EEG clin. Neurophysiol., 9:* 673.

ELKES, J. 1957. Effects of psychosomimetic drugs in animals and man. In H. A. Abramson (Ed.), *Neuropharmacology: Transactions of the Third Conference.* New York: Josiah Macy, Jr. Foundation.

ELKES, J. 1958. Pharmacological correlates. In W. Dorfman (Ed.) *Transactions, Fifth Annual Meeting, Academy of Psychosomatic Medicine.* New York: Academy of Psychosomatic Medicine.

EYSTER, M. E. 1960. The psychologic effects of ACTH and cortisone therapy. *N. Carolina med. J., 21:* 186.

FEDERN, P. 1952. *Ego psychology and the psychoses.* E. Weiss, ed. New York: Basic Books.

FENICHEL, O. 1945. *Psychoanalytic theory of neurosis.* New York: Norton.

FISHER, C. 1962. Fluctuations in the dream-sleep cycle in relation to psychopathological states. Read before Westchester Psychoanalytic Society, April 1962.

FORRER, G. R. 1960. Benign auditory and visual hallucinations. *Arch. gen. Psychiat., 3:* 95.

FRENCH, J. D. 1952. Brain lesions associated with prolonged unconsciousness. *Arch. Neurol. Psychiat., 68:* 727.

FRENCH, J. D., and MAGOUN, H. W. 1952. Effects of chronic lesions in the central cephalic brain stem of monkeys. *Arch. Neurol. Psychiat., 68:* 591.

FRENCH, J. D., VON AMERONGEN, F. K., and MAGOUN, H. W. 1952. An activating system in the brain stem of monkeys. *Arch. Neurol. Psychiat., 68:* 577.

FREUD, A. 1946. *The ego and the mechanisms of defence.* New York: International Universities Press.

FREUD, S. (1895b). On the grounds for detaching a particular syndrome from neurasthenia under the description "Anxiety Neurosis." In *Collected Papers, 1.* London: Hogarth.

FREUD, S. (1900a). *The interpretation of dreams.* In *Standard Edition, 4-5.* London: Hogarth.

FREUD, S. (1905c). *Wit and its relation to the unconscious.* In A. A. Brill (Ed.), *The basic writings of Sigmund Freud.* New York: Random House.

FREUD, S. (1905d). *Three essays on the theory of sexuality.* In *Standard Edition, 7.* London: Hogarth.

FREUD, S. (1909a). Some general remarks on hysterical attacks. In *Standard Edition, 9.* London: Hogarth.

FREUD, S. (1909b). Analysis of a phobia in a five-year-old boy. In *Standard Edition, 10.* London: Hogarth.

FREUD, S. (1911c). Psycho-analytic notes on an autobiographical account of a case of paranoia. In *Standard Edition, 12.* London: Hogarth.

FREUD, S. (1912c). Types of onset of neurosis. In *Standard Edition, 12.* London: Hogarth.

FREUD, S. (1912-13). *Totem and taboo.* In *Standard Edition, 13.* London: Hogarth.

FREUD, S. (1914c). On narcissism: an introduction. In *Standard Edition, 14.* London: Hogarth.

FREUD, S. (1915c). Instincts and their vicissitudes. In *Standard Edition, 14.* London: Hogarth.

FREUD, S. (1915d). Repression. In *Standard Edition, 14.* London: Hogarth.

FREUD, S. (1915e). The unconscious. In *Standard Edition, 14.* London: Hogarth.

FREUD, S. (1917d). A metapsychological supplement to the theory of dreams. In *Standard Edition, 14.* London: Hogarth.

FREUD, S. (1917e). Mourning and melancholia. In *Standard Edition, 14.* London: Hogarth.

FREUD, S. (1920g). *Beyond the pleasure principle.* In *Standard Edition, 18.* London: Hogarth.

FREUD, S. (1923b). *The ego and the id.* J. Riviere, trans. London: Hogarth.

FREUD, S. (1926d). *Inhibitions, symptoms and anxiety.* In *Standard Edition, 20.* London: Hogarth.

FREUD, S. (1927c). *The future of an illusion.* In *Standard Edition, 21.* London: Hogarth.

FREUD, S. (1927e). Fetishism. In *Standard Edition, 21.* London: Hogarth.

FREUD, S. (1928). Humour. In *Collected Papers, 5.* London: Hogarth.

FREUD, S. (1930a). *Civilization and its discontents.* In *Standard Edition, 21.* London: Hogarth.

FREUD, S. (1933a). *New introductory lectures on psychoanalysis.* W. J. H. Sprott, trans. New York: Norton.

FREUD, S. (1933b). *Why war?* In *Collected Papers, 5.* London: Hogarth.

FREUD, S. (1937c). Analysis terminable and interminable. In *Collected Papers, 5.* London: Hogarth.

FREUD, S. (1939a). *Moses and monotheism.* K. Jones, trans. New York: Knopf.

FREUD, S. (1940a). *An outline of psychoanalysis.* J. Strachey, trans. New York: Norton.

FREUD, S. 1954. *The origins of psychoanalysis. Letters to Wilhelm Fliess, drafts and notes: 1887-1902.* M. Bonaparte, A. Freud, E. Kris, eds. New York: Basic Books.

FREUD, S. 1960. *Letters of Sigmund Freud.* E. L. Freud, ed.; T. and J. Stern, trans. New York: Basic Books.

FREUD, S., and BREUER, J. (1895d). *Studies on hysteria.* In *Standard Edition, 2.* London: Hogarth.

FREYHAN, F. 1958. Occurrence and management of extra-pyramidal syndromes in psychiatric treatment with trifluoperazine. In *Trifluoperazine, Clinical and pharmacological aspects.* Philadelphia: Lea and Febiger.

FREYHAN, F. 1960. Neuroleptic effects: facts and fiction. In G. Sarwer-Foner (Ed.), *The dynamics of psychiatric drug therapy.* Springfield, Ill.: C. C. Thomas.

FRIEDMAN, P. 1948. The road back for the DP's. *Commentary, 6:* 502.

FRIEDMAN, P. 1949. Some aspects of concentration camp psychology. *Am. J. Psychiat., 105:* 601.

FRIEDMAN, P. 1959. The phobias. In S. Arieti (Ed.), *American handbook of psychiatry, 1.* New York: Basic Books.

FUNKENSTEIN, D., GREENBLATT, M., and SOLOMON, H. 1952. Norepinephrine-like and epinephrine-like substances in psychotic and psychoneurotic patients. *Am. J. Psychiat., 108:* 652.

GIBBY, R., ADAMS, H., and CARRERA, R. 1960. Therapeutic changes in patients following partial sensory deprivation. *Arch. gen. Psychiat., 3:* 33.

GIBERTI, F., and GREGORETTI, L. 1955. Prima esperienze di antagonismo psicofarmacologico; psicosi sperimentale da LSD e trattamento con clorpromazine e reserpina. *Sist. nerv., 4:* 301. Cited in Wikler, 1957.

GOLDMAN, H. 1959. Treatment of post-alcoholic syndrome with triflupromazine hydrochloride. *J.A.M.A., 171:* 1502.

GOSLINE, E., BLUESTONE, H., and SAUNDERS, J. 1960. Betaphenylisopropylhydrazine and its use in psychoses. *J. clin. exper. Psychopath., 21:* 220.

HALL, A. 1945. The origin and purposes of blinking. *Brit. J. Ophth., 29:* 445.

HEATH, R. G. 1959. Clinical studies with taraxein. In H. A. Abramson

(Ed.), *Neuropharmacology: Transactions of the Fourth Conference.* New York: Josiah Macy, Jr. Foundation.

HEBB, D. O. 1954. The mammal and his environment. *Am. J. Psychiat.,* *111:* 826.

HEISE, G. A., 1960. Behavioral analysis of tetrabenazine in animals. *Dis. nerv. Syst., 21* Suppl.: 111.

HESS, E. H. 1957. Effects of meprobamate on imprinting in waterfowl. *Ann. N. Y. Acad. Sci., 67:* 724.

HOLT, L. E., Jr., and SNYDERMAN, S. E. 1960. Disturbances of amino acid metabolism. *Bull. N. Y. Acad. Med., 36:* 431.

HYDE, R. W. 1960. Psychological and social determinants of drug action. In G. Sarwer-Foner (Ed.), *The dynamics of psychiatric drug therapy.* Springfield, Ill.: C. C. Thomas.

IRWIN, S. 1960. Factors influencing sensitivity to stimulant and depressant drugs in animals. In G. Sarwer-Foner (Ed.), *The dynamics of psychiatric drug therapy.* Springfield, Ill.: C. C. Thomas.

IRWIN, S., and TABACHNICK, I. 1961. Correlation between locomotor stimulant and brain monoamine-oxidase inhibitory activity of iproniazid, nialamide, and pheniprazine in the rat. *Federat. Proc., 20* (1), (Part 1): 396.

ISBELL, H., and LOGAN, C. 1957. Studies on the diethylamide of lysergic acid (LSD-25). *Arch. Neurol. Psychiat., 77:* 350.

KAPLAN, S., MAAS, J., PIXLEY, J., and ROSS, W. 1960. Use of imipramine in diabetics. *J.A.M.A., 174:* 511.

KAPPERS, C., HUBER, C., and CROSBY, E. 1936. *The comparative anatomy of the nervous system of vertebrates including man.* New York: Macmillan.

KILLAM, K., and KILLAM, E., 1960. Central action of chlorpromazine and reserpine. In H. A. Abramson (Ed.), *Neuropharmacology: Transactions of the Fifth Conference.* New York: Josiah Macy, Jr. Foundation.

KIMBALL, R., FRIEDMAN, A., and VALLEJO, E. 1960. Effect of serotonin in migraine patients. *Neurology, 10:* 107.

KINROSS-WRIGHT, J. 1959. Newer phenothiazine drugs in treatment of nervous disorders. *J.A.M.A., 170:* 1283.

KLÜVER, H. 1951. Functional differences between the occipital and temporal lobes with special reference to the interrelations of behavior and extracerebral mechanisms. In L. A. Jeffress (Ed.), *Cerebral mechanisms in behavior. The Hixon Symposium.* New York: Wiley.

LEAKE, C. 1958. *The amphetamines, their actions and uses.* Springfield, Ill. C. C. Thomas.

LEMERE, F. 1957. New steroid hormone tranquilizing agent (Cetadiol). *Am. J. Psychiat., 113:* 930.

LEWIN, B. D. 1950. *The psychoanalysis of elation.* New York: Norton.

LILLY, J. 1956. Mental effects of reduction of ordinary levels of physical stimuli on intact, healthy persons. In *Psychiatric Research Reports, No. 5.* Washington: American Psychiatric Association.

LILLY, J. 1956a. Problems of isolation. In *Symposium No. 2: Illustrative strategies for research on psychopathology in mental health.* New York: Group for the Advancement of Psychiatry.

LILLY, J. 1959. "Stop" and "start" systems. In H. A. Abramson (Ed.), *Neuropharmacology: Transactions of the Fourth Conference.* New York: Josiah Macy, Jr. Foundation.

LINN, L., KAHN, R. L., COLES, R., COHEN, J., MARSHALL, B., and WEINSTEIN, E. 1953. Patterns of behavior disturbance following cataract extraction. *Am. J. Psychiat., 110:* 281.

LJUNGBERG, E. 1958. Treatment of psychiatric patients with carbutamide. Abstract in *J.A.M.A., 168:* 211.

LOOMER, H. P., SAUNDERS, J. C., and KLINE, N. S. 1957. A clinical and pharmacodynamic evaluation of iproniazid as a psychic energizer. In R. A. Cleghorn (Ed.), *Research in affects. Psychiatric Research Reports, No. 8.* Washington: American Psychiatric Association.

LORENZ, K. (1937). The nature of instinct. In C. H. Schiller (Ed.), *Instinctive behavior.* New York: International Universities Press, 1957.

LORENZ, K. (1939). Comparative study of behavior. In C. H. Schiller (Ed.), *Instinctive behavior.* New York: International Universities Press, 1957.

LORENZ, K. (1952). The past twelve years in the comparative study of behavior. In C. H. Schiller (Ed.), *Instinctive behavior.* New York: International Universities Press, 1957.

LORENZ, K., and TINBERGEN, N. (1938). Taxis and instinct. In C. H. Schiller (Ed.), *Instinctive behavior.* New York, International Universities Press, 1957.

LUCKIESH, M., and MOSS, F. 1942. The eyelid reflex in emmetropia. *Brit. J. Ophth., 26:* 153.

LUTTRELL, R., and MORRISON, A. 1955. A preliminary report on the tranquilizing effect of reserpine. In R. Miner and F. Yonkman (Eds.), *Reserpine in the treatment of neuropsychiatric, neurological and related clinical problems. Ann. N. Y. Acad. Sci., 61:* 183.

MAGOUN, H. W. 1952. An ascending reticular activating system in the brain stem. *Arch. Neurol. Psychiat., 67:* 145.

MAGOUN, H. W. 1958. Non-specific brain mechanisms. In H. Harlow and C. Woolsey (Eds.), *Biological and biochemical bases of behavior.* Madison, Wisc.: Univ. of Wisconsin.

MALITZ, S., HOCH, P., and LESSE, S. 1956. A two-year evaluation of chlorpromazine in clinical research and practice. *Am. J. Psychiat.*, *113*: 540.

MAY, R. H. 1959. Catatonic-like states following phenothiazine therapy. *Am. J. Psychiat.*, *115*: 1119.

McCULLOCH, W. S. 1944. Cortico-cortical connections. In P. Bucy (Ed.), *The precentral motor cortex.* Urbana, Ill.: Univ. of Illinois.

MENDELSON, J., KUBZANSKY, P., LEIDERMAN, P., WEXLER, D., duTOIT, C., and SOLOMON, P. 1960. Catecholamine excretion and behavior during sensory deprivation. *Arch. gen. Psychiat.*, *2*: 147.

METTLER, F. 1948. *Neuroanatomy.* St. Louis: Mosby.

MIRSKY, I. A., MILLER, R., and STEIN, M. 1953. Relation of adrenocortical activity and adaptive behavior. *Psychosomat. Med.*, *15*: 574.

NUNBERG, H. (1920). On the catatonic attack. In *Practice and theory of psychoanalysis.* New York: Nervous and Mental Disease Monographs, No. 74, 1948.

NUNBERG, H. (1926). The sense of guilt and the need for punishment. *Int. J. Psychoanal.*, *7*: 420. Reprinted in *Practice and theory of psychoanalysis.* New York: Nervous and Mental Disease Monographs, No. 74, 1948.

NUNBERG, H. (1931). The synthetic function of the ego. *Int. J. Psychoanal.*, *12*: 123. Reprinted in *Practice and theory of psychoanalysis.* New York: Nervous and Mental Disease Monographs, No. 74, 1948.

NUNBERG, H. (1934). The feeling of guilt. *Psychoanal. Quart.*, *3*: 589. Reprinted in *Practice and theory of psychoanalysis.* New York: Nervous and Mental Disease Monographs, No. 74, 1948.

NUNBERG, H. (1942). Ego strength and ego weakness. *Am. Imago, 3:* 25. Reprinted in *Practice and theory of psychoanalysis.* New York: Nervous and Mental Disease Monographs, No. 74, 1948.

NUNBERG, H. (1943). Limitations of psychoanalytic therapy. *Bull. N. Y. Acad. Med.*, *19:* 729. Reprinted in *Practice and theory of psychoanalysis.* New York: Nervous and Mental Disease Monographs, No. 74, 1948.

NUNBERG, H. 1955. *Principles of psychoanalysis.* New York: International Universities Press.

NUNBERG, H. 1961. *Curiosity.* New York: International Universities Press.

OLDS, J. 1957. Brain response to drugs mapped through self-stimulation. In H. A. Abramson (Ed.), *Neuropharmacology: Transactions of the Third Conference.* New York: Josiah Macy, Jr. Foundation.

OLDS, J. 1958. Self-stimulation of the brain. *Science, 127:* 315.

OLDS, J., KILLAM, K., and BACH-Y-RITA, P. 1956. Self-stimulation of the brain used as a screening method for tranquilizing drugs. *Science, 124:* 265.

Ostow, M. 1954. A psychoanalytic contribution to the study of brain function. I. The frontal lobes. *Psychoanal. Quart., 23:* 317.

Ostow, M. 1955a. A psychoanalytic contribution to the study of brain function. II. The temporal lobes; and III. Synthesis. *Psychoanal. Quart., 24:* 383.

Ostow, M. 1955b. Psychic contents and processes of the brain. *Psychosomat. Med., 17:* 396.

Ostow, M. 1958. The death instincts—a contribution to the study of instincts. *Int. J. Psychoanal., 39:* 1.

Ostow, M. 1959a. The biological basis of human behavior. In S. Arieti (Ed.), *American handbook of psychiatry, 1.* New York: Basic Books.

Ostow, M. 1959. The structural model: ego, id, and superego. *Ann. N. Y. Acad. Sci., 76:* 1098.

Ostow, M. 1960a. The effects of the newer neuroleptic and stimulating drugs on psychic function. In G. Sarwer-Foner (Ed.), *The dynamics of psychiatric drug therapy.* Springfield, Ill.: C. C. Thomas.

Ostow, M. 1960b. The use of drugs to overcome technical difficulties in psychoanalysis. In G. Sarwer-Foner (Ed.), *The dynamics of psychiatric drug therapy.* Springfield, Ill.: C. C. Thomas.

Ostow, M. 1960c. The psychic function of depression: A study in energetics. *Psychoanal. Quart., 29:* 355.

Ostow, M. 1960d. A note on sweating in mental illness. *Psychosomatics, 1:* 156.

Ostow, M. 1960e. Visual hallucinations in recovery from schizophrenia. *Comprehen. Psychiat., 1:* 253.

Ostow, M. 1960f. The metapsychology of autoscopic phenomena. *Int. J. Psychoanal., 41:* 619.

Ostow, M. 1961. The clinical estimation of ego libido content. *Int. J. Psychoanal. 42:* 486.

Ostow, M., and Kline, N. S. 1959. The psychic action of reserpine and chlorpromazine. In N. S. Kline (Ed.), *Psychopharmacology frontiers.* Boston: Little, Brown.

Ostow, M., and Ostow, M. 1945. The frequency of blinking in mental illness. *J. nerv. ment. Dis., 102:* 294.

Pennes, H., and Hoch, P. 1957. Psychotomimetics, clinical and theoretical considerations: Harmine, Win-2299, and Nalline. *Am. J. Psychiat., 113:* 887.

Petrie, A., Collins, W., and Solomon, P. 1958. Pain sensitivity, sensory deprivation and susceptibility to satiation. *Science, 128:* 1431.

Pfeiffer, C., Jenney, E., Gallagher, W., Smith, R., Bevan, W., Jr., Killam, K., Killam, E., and Blackmore, W. 1957. Stimulant effect of 2-dimethylaminoethanol—possible precursor of brain acetylcholine. *Science, 126:* 610.

PIOTROWSKI, Z., and BRICKLIN, B. 1958. A long-term prognostic criterion for schizophrenics based on Rorschach data. *Psychiat. Quart.*, *32*, Suppl., Part 2: 315.

PIOTROWSKI, Z., and LEVIN, D. 1959. A case illustrating the concept of the alpha schizophrenic. *J. proj. Techniques*, *23*: 223.

PLETSCHER, A. 1959. Alterations of monoamine metabolism caused by drugs acting on the central nervous system. In N. S. Kline (Ed.), *Psychopharmacology frontiers*. Boston: Little, Brown.

PONDER, E., and KENNEDY, W. 1928. On the act of blinking. *Quart. J. Physiol.*, *18*: 89.

RADO, S. (1933). The psychoanalysis of pharmacothymia (drug addiction). *Psychoanal. Quart.*, *2*: 1. Reprinted in *Psychoanalysis of behavior*. New York: Grune and Stratton, 1956.

RIFKIN, H. Personal communication.

ROBIE, T. 1961. A new and safer antidepressant. *J. Neuropsychiat.*, *2*, Suppl. 1: 31.

ROME, H., and BRACELAND, F. 1952. The psychological responses to ACTH, cortisone, hydrocortisone, and related steriod substances. *Am. J. Psychiat.*, *108*: 641.

ROSNER, A. 1942. Psychiatric sequelae of epidemic encephalitis. In J. B. Neal (Ed.), *Encephalitis, a clinical study*. New York: Grune and Stratton.

SARWER-FONER, G. 1957. Psychoanalytic theories of activity-passivity conflicts and of the continuum of ego defenses. *Arch. Neurol. Psychiat.*, *78*: 413.

SARWER-FONER, G. 1960. Some therapeutic aspects of the use of the neuroleptic drugs in schizophrenia, borderline states, and in the short-term psychotherapy of the neuroses. In G. Sarwer-Foner (Ed.), *The dynamics of psychiatric drug therapy*. Springfield, Ill.: C. C. Thomas.

SARWER-FONER, G., and KORANYI, E. 1957. The clinical investigation of Pacatal in open psychiatric settings. *Can.M.A.J.*, *77*: 450.

SARWER-FONER, G., and OGLE, W., 1956. Psychosis and enhanced anxiety produced by reserpine and chlorpromazine. *Can.M.A.J.*, *74*: 526.

SAUNDERS, J. C. 1959. Etiology of psychosis theorized from drug actions. In N. S. Kline (Ed.), *Psychopharmacology frontiers*. Boston: Little, Brown.

SCHERBEL, A. L. 1957. The effect of isoniazid and iproniazid in patients with rheumatoid arthritis. *Cleveland Clin. Quart.*, *24*: 90.

SCHWAB, R., ENGLAND, A., and PETERSON, E. 1959. Akinesia in Parkinson's disease. *Neurology*, *9*: 65.

SCHWARZ, B., SEM-JACOBSEN, C., and PETERSEN, M. 1956. Effects of mescaline, LSD-25, and adrenochrome on depth electrograms in man. *Arch. Neurol. Psychiat., 75:* 579.

SELYE, H. 1956. Stress and psychiatry. *Am. J. Psychiat., 113:* 423.

SEROTONIN. 1956. Editorial. *J.A.M.A., 161:* 460.

SHAGASS, C., and NAIMAN, J. 1955. The sedation threshold, manifest anxiety, and some aspects of ego function. *Arch. Neurol. Psychiat., 74:* 397.

SHAGASS, C., NAIMAN, J., and MIHALIK, J. 1956. An objective test which differentiates between neurotic and psychotic depression. *Arch. Neurol. Psychiat., 75:* 461.

SHARP, W. 1960. Convulsions associated with anti-depressant drugs. *Am. J. Psychiat., 117:* 458.

SILVERMAN, A., COHEN, S., and SHMAVONIAN, B. 1959. Investigation of psychophysiologic relationships with skin resistance measures. *J. psychosomat. Research, 4:* 65.

SMITH, M. E. 1960. Clinical comparison of tetrabenazine, reserpine, and placebo in chronic schizophrenics. *Dis. nerv. Syst., 21* Suppl.: 120.

SMITH, W. R. 1956. *The religion of the Semites.* Second edition. New York: Meridian.

SOLOMON, P., LEIDERMAN, H., MENDELSON, J., and WEXLER, D. 1957. Sensory deprivation. *Am. J. Psychiat., 114:* 357.

STACKHAUSEN, F. 1960. Clinical studies with tetrabenazine. *Dis. nerv. Syst., 21* Suppl.: 115.

STANDARD NOMENCLATURE OF DISEASE: FOURTH EDITION. 1952. In *Diagnostic and statistical manual of mental disorders.* Washington: American Psychiatric Association.

STOLL, W. (1947). Lysergsäure-diäthylamid, ein Phantastikum aus der Mutterkorngruppe. *Schweiz. Arch. Neurol. Psychiat., 60:* 1. Abstracted in Wikler, 1957.

STRAUSS, H., LINN, L., and OSTOW, M. 1955. Electroencephalographic and neuropsychiatric observations in patients with senile cataract. *Mschr. Psychiat. Neurol., 130:* 321.

THORPE, W., 1956. *Learning and instinct in animals.* Cambridge: Harvard.

TINBERGEN, N. 1951. *The study of instinct.* London: Oxford.

TISLOW, R., KOUZMANOFF, S., GORE, E., HADLEY, F., HOSKO, M. J., JR., and SEIFTER, J. 1960. Studies on experimental catatonia in animals. In G. Sarwer-Foner (Ed.), *The dynamics of psychiatric drug therapy.* Springfield, Ill.: C. C. Thomas.

TYLER, D. 1955. Psychological changes during sleep deprivation. *Dis. nerv. Syst., 16:* 293.

UDENFRIEND, S. 1960. Amine metabolism and its pharmacological implications. In H. A. Abramson (Ed.), *Neuropharmacology: Transactions of the Fifth Conference.* New York: Josiah Macy, Jr. Foundation.

VERNON, J., and HOFFMAN, J. 1956. Effect of sensory deprivation on learning rate in human beings. *Science, 123:* 1074.

VOELKEL, A. H. 1959. Drugs influencing monoamine metabolism. In N. S. Kline (Ed.), *Psychopharmacology frontiers.* Boston: Little, Brown.

VON UEXKÜLL, J. (1934). A stroll through the worlds of animals and men. In C. H. Schiller (Ed.), *Instinctive behavior.* New York: International Universities Press, 1957.

WALASZEK, E., and ABOOD, L. 1956. Effect of tranquilizing drugs on fighting response of Siamese fighting fish. *Science, 124:* 140.

WEXLER, D., MENDELSON, J., LEIDERMAN, P., and SOLOMON, P. 1958. Sensory deprivation: a technique for studying psychiatric aspects of stress. *Arch. Neurol. Psychiat., 79:* 225.

WIKLER, A. 1957. *The relation of psychiatry to pharmacology.* Baltimore: Williams and Wilkins.

WILSON, S. A. K. 1940. *Neurology.* Baltimore: Williams and Wilkins.

WINKELMAN, N. W., JR. 1960. Chlorpromazine and prochlorperazine during psychoanalytic psychotherapy: Theoretical formulations concerning the ego, energy relationships, anxiety and the psychic therapeutic process. In G. Sarwer-Foner (Ed.), *The dynamics of psychiatric drug therapy.* Springfield, Ill.: C. C. Thomas.

WORLD HEALTH ORGANIZATION. 1958. *Technical report series, No. 152. Ataractic and hallucinogenic drugs in psychiatry.* Geneva: World Health Organization.

ZBINDEN, G., RANDALL, L., and MOE, R. 1960. Clinical and pharmacological considerations on mode of action of monoamine oxidase inhibitors. *Dis. nerv. Syst., 21* Suppl.: 89.

ZISKIND, E. 1958. Isolation stress in medical and mental illness. *J.A.M.A., 168:* 1427.

Date Due